KU-798-032

OXFORD

302210013C

The flowing landscapes of geologic time may be likened to a kinetoscope panorama. The scenes transform from age to age, as from act to act; seas and plains and mountains follow and replace each other through time, as the traveller sees them replace each other in space. . . . Science demonstrates that mountains are transient forms, but the eye of man through all his lifetime sees no change, and his reason is appalled at the thought of duration so vast that the millenniums of written history have not recorded the shifting of even one of the fleeting views whose blendings make the moving picture.

JOSEPH BARRELL

Franz Josef Glacier, New Zealand.

C. A. Cotton, photo.

59—

GEOMORPHOLOGY

An Introduction to the Study of Landforms

BY

C. A. COTTON

Victoria University College, Wellington, New Zealand

THIRD EDITION

Revised and Enlarged

WHITCOMBE & TOMBS LIMITED

CHRISTCHURCH AUCKLAND WELLINGTON DUNEDIN INVERCARGILL

LONDON MELBOURNE SYDNEY

1942

TO THE GEOMORPHOLOGISTS OF ALL NATIONS
AND MORE ESPECIALLY TO DOUGLAS JOHNSON
OF AMERICA AND HENRI BAULIG OF FRANCE

PREFACE

This book may be regarded as a new and revised edition of *Geomorphology of New Zealand, Part I: Systematic,* which was published in 1922 (reprinted 1926) by the Dominion Museum, Wellington, as New Zealand Board of Science and Art Manual No. 3. The old *Geomorphology,* which has been out of print for some years, has enjoyed a considerable popularity notwithstanding that a rashly promised sequel which was to present a regional treatment of New Zealand landforms has failed to appear.

Geomorphology makes its appeal not only to geologists and geographers but also to all who love Nature and have eyes for the natural landscape. To geologists the form of the surface is of interest because landforms result from the operation and interaction of processes which are active also in the production, transportation, and deposition of the materials that make rocks. It has a further interest which transcends this, however, in that it gives access to a record—which is in many cases the only record available—of a late period in the history of the earth very scantily documented by stratigraphy. Farther back in geological history, indeed, there are many gaps in the stratigraphical record, erosion intervals marked by unconformities, the correct interpretation of which can be made possible only by analogy of buried landscapes with landforms and landscapes as they exist to-day.

Geography on the other hand, is concerned with the surface of the earth as the environment of organised beings and notably as the abode of man. From the geographical point of view, therefore, geomorphology is concerned with the description of the natural landscape and the classification and labelling of landforms. For this reason the science has advanced largely as a development of the method of "explanatory description" advocated by W. M. Davis. In the present book the treatment is intentionally Davisian in the sense that explanation is assumed to be a necessary part of landscape description.

The presentation of the "normal" cycle is Davisian also; for Davis's down-wearing theory is accepted in explanation of the origin of peneplains without reference to alternative hypotheses of slope retreat.

Though not written in the conventional form of a school book, the old *Geomorphology* has been found useful as a textbook by first-year students of geology and geography in the University and Teachers' Training Colleges; and I venture to believe that this revised edition is suitable for use also by pupils in the higher classes in secondary schools. Abridgement for a first reading may be left to the discretion of teachers, whose predilections, as well as the availability of local examples of landforms, must govern the choice of matter. I hope it is quite obvious that the book has not been written up to meet the requirements of any examination syllabus.

In this elementary treatment of geomorphology, which attempts to cover in one small volume a wide field of study, limitation of space has made it impossible to indicate the sources and authorship of terms employed in a technical sense (for very few of which I admit personal responsibility) or to trace the origin of geomorphic doctrines and theories. For some information on such matters, as well as for fuller treatment of some aspects of geomorphology, the reader is referred to other works, to which the brief list in the Appendix will serve as an introduction.

I am particularly grateful to all those colleagues and correspondents who have supplied me with and allowed me to use illustrative material; and I am no less indebted to the professional photographers whose keen eye for scenic beauty has so often led to the production of pictures of the greatest value as illustrations of landforms. Wherever it has been possible acknowledgment for the illustrations has been made in credit lines.

I am indebted to the New Zealand Government for permission to draw on *Geomorphology of New Zealand, Part I* for portions of the text and for many of the illustrations.

C. A. Cotton.

Lower Hutt

January 1942

CONTENTS

PART I

Contents

PART II

Contents

PART I

ELEMENTS OF GEOMORPHOLOGY

CHAPTER I

THE CRUST OF THE EARTH

Uniformitarianism. Geological processes. The material of the lithosphere: rocks. Rock structures. "Structure" or terrain.

Uniformitarianism.—It is recognised that the present condition of the earth's surface is due in great part to the long-continued action of processes still in operation. Over a century ago it was asserted that there is "no trace of a beginning and no prospect of an end." Nowadays, however, such pronounced "uniformitarian" views, as they are termed, are regarded as extreme. The importance of physical geology hinges, nevertheless, on the acceptance of the present as a "key to the past," and this key unlocks so many doors that we cannot but believe it is the right one.

Geological Processes.—Among the more important of the *processes* with which physical geology concerns itself are the work of rain, rivers, wind, waves, and ice, volcanic action, and earth movements.

The raw materials on which the various agents work consist of layers and masses of *rock*, and, although the study of processes may, from one point of view, be regarded as a preliminary to the study of rocks, at least a rudimentary idea of rocks is required as a basis for the study of processes.

The Material of the Lithosphere: Rocks.—It is only the superficial rocks that concern the student of landforms. Geology, indeed, knows little about the nature of the materials forming the deeper, inaccessible parts of the globe.

Lithosphere is a term used to designate the outer shell of the solid globe, containing all accessible rocks. It is somewhat better term than "crust of the earth," which is, however, often used, for the latter seems to imply belief in the now discredited theory that these rocks are merely a thin hardened crust or skin surrounding a mobile liquid interior.

The materials of the lithosphere are rocks and minerals. The fundamental units of geology are rocks, and rocks are made up of minerals, each of which is either a native element or a definite chemical compound of certain elements. Rocks are not necessarily hard; the loose sand of a sandhill is technically a rock.

All rocks fall naturally into three great divisions, termed (1) *sedimentary,* (2) *igneous,* and (3) *metamorphic.*

Sedimentary rocks include all those that have accumulated on the surface of the earth (some of them under the sea) through the operation of water, ice, air, gravity, or organic agency. This class includes rocks formed from deposits of sediment, coarse or fine—namely, the conglomerates, sandstones, shales or mudstones, and some slates, as well as limestones, most of which are composed largely of shells and other animal remains, and coal, which is formed from accumulations of vegetable matter. Sedimentary rocks are as a general rule, disposed in layers, termed *beds* or *strata,*[1] piled one upon another (fig. 1). A thick stratum of one kind of rock is often termed a *formation.* On account of their *stratification* (arrangement in layers) this division of rocks is sometimes termed the *stratified* rocks. The rocks formed from mechanical sediment, as distinguished from organic material, are called *clastic.*

Igneous rocks are those that have solidified from the liquid state either beneath or on the surface of the earth. Those which have flowed out in sheets on the surface as lava before solidifying are termed *volcanic* (Chapter XXV). Lava sheets may be found as beds alternating with beds of sediment, which have buried successive layers of lava. The fragmentary material ("volcanic ash") thrown out by volcanoes also forms strata, and when it has been spread and deposited as "tuff" by water may be interbedded and more or less mixed with clastic or organic sediment.

Igneous rocks that have solidified without reaching the surface are termed *intrusive,* each body of such rock being an *intrusion.* The smaller intrusions have generally solidified in fissures, often

[1] Sing., *stratum;* pl., *strata.*

Fig. 1.— Stratified rocks, Oamaru, N.Z. These strata, originally laid down horizontally, have been subsequently tilted into an inclined attitude, and still later their edges have been exposed to view by erosion in a sea-cliff.

A. C. Gifford, photo.

Fig. 2.—Dyke of igneous rock on the foreshore near Oamaru, New Zealand.

A. C. Gifford, photo.

nearly vertical, forming thin sheets, which are called *dykes* (fig. 2). Thin sheets injected between strata are called *sills*. The rocks forming large intrusions are termed *plutonic*. The commonest is granite, and all have the coarse grain and texture termed *granitic*. Masses of plutonic rock are frequently so large that, when exposed by erosion, they form the land surface over hundreds of square miles. Since in such masses there is no stratification, they are termed *massive*. Igneous rocks are, generally speaking, harder and more resistant to the processes that are wearing down the land than are the sedimentary rocks associated with them. This is not

Fig. 3.—Foliated metamorphic rock (mica schist) outcropping on the Rock and Pillar Range, Otago, New Zealand.

W. D. Reid, photo.

an invariable rule, however; and some igneous rocks—dykes especially—are relatively weak because they are much more susceptible to the process of rock-decay than are the sedimentary rocks which enclose them.

Metamorphic rocks have been formed from either sedimentary or igneous rocks, chiefly by the long-continued action of heat and pressure. These have caused a rearrangement of the elements of the rocks into new minerals, which are generally of flaky form. On account of the abundance of mica and the arrangement of the minerals in layers (foliation) most metamorphic rocks (schists) are softer and more easily broken and worn away than are igneous rocks (fig. 3).

Rock Structures.—All rocks are subject to movements of various kinds, and so they do not remain in the positions and attitudes in which they were formed (fig. 4). Stratified rocks, originally

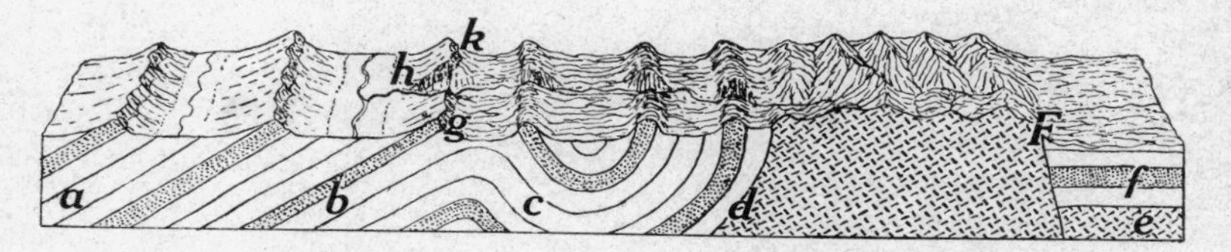

Fig. 4.—Diagram of structures, *ad, f,* stratified rocks; *de,* massive rock; *ab,* homocline; *bc,* anticline; *cd* syncline; *f,* strata still horizontal; *F,* fault; *ghk,* outcrop of stratum *b.*

laid down horizontally or nearly so, are sometimes found still in that attitude, though they may have been uplifted bodily, but far more often they are tilted or bent (*folded*) into arches and troughs, termed *anticlines* and *synclines* (figs. 4, 5). Strata which are inclined

Fig. 5.—Small anticline exposed in a sea-cliff, Fitzroy Bay, Wellington, New Zealand.

C. A. Cotton, photo.

Fig. 6.—Homoclinal outcrop of limestone, Waipara district, New Zealand.
C. A. Cotton, photo.

Fig. 7.— Outcrop of volcanic lavas tilted steeply by earth movement, Marlborough, New Zealand.
C. A. Cotton, photo.

(which *dip*) constantly in one direction form a *homocline*[1] (fig. 6). In some cases the beds are quite vertical.

Sheet-like igneous rocks may exhibit folding like sedimentary strata, but such structures are not obvious in massive rocks.

Fig. 8.—Faults in the Oamaru series, New Zealand.

A. C. Gifford, photo.

The band traced on the surface of the ground by a rock layer is its *outcrop* (figs. 4-7), and the direction of a band which would be traced on an imaginary horizontal surface is its *strike*. The strike

[1] The term *monocline* is sometimes used in this sense, but is better reserved for another structure which is described in Chapter XIV.

Fig. 9.—Hexagonal columns separated by shrinkage cracks in the basalt of the Giants' Causeway, North Ireland.

C. A. Cotton, photo.

Fig. 10.—Several systems of joints intersecting in sedimentary rock, Wellington, New Zealand.

C. A. Cotton, photo.

is at right angles to the direction of steepest inclination, the *dip,* of the stratum.

Faults (figs. 4 and 8) are surfaces of fracture in the rocks along which movement has taken place, all on one side of the break having moved relatively to all on the other side. A break in the surface of the ground may accompany the formation of a fault in the rocks beneath, but if the fault is an old one the chances are that erosion has removed all trace of it at the surface or has developed relief forms in connection with it which are quite different from the original break (Chapter XIII).

Joints (figs. 9 and 10) are fissures or cracks in rocks. In almost every rock there are joints, and frequently several systems of joints intersect, dividing the rock into large or small pieces which may be of regular geometrical shapes, as in the case of the hexagonal columns which develop at right angles to cooling surfaces in lava flows and in injected sheets (sills) and other intrusive bodies of rock (fig. 9).

Such jointing, which results from shrinkage during cooling of the igneous rock after its solidification, forms open crevices and greatly weakens the rock—that is, makes it much less resistant to erosion than an unjointed rock would be. Other joints, which originate in the process of rock folding, are mere cracks with the walls closely pressed together; but even these allow water to enter and facilitate weathering and erosion of rocks that are close to the surface (fig. 10).

"Structure" or Terrain.—In geomorphology the term "structure" is commonly more comprehensive than in geological writings. As used in Davis's all-inclusive formula for explanatory description of landforms—"structure, process, and stage"—it "indicates the product of all *constructional* agencies. It includes the nature of the material, its mode of aggregation, and even the form before the work of erosive agencies begins. In other words, it stands for that upon which erosive agents are, and have been, at work" (Fenneman). Another convenient name for the assemblage of rocks and structures underlying a landscape is *terrain*.

CHAPTER II

EROSION: THE WEATHERING OF ROCKS

Erosion. Weathering: the work of rain and associated agents. Mechanical weathering or rock-breaking. Rock-breaking by organic agencies. Rock-decay. Residual clay. Spheroidal weathering. Depth of weathering.

Erosion.—All rock masses that are exposed at the surface of the earth are subject to constant chemical and mechanical action, by which they are decomposed and worn away. *Erosion* is a comprehensive term denoting the sum of such processes, and *denudation* as generally applied is synonymous with erosion. By these processes the lithosphere is said to be *eroded* or *denuded*. The majority of surface features—viz., hills, valleys, etc.—are the work of erosion, which, however, is not a finished process but is still in progress. The material that is removed as waste by erosion goes to form new sedimentary rocks.

There are three natural divisions of erosion—viz., (1) *rock-breaking,* (2) *rock-decay,* and (3) *transportation.*

The most important of the eroding agents are running water, rain, certain physical and organic processes, wind, glaciers, and wave action. Wind and glaciers are important only within strictly limited areas, while wave action is important only around the margin of the land. The remaining processes—running water, rain, and certain associated physical and organic processes, are responsible for the erosion now in progress over the greater part of the surface of the habitable lands. Hence they are termed the *normal*[1] processes.

Weathering: the Work of Rain and Associated Agents.—The work of rock-breaking (disintegration) and rock-decay (decomposition and solution) accomplished by rain and associated processes is termed *weathering.* Two phases of weathering, rock-breaking and rock-decay, may be considered separately.

---

[1] "The term 'normal erosion' is plainly open to criticism on the ground that one mode is just as normal as another, but no other satisfactory term has been proposed" (Fenneman).

Mechanical Weathering or Rock-breaking.—In arid regions and also on all mountain-tops there is a great daily range of temperature due to the intensity of solar radiation (insolation) by day and rapid loss of heat due to radiation and to contact with cold air at night. So the bare rock surfaces which are commonly exposed in such situations are rapidly heated and as rapidly cooled. In heterogeneous rocks, especially those of coarse grain, like granite,

Fig. 11.—Granite suffering disintegration and crumbling into coarse sand, Rocky Mountains, Colorado.

C. A. Cotton, photo.

the different mineral constituents expand differently when heated, and as there are not generally any spaces to accommodate grains expanding more than their neighbours, enormous strains result from such differential expansion. Granite and similar rocks consequently crumble at the surface into coarse sand or fine rubble (fig. 11).

Homogeneous (one-mineral) rocks like quartzite and limestone (composed of the minerals quartz and calcite respectively) do not so readily crumble in this manner. Instead they blister, and expansion of a thin superficial layer of the poorly conducting rock as it is rapidly heated results in a flaking off (*exfoliation*) of the surface (figs. 12, 13).

Fig. 12.—Exfoliation from an exposed face of limestone, North Canterbury, New Zealand. *C. A. Cotton, photo.*

Fig. 13.—Whaleback surfaces rounded by exfoliation, Marlborough, New Zealand. *C. A. Cotton, photo.*

Fig. 14.—A monolithic dome resulting from exfoliation of granite, Frazer Peaks, Stewart Island, New Zealand. *L. Cockayne, photo.*

Fig. 15.—Half Dome, a granite monolithic dome steepened on one side by glacial erosion, Yosemite, California.

C. A. Cotton, photo.

Neither superficial crumbling nor exfoliation is necessarily always a purely physical process: both may be aided by a swelling of mineral grains already in progress as they undergo hydration and other incipient chemical changes such as ultimately destroy them in the process of ordinary weathering (fig. 22). A large-scale exfoliation which results in the separation of gigantic flakes from some rock surfaces may be caused entirely by expansion due to these chemical processes. Some smooth dome-like hills and even mountains owe their form to this large-scale exfoliation from the surface

Fig. 16.—Spalled block, Hooker Valley, New Zealand.
C. A. Cotton, photo.

of large masses of hard rock which are monolithic in the sense of being free from joints. Such geomorphic *monoliths,* as these domes have been called, are commonest in granite (figs. 14, 15).

Rock outcrops which neither crumble nor exfoliate readily may suffer *spalling* as a result of rapid change of temperature, falling apart into large angular blocks as though they had been struck with some enormous sledge-hammer. Isolated blocks may be seen to have split apart as a result of the spalling process (fig. 16), though every apparent example cannot be ascribed to the effects of insolation, much spalling having resulted from forest fires.

A *felsenmeer,* or block-strewn surface, such as is generally present where the ground is reasonably level on cold mountain-tops rising above the level at which vegetation can exist, may be ascribed to the spalling effects of rapid temperature changes together with *freeze-and-thaw* action, or *frost-riving.* This is another physical process which is effective as a rock-breaker. Water freezing in crevices expands and forces apart their rock walls. After a thaw water freezes again in the same crevice, and repeated freezings eventually prise off rock fragments (fig. 17).

Fig. 17.—Frost-riven and other fragments from a crumbling outcrop of sedimentary rock stream down talus slopes to be carried away by a river, Clarence Valley, New Zealand.

C. A. Cotton, photo.

Daily temperature changes do not penetrate far into the ground, and so disintegration due to this cause is a surface phenomenon. Where waste accumulates it blankets the rock and thus protects it from further disintegration, but owing to the removal of the waste from desert surfaces by wind and from mountain peaks by gravity fresh surfaces are there constantly exposed, and disintegration goes on apace.

Streams of angular fragments forming *talus slopes* (fig. 17), also termed *screes,* below exposed outcrops of rock testify to the activity of the physical processes. After some talus material has accumulated more rubble glissades down its sloping surface and is delivered to streams which actively remove it.

Rock-breaking by Organic Agencies.—Under forest much rock-breaking results from the prising effect due to growth of tree roots which have entered hair cracks as fibres and forced their walls apart (fig. 18). The bedrock is disintegrated and is easily pene-

Fig. 18.— Rock crevice enlarged by the growth of tree roots, which are prising off slabs of rock, near Wellington, New Zealand.
C. A. Cotton, photo.

trated by water, thus greatly accelerating chemical weathering (rock-decay). Burrowing animals also help to destroy soft rocks; and, where rock-decay is in progress, a great quantity of soil is finely comminuted and deposited on the surface by earthworms, which pass it through their bodies. Such fine material is readily washed away by the run-off during rain showers.

Rock-decay.—Rock-decay involves chemical processes and is largely the work of rain-water, accomplished during its downward passage through the soil and subsoil, though bacteria are also active in the soil. The activity of rain-water is due mainly to the chemical and solvent action of dissolved substances, chief among which are oxygen and carbon dioxide. These gases are dissolved from the atmosphere by the falling rain, and during its passage through the upper layer of soil the water takes up a further

Fig. 19.—Limestone outcrop fluted by the solvent action of rain, near Whangarei, New Zealand.

C. A. Cotton, photo.

amount of carbon dioxide resulting from plant decay. Above the level of water-saturation air is present in the crevices of the rocks, and the oxygen of this aids in producing rock-decay. The most important chemical processes involved in the attack made by rain-water on the mineral constituents of rocks are oxidation, hydration, and carbonation. These are accompanied by solution either of original constituents of the rock or, more commonly, of substances separated from rock constituents by chemical action.

The simplest action of rain-water is solution of limestone, a rock consisting of a single mineral, calcite, the chemical composition of which is carbonate of lime. This compound is soluble in water containing carbon dioxide. The effects of solution by rain-water are to be seen on all outcrops of pure limestone, which show grooves (*lapiés*) due to rain-water collecting as streams and deepening by solution the furrows in which it flows (fig. 19).

Fig. 20.—Solid rock (below) passing up into residual clay and soil, Tinakori Hills, Wellington, New Zealand.

C. A. Cotton, photo.

Residual Clay.—The effects of rain in producing rock-decay are to be seen in practically all rocks, but especially in igneous rocks with abundant silicate minerals. These latter, especially feldspar, are broken up, the alkalies present in them are removed in solution as carbonates, and the alumina, combined with some of the silica, is hydrated and forms clay. Iron derived from minerals in which it is present in the rock is oxidised to the ferric state and hydrated to form the mineral limonite, which stains the clay yellow or brown. The grains of minerals such as quartz and white mica, which are but very slightly acted upon by rain-water, remain scattered through the clay. In this way is formed *residual* clay. so called because it is the residue resulting from the decay of a rock.

Weathering is most complete at the surface of the ground. A little below the surface the rock is only partially weathered, and some distance down there is fresh or unweathered rock (fig. 20). This is easily understood when it is remembered that weathering works downward from the surface, and also that the surface of the ground is being worn away. A layer below the surface now will at some future time be at the surface, but by that time it will be more thoroughly weathered than it is now.

Fig. 21.—Spheroidal weathering of basalt lava rock, near Mosgiel, New Zealand. *M. Ongley, photo.*

Spheroidal Weathering.—Rain-water passing down through rock makes its way along the natural crevices or joints present. When these are rather widely spaced they separate compact blocks of rock, which slowly weather on all their surfaces. As sharp angles on such blocks are attacked from two sides, they become rounded off. Hence as the weathered layer around the outside becomes thicker the diminishing core becomes more and more nearly round, or spheroidal. In a residual clay such spheroidal cores are frequently abundant, and when some of the clay is washed away they may lie on the surface. They must not be mistaken for stream-worn boulders (figs. 21 and 22).

Fig. 22.—Spheroidal weathering of feldspathic sandstone, Curio Bay, Waikawa, New Zealand.

C. A. Cotton, photo.

Fig. 23.—Granite tors, Tamworth district, New South Wales.

C. A. Cotton, photo.

The huge blocks forming singly or in piles the salient features known as *tors,* sometimes resembling ruined masonry, which surmount many plateaux formed of granitic rocks have originated in a similar way (fig. 23). In Central Otago, New Zealand, tors of mica schist break the monotony of the upland plateaux. Where the schist foliation is nearly horizontal and joints are vertical they also have the appearance of masonry (fig. 24).

Fig. 24.—Schist tors Rough Ridge, Otago, New Zealand.
C. A. Cotton, photo.

Depth of Weathering.—The depth to which weathering proceeds depends upon the depth to which rain-water can sink vertically before reaching a continuous body of water (the *ground water*). The *level of ground water,* or the *water-table,* below which the rocks are saturated and all cavities are filled with water is deeper on hills than on flat country, and, other things being equal, is deeper also where the rocks are shattered or porous. The ground-water level also varies with the seasons, being close to the surface after long-continued rains. It is the deepest level reached by the water surface that sets a limit to the depth at which ordinary rock-decay can take place.

CHAPTER III

EROSION: REMOVAL OF ROCK DEBRIS

The mantle of waste. Gravity transportation or mass movements: landslides. Solifluction. Soil creep. Water transportation. Earth pillars. Rivers. Corrasion and transportation by running water. Chemical corrosion and transportation in solution. Mechanical corrasion and transportation in suspension. The quantity of waste transported.

The Mantle of Waste.—On all surfaces except the steepest, from which fragments fall or stream down, the waste that results from weathering, and in particular the debris of rock-decay, accumulates as a mantle of soil and subsoil, the latter consisting of clay mixed with partially weathered residual fragments of rock. It is the presence of the waste mantle that allows of the growth of vegetation; and vegetation in its turn helps to bind the waste and retard its removal and so to increase the thickness of the layer. The roots of forest trees are especially effective as soil binders or retainers. The thickness of the waste mantle does not increase indefinitely, however, for the waste—its upper layer at least—is continually being removed. This removal of waste, which results in a general lowering or wasting-away of the land surface is effected in part by washing-away of fine particles in wet weather, as will be described in due course. There are, however, other processes of downhill transportation directly controlled by gravity.

Gravity Transportation or Mass Movements: Landslides.—Landslides[1] occur when masses of the waste mantle and perhaps underlying bodies of partly disintegrated rock become so saturated with water that the friction holding them in place on slopes is overcome and they move downhill. Earthquakes provide a trigger effect which sets many landslides in motion. Innumerable small landslides occur during heavy rains, and occasionally whole hillsides thus slip away, coming to rest on lower ground as glacier-like

[1] Also termed "landslips"; and in New Zealand commonly "slips."

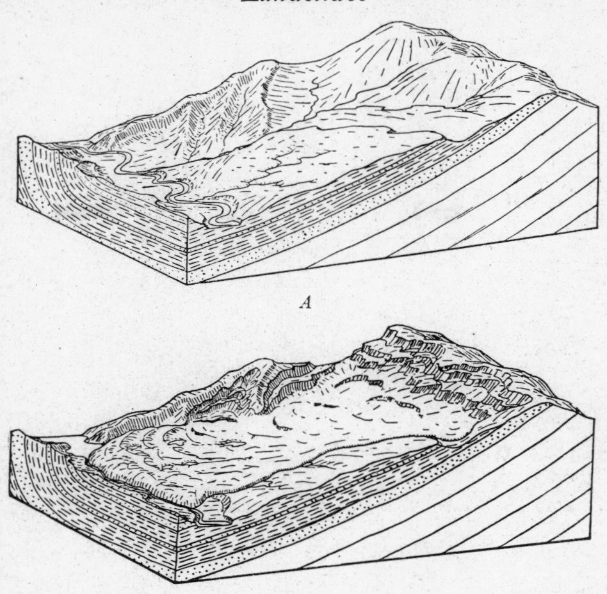

Fig. 25.—Slump and earth flow (the Gros Ventre Slide, Wyoming). *A* is a restoration of the landscape before the occurrence of the landslide; *B* shows the features developed after the earth flow, which was a rather slow-moving one, had come to rest. (After Blackwelder.)

Fig. 26.— Slump and earth flow, East Wairarapa, New Zealand.
Hadmar Sticht, photo.

Fig. 26A.—An earth flow, Motunau, New Zealand.

R. Speight, photo.

Fig. 27.—A great landslide leaves an amphitheatre scar and forms a temporary lake, as in the case of Gohna slide, which occurred in India in 1893. (After W. M. Davis.)

Fig. 28.—Rock fall from the roof of a limestone cavern, Jenolan, New South Wales.

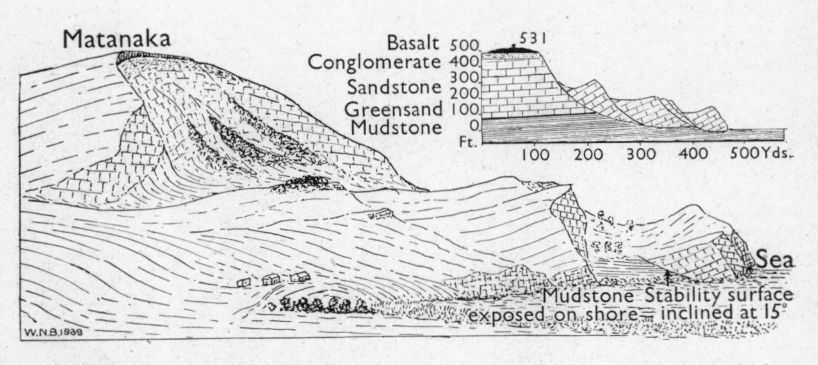

Fig. 29.—Slump at Cornish Head, Waikouaiti, New Zealand. (From a drawing by W. N. Benson, F.R.S.)

earth flows which in extreme cases extend for miles. These have characteristic hummocky surfaces (figs. 25, 26) diversified in many cases by tarns (fig. 26A), and may impound water to form lakes of larger size by blocking valleys (fig. 27). Such lakes are generally short-lived, however. If they outflow over the landslide dams the overflow channels are generally enlarged so rapidly that the lakes are drained after the manner of the bursting of a dam, and many disastrous floods have been thereby caused in lower valleys. A number of temporary lakes of this kind, soon drained after they overflowed, were formed by landslides that resulted from the Murchison earthquake of 1929 in New Zealand.

Accumulations of angular boulders brought down by gravity are termed *rock falls* (fig. 28) and *rock slides.* Rock-sliding is facilitated by the presence of flat surfaces of separation inclined a little less steeply than the slope of the surface of the ground. These may be fault surfaces or major joints; but most commonly they are stratification planes, especially where permeable overlie impervious rock formations.

Another type of landslide movement is the *slump,* which takes place along a curved ("spoon-shaped") surface (fig. 29) as a kind

Fig. 30.—Terraces ("terracettes") in slumped ground in the unstable "hydraulic limestone" formation of North Auckland, New Zealand.

J. Wood, photo.

Fig. 31.—Forward movement of slumped ground closes a newly-made cut, North Auckland, New Zealand.

J. Wood, photo.

Fig. 32.—The Whitecliffs landslide, formed during the 1929 earthquakes, West Nelson, New Zealand.

Photo from N.Z. Geol. Survey.

of superficial faulting and leaves an amphitheatre-shaped scar in the landscape (fig. 27). Commonly this landslide-faulting surface branches, and terrace-like strips remain in the scar, each with a backward tilt resulting from rotation during movement down the concave curve of the sole (figs. 29, 30). Slumped ground may move forward almost as a whole (fig. 31), and may buckle the surface in front of the toe of the slide so that it rises to form a ridge. Thus the Whitecliffs slide (fig. 32) which broke away from the coastal cliffs of western Nelson (New Zealand) in 1929 thrust up and exposed a strip of sea-floor over a mile long so that in places it is now 100 feet above sea-level.

Solifluction.—In the frigid zone a slurry of saturated rock debris flows down even very moderate slopes, especially where the deeper ground remains frozen all the year. This *solifluction* results in the formation of irregular terraces and boulder ridges.

Soil Creep.—There is an imperceptible but general mass movement, or *creep,* always in progress on most slopes in low and middle latitudes which accounts for the downhill migration of much waste. Creep is not strictly comparable to the flow of a fluid. Small to-and-fro movements of fragments are always going on as the result of alternate heating and cooling, freezing and thawing,

Fig. 33.—Effects of soil creep, East Wairarapa, New Zealand.
Hadmar Sticht, photo.

wetting and drying. Owing to the constant pull of gravity there is a preponderance of downhill over uphill movements, and this results in downhill creep. Evidence of creep may be seen where trees and posts have been tilted from the vertical by the more rapid movement of a superficial layer (fig. 33), and also in a downhill sag of the edges of the strata of partially weathered rocks, which is sometimes termed "outcrop curvature" (fig. 34).

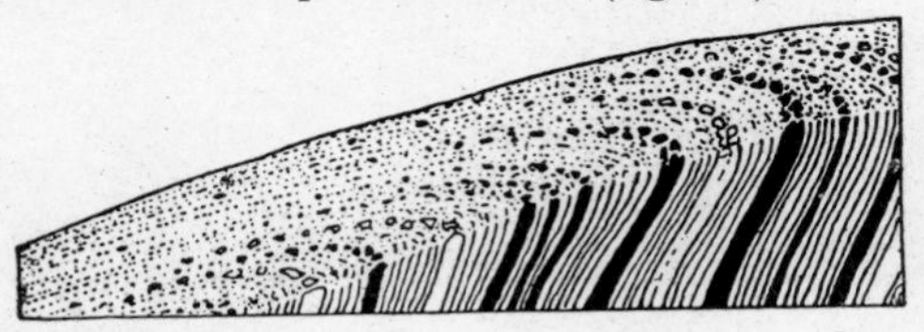

Fig. 34.—Downhill creep of waste. (After W. M. Davis.)

Even angular talus material creeps downhill, especially in cold climates where freeze-and-thaw alternations are frequent. The superficial layer of creeping material on a slope may arrange itself in down-slope ridges of coarse fragments and furrows in which finer material is exposed (*stone stripes*). Where slopes lead to level ground the stone-stripe pattern changes to *soil polygons,* or *stone rings,* which are common in Spitsbergen and other cold regions. This pattern of rings or hexagons of coarse fragments occurs on various scales, the coarser the material the larger the diameter of the rings, up to about 10 feet. It appears to result from a heaving of the ground due to freezing, which causes radial movements around evenly spaced centres. It is possible that the pattern is developed only over a permanently frozen subsoil. Where this is the case the superficial material is undrained, and water which consequently remains in it during the summer is frequently frozen. Phenomena of the fringe around permanently frozen or ice-covered regions are termed "periglacial." Among periglacial features which may have resulted from creep of bouldery waste are *rock glaciers,* resembling ice glaciers in form, but with a ridged or wrinkled surface,[1] and the boulder fillings of valley-bottoms (*stone rivers*) of the Falkland Islands, which are said to creep gradually downstream.

Water Transportation.—The chief agents removing the waste produced by weathering are rain and running water. The latter

[1] Possibly these are a variety of stranded glacial moraines, however.

Fig. 35.—Badland erosion in consolidated gravels (conglomerate), White Bluffs, Marlborough, New Zealand. *F. H. Clift, photo.*

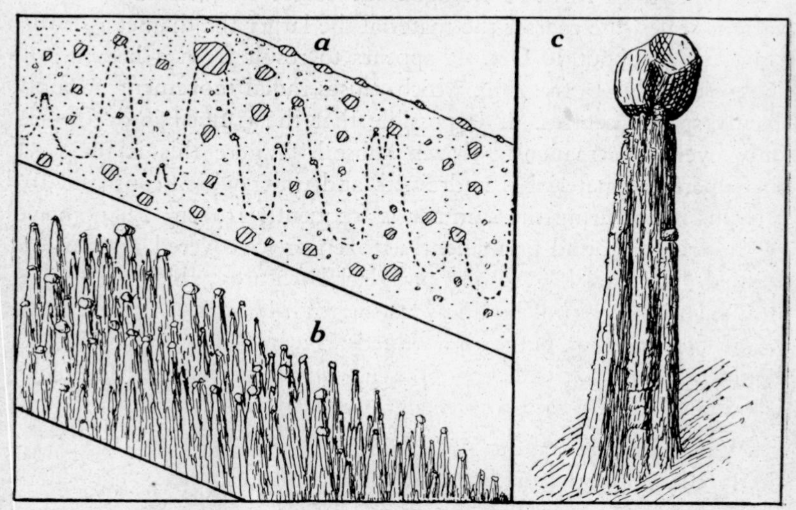

Fig. 36A.—Earth pillars; *a,* section of a clay containing boulders, showing profiles of the surface before and after it has been carved by raindrop impact; *b,* a group of earth pillars; *c,* an earth pillar at Bozen, Tyrol.

is the more effective of the two, but raindrops as they fall loosen particles of fine waste, mix up with them, and so take them into suspension as mud, thus co-operating with running water, which gathers as ephemeral streams and flowing sheets on the surface (when the ground is saturated) and washes the mud away into the channels of permanent streams.

Fig. 36B.—Earth pillars near Bozen (Bolzano), South Tyrol.

C. A. Cotton, photo.

Bare ground is carved by rain-wash into innumerable closely-spaced, steep-sided ridges and valleys of miniature dimensions, producing an almost impassable land surface generally referred to as "badlands" or *badland erosion* (fig. 35).

Earth Pillars.—A demonstration of the effect of raindrop impact is afforded by *earth pillars* (figs. 36A, 36B). These are carved under special conditions—namely, where the raindrops fall vertically in sheltered situations upon material consisting of clay with embedded boulders. As the surface is worn down, the boulders protect the clay immediately beneath them from the impact of falling drops, and so each boulder becomes the cap of a column of clay.

It must not be supposed that rain is particularly active as an eroding agent when falling vertically; but it is only under favourable conditions that vertically falling raindrops can cut earth pillars, which then afford a demonstration of the universal erosive action of rain.

Fig. 37.—Earth fingers, Seatoun, Wellington, New Zealand.
C. A. Cotton, photo.

Rain, indeed, does most erosive work when the impact of the drops is greatest—that is, when the drops are large and especially when they are driven by wind. In the neighbourhood of Wellington, New Zealand, where showers of wind-driven rain occur frequently, the sides of some road cuttings exhibit miniature earth pillars in a nearly horizontal attitude. These might be called *earth fingers* (fig. 37).

Rivers.—When rain falls, generally some of the water runs off the surface of the ground immediately. The proportion of this *run-off* to the total precipitation is very variable, being obviously greatest at any place when heavy rain falls after the ground has

miles along a river-bed. In this way *river gravel* originates. The wearing action is much less marked on finer particles—those which are termed *sand* and *mud*—because the films of water which cling to them by surface tension act as cushions and prevent actual grinding of the grains. Sand that has been carried by water is somewhat angular in contrast with wind-carried sand, which may be worn until the grains are well rounded. Sand grains present along with gravel are liable, however, to be pounded into fine powder by the milling effect of the gravel as it is rolled along, but in rivers such grinding is perhaps less effective in destroying sand than it has been shown to be on gravel beaches.

In mountainous countries such as New Zealand the river-beds, in some cases of great width, are composed of stream-worn gravel. The constituent pebbles are generally well rounded, but retain flat sides here and there, which indicate that they have been formed by the grinding-away of the corners and edges of fragments originally angular and bounded by flat joint surfaces. If the pebbles are traced to their sources it is found that farther and farther upstream they are less and less rounded until, among the mountains, the talus slopes of rough, angular rubble—called "shingle slips" in New Zealand—are reached, which are the source of supply of waste to these rivers.

In general, in small streams and near the heads of streams, where the waste has not travelled far, rounding of boulders and pebbles is incomplete (fig. 39).

The size of fragments that can be carried in suspension by flowing water depends on the velocity of the stream. A sluggish stream with a velocity of 0·17 mile per hour will be capable of carrying only the finest silt, while one flowing two miles per hour (a fairly rapid stream) will sweep along pebbles the size of eggs (A. Geikie). The shape also of fragments has an influence on the size that can be carried. Thus flake-shaped fragments of relatively large size will be carried, for they sink but slowly. For fragments of the same shape the transporting power of streams varies as the sixth power of the velocity.

It is not the maximum or even the mean velocity of a stream that determines the maximum size of fragment that can be carried, but rather the minimum—that is to say, the velocity of the bottom water, for the largest pebbles always slide or roll along the bottom.

Fragments in suspension do not, of course, float. Each fragment is always sinking, slowly or rapidly, according to its size, shape, and specific gravity, which affect the resistance offered to sinking by the viscosity of the water. In running water, however, the motion is not uniformly forward but turbulent, and fragments remain in suspension owing to their being lifted from time to time by upward currents with a velocity greater than that with which the fragments are sinking.

Fig. 39.—Coarse waste (boulders), partly rounded, in a tributary of the Ngakawau River, New Zealand.
C. A. Cotton, photo.

While the larger stones are rolled along the bottom, very large boulders are moved along by torrents in another way. Their forward motion is not continuous. Occasionally, during floods, the stream scours away the gravel on which a large boulder rests, leaving it badly supported. After a time, pressed onward by the stream and unsupported in front, it rolls forward a short distance, and this process is repeated many times, though perhaps at long intervals.

The Quantity of Waste Transported.—The amount of waste actually carried by a stream depends not on its carrying capacity alone, but also on the amount available. Sometimes solid material as much as one-tenth of the weight of the water is carried by small streams in flood. The amount may fall as low as one eight-thousandth. In the case of the Mississippi the average is about 1/1800 by weight. The total amount of suspended material removed by the Mississippi in a year is 340,500,000 tons. (This is additional to 136,400,000 tons removed in solution.) By chemical and mechanical erosion the whole drainage area of the Mississippi is lowered at the rate of 1 inch in 500 years, and the rate of lowering for the whole of the United States has been calculated to be 1 inch in 760 years. Estimates made in South Africa on a different basis of calculation indicate that an almost identical average rate of erosional lowering of the land surface has been in progress for a vast period.

CHAPTER IV

YOUTH OF RIVERS

Normal erosion. The geomorphic cycle. Consequent drainage. Youth. Young valleys. Vertical corrasion. Falls and rapids. Lakes.

Normal Erosion.—The subaerial, as distinguished from the marine eroding agencies fall in two groups, *normal* and *special,* and it is by the normal group, running water and the weathering processes, that the shaping of the land surface is mainly effected. Wind erosion and ice erosion (both of which are in the "special" category) seldom, if ever, work alone. The normal agents, however, can work without help from the special agents; and on practically all the habitable parts of the land surface the normal agents are at present working alone.

It is now universally recognised that, generally speaking, valleys have been excavated or cut to their present forms by the streams that flow in them. This explanation of the origin of valleys (and consequently also of hills and ridges, which are merely the residual parts of the terrain left standing after the excavation of valleys) gained acceptance only in the nineteenth century. One of the most forcible arguments urged in favour of the hypothesis was that now embodied in what has been termed Playfair's *law of accordant junctions.* This is based on the observed fact that in most landscapes tributary valleys join the mains at a common level. Exceptions to Playfair's law may be found, but they are all capable of explanation in such ways as not to contradict the principle (see p. 43).

Many rivers are guided, as will be shown in later chapters, by relatively depressed areas and strips of the land surface, features which, being due to earth movements, are termed *tectonic.* Thus guided the rivers proceed to shape valleys for themselves, but the depression as a whole, as modified in form by the river is often termed the "valley" of the river, though such usage may not be strictly correct. Adjacent mountain masses also are not wholly residual—that is, do not owe their full relief to excavation of valleys around them by rivers (*circumdenudation*). These tectonic forms, however, may be traced only in major landscape features, and in many regions they have entirely disappeared owing to the depth to which erosion has been carried. Smaller valleys, hills, and ridges may generally be regarded without any doubt as the results of the activity of the processes of erosion.

In the latter half of the nineteenth century a corollary to Playfair's law gained acceptance—namely, that, if sufficient time is allowed, the slopes of valley sides become more and more gentle, valley floors become broader and broader, and the intervening ridges and spurs become lower and lower; and that, as the material of the land above sea-level is gradually carried away, particle by particle, the whole surface will be eventually reduced to very faint relief.

When the enormous age of the earth is taken into account, the fact that the land surface is not a continuous plain sloping gently to sea-level seems at first to be inconsistent with the principle just stated; but the contradiction is only apparent. The explanation is that, from time to time, parts of the lithosphere have been uplifted, so that the work of erosion has had to be begun afresh on them. Some parts of the earth's surface have been worn down almost to sea-level over and over again in the course of later "geological time."

In the study of landforms it is important to bear always in mind that no feature of the earth's surface is a finished product. The agencies which effect changes of form are everywhere at work: every part of the surface is even now undergoing some change, and its future landscape forms will differ from the present as the present differ from the past.

The Geomorphic Cycle.—In the study of landforms and landscapes it is convenient to picture a complete series of forms developed during the process of down-wearing of the land by erosion, and land surfaces corresponding to nearly every stage of such a series are known in nature. The successive landscapes, or aspects of the landscape, produced by erosion following uplift of a portion of the earth's surface of whatever form above sea-level comprise a *cycle of erosion* or *geomorphic cycle*. The surface upon which eroding agents begin to work is the *initial surface* and its relief is the *initial relief*. At the other end of the sequence, after valleys have been cut by erosion and the residual relief thus produced has been destroyed by a continuation of the same processes, the thoroughly worn-down surface eventually resulting is termed a *peneplain*. Development of a peneplain depends, however, on a long immunity from further earth movements, and if we were to judge of the frequency of such occurrences by the visible evidence of recent movements of the land in mobile belts of the lithosphere—in New Zealand, for example—the conclusion would be inescapable that no cycle can reach an advanced stage. In relatively stable regions such as Africa, western Europe, and eastern North America, and even in parts of what are now the mobile belts, the geomorphic cycle has proceeded far enough in the past, however, to develop very extensive peneplains. Portions of these still survive, though they have been attacked by erosion in new cycles.

A cycle is introduced generally by the uplift (relative to sea-level) of a portion of the lithosphere. It simplifies the elementary study of landforms to regard such uplift as rapid. It is not to be regarded as ever sudden, or catastrophic, however, but it may conceivably take place so rapidly that the amount of erosion that goes on during uplift is negligible. This will be so especially in terrains of resistant rock. All uplifts are not as rapid as this, and it must be borne in mind that the case of rapid uplift is a special case of the geomorphic cycle selected in order to simplify introductory study. Ultimately—in late stages of the cycle—the results produced by erosion will be much the same whether the initial uplift has been slow or rapid.

The initial surface thus uplifted may have previously been a land surface, or it may have been part of the sea floor. It may have been previously flat, or it may have had any conceivable kind of relief. The initial relief after uplift may be the former relief without modification, or it may be modified by inequality of uplift.

The uplifted mass may have any conceivable kind of geological structure. It may, for example, consist of massive rock, or, on the other hand, of stratified rocks with some of the strata more resistant to erosion than others, and these may be horizontal, tilted, or folded and faulted.

The amount of uplift (relative to sea-level) may be uniform throughout, as would be the case if a cycle were initiated by sinking of the ocean level; or, on the other hand, uplift may be uneven.

The possible initial forms upon which erosion may begin to work to etch out *sequential* forms are thus many and varied, and it follows that the sequential forms produced during the course of the cycle are not always alike, but present an infinite variety. Allowance being made, however, for initial differences of form and structure, certain features are characteristic of the landscape in the various stages of the cycle of erosion—sufficiently so, indeed, to make such stages of great systematic value in classification and description.

A theoretically simple case with which to begin the study of the cycle of erosion is that in which a previously flat or almost flat surface is uplifted to become the initial form. Consideration of the case in which moderate or strong relief of the land is inherited from a period anterior to the uplift introducing the cycle will, therefore, be reserved for a later chapter (Chapter XVI). A nearly flat initial surface might be a *plain of deposition* resulting from deposition of waste in flat layers or strata either beneath the sea or on land, where waste is spread by rivers, or it might be a plain or peneplain which is the result of long-continued earlier erosion. The abundance of sedimentary rocks of marine origin now forming land makes it clear that the history of most land areas began with emergence of a former sea-bottom. In a great many cases uplift has been renewed later in such areas, perhaps more than once, so that the existing landforms do not belong to the cycle of erosion initiated by that emergence; but clearly there must have been such a "first" cycle, the sequence of events in which can be deduced. Examples illustrating or analogous to first cycle forms have often to be drawn from landscapes in a later ("*n*th") cycle, however.

Uplift may be assumed to be slightly irregular, so that the initial surface is diversified by small initial inequalities and gentle slopes, the initial relief being just sufficient to give a definite direction to drainage (fig. 40). Corrugations of the surface and of the strata underlying it are normally much less strongly marked than those shown in the diagram. The strata immediately underlying the surface of a plain of deposition are warped during uplift to the same extent as the surface, to which they remain parallel. The topmost layer of sediment is in this case uniformly weak and unconsolidated, but some of the buried strata may be quite hard, and some are almost certain to be more resistant to erosion than the others. Moreover, there will be present, in any ordinary case, beneath the recently deposited formations, or *cover,* an *undermass* of older rocks with a more complex, perhaps intensely deformed, structure. These may not be deeply buried, and they will perhaps be quickly exposed by erosion. Such an arrangement of cover and undermass may be termed *compound structure.*

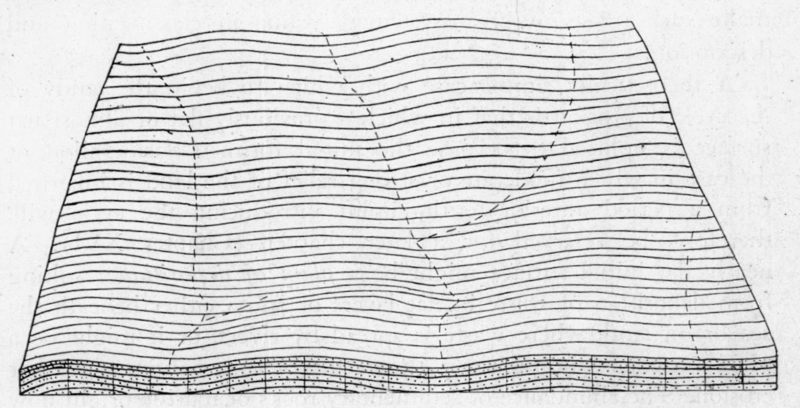

Fig. 40.—Diagram of an initial surface and consequent drainage.

Consequent Drainage.—When rain falls on the initial surface some of the run-off collects and flows along the initial hollows and wrinkles. Streams that have been guided thus by the initial slopes are termed *consequent,* their direction of flow being consequent upon the slope. The valleys which are soon cut by these streams, aided by the waste they pick up, are called *consequent valleys,* and the water-partings or divides between these are *consequent divides,* for their positions are likewise consequent upon the initial form of the surface. Consequent river systems and valley systems thus come into existence.

Youth.—The stage of the cycle entered upon when the work of erosion begins on the uplifted surface is termed the stage of *youth*. Later stages are termed *maturity* and *old age.*

The characteristics of youth and of maturity in the rivers and their valleys and in the landscape surface as a whole must be considered separately. The features of young valleys may be taken up first, and it will be necessary to find examples of some youthful landforms in other than the simple first-cycle case previously postulated.

Young Valleys.—The young valleys which the streams are excavating in the stage of youth are generally narrow and steep-walled—mere trenches in the uplifted surface, the floors of which are covered from side to side by the streams during even moderate floods (fig. 41). There are generally rapids, and often falls, and

Fig. 41.—Young valley cut through limestone by a small stream, Broken River Basin, New Zealand.

C. A. Cotton, photo.

sometimes lakes, along their courses. At first all the tributaries are, like the main streams, consequent, occupying subsidiary wrinkles or flowing down the side slopes of the larger hollows of the initial surface. Where the initial slopes are gentle these tributaries are not numerous. While they are young they do not necessarily join the main stream with *accordant* junctions, the tributary streams sometimes failing to deepen their valleys as rapidly as the main, so that the junctions remain *discordant* or "hanging" (fig. 42). This feature is well seen in many New Zealand valleys. Where the rocks

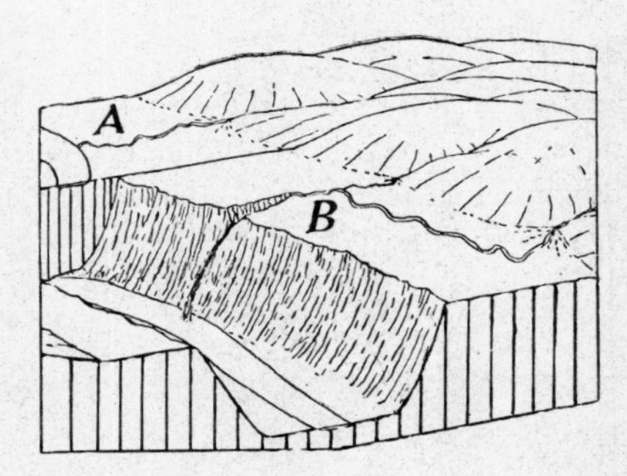

Fig. 42.—*A*, accordant junction of a tributary with a main stream. *B*, discordant junction.

Fig. 43.—Above: Diagram of a stream-bed, showing potholes. Below: Pothole, Dartmoor, England.

of the terrain are soft and the main streams are large and vigorous as, for example, in the case of the Rangitikei and Awatere Rivers, in New Zealand, the main streams have cut for themselves deep, steep-sided trenches in a cycle recently initiated (not a "first" cycle, however). In their rate of downward cutting they have outstripped their small tributaries, which now cascade from mere notches on the walls of the main trenches as in fig. 42, *B*.

Vertical Corrasion.—All the above-mentioned features of young valleys, with the exception of lakes, result from the concentration of the erosive activity of young streams on downward corrasion. To begin with the consequent courses have quite uneven declivities, and these are generally so steep as to give the streams high velocities and power to transport a greater quantity of waste than is supplied to them. No waste, therefore, accumulates in the stream beds. The bedrock is exposed and rapidly worn down by the waste that is dragged over it by the current.

Fig. 44.—A saw-cut gorge in limestone, a tributary of the Ure, Marlborough, New Zealand.

B. C. Aston, photo.

Where the waste is of coarse texture but limited in quantity, much of the deepening where hard rock is exposed in the stream bed is due to the excavation of *potholes*—round vertical shafts up to several feet across and with a depth often greater than their diameter (fig. 43)—which result where boulders or large pebbles are carried around for a long time by eddies. As the first boulders are worn away in the process of grinding, others take their place, and so some well-rounded stones are generally to be found in each pothole.

Fig. 45.—V-shaped young valley, Kaikoura Mountains, New Zealand.
C. A. Cotton, photo.

The processes just described, which corrade vertically downward, would cut valleys of the same width throughout their depth—parallel-sided trenches, vertical-walled in the case of straight streams and sloping-walled in the case of curved streams (which, as will be explained in Chapter VIII, cut sideways as well as downward). There are some well-known young valleys of this "saw-cut" form in Switzerland. A New Zealand example is shown in fig. 44. These narrow trenches are not common in nature, however, for few rocks will stand up for long as vertical or overhanging cliffs,

Fig. 46.—A narrow, V-shaped, young valley, Shotover River, New Zealand.
C. A. Cotton, photo.

and so young valleys are generally opened out to a V shape by slipping down of material from the sides (figs. 45, 46).

As shown in fig. 47 the amount of rock debris which thus slips into a stream and is washed down into the bottom of a valley and carried away by running water is much greater than that actually

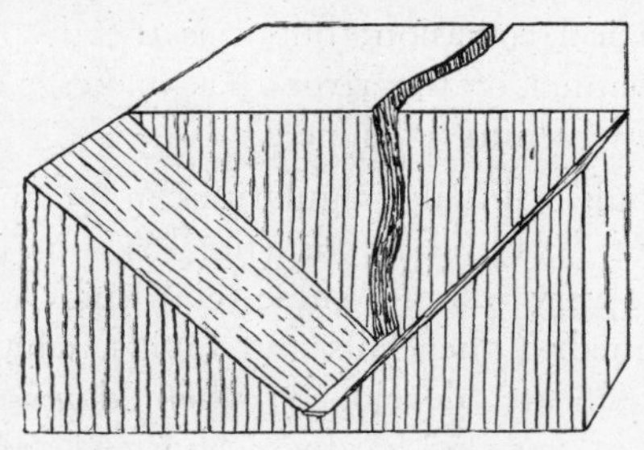

Fig. 47.—Diagram to compare the volume of material actually excavated by vertical corrasion (rear block) with that removed by a stream as a valley is opened out to a V shape (front block).

Fig. 48.—A consequent waterfall over the edge of a lava flow, Iceland.

excavated by vertical corrasion; but it is the deepening of a saw cut along the channel of the river that makes crumbling of the banks and valley-widening possible.

Falls and Rapids.—Initial irregularities in stream gradients give rise to consequent falls and rapids (fig. 48), but unless the rocks at the surface are very resistant these tend quickly to disappear as valleys are deepened. Other falls and rapids, which are generally much longer-lived, are developed when down-cutting streams encounter rocks of varying hardness (figs. 49, 50). These, since they are not related to the initial form of the surface, are not "consequent." Strictly they must be classed with "subsequent" fea-

Fig. 49.—Huka Falls, Waikato River, New Zealand, formed where the edge of a resistant lava layer has been exposed by the river cutting downward.

F. G. Radcliffe, photo.

Fig. 50.—Aratiatia Rapids, Waikato River, New Zealand, formed at the junction of resistant lava (upstream) with weaker material (downstream).

F. G. Radcliffe, photo.

tures such as are described in Chapter VI. Some rocks, such as those consisting of imperfectly consolidated and indurated materials and also much-jointed and shattered rocks, yield very rapidly to stream corrasion. Others are worn away infinitely more slowly.

When, therefore, a down-cutting stream crosses a geological boundary from a resistant to a weak rock, the weak rock downstream has the channel cut more deeply into it than the resistant rock upstream, and at the boundary there is an abrupt steepening of the gradient. At this point there will be a fall or rapid, according to the nature of the junction between the two kinds of rock.

Where the junction is vertical, or even slightly overhanging, rapids rather than distinct falls are generally formed (fig. 51),

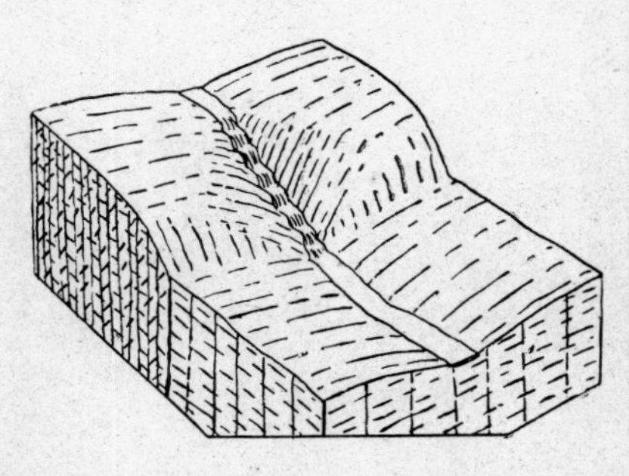

Fig. 51.—Development of a rapid at the junction of resistant and weak rocks.

because at the steep slope where the stream is leaving the resistant rock (after the channel has been more deeply excavated in the weaker rock below) the velocity is increased, and the stream thus has its capacity for corrasion enormously increased, with the result that the edge of the resistant rock is cut away much more quickly than the channel is deepened farther upstream. A steep descent only instead of an abrupt drop in the stream course is the result.

The chief *fall-makers,* as distinguished from rapid-makers, are horizontal and gently inclined beds of resistant rock, which may be either sedimentary strata or lava sheets, overlying weaker rocks. The Falls of Niagara may be regarded as the type of such falls in horizontal strata. Once a fall is established either at the edge of a hard layer on the initial surface, or where the edge is exposed by erosion, the weaker material underlying the fall-maker is easily

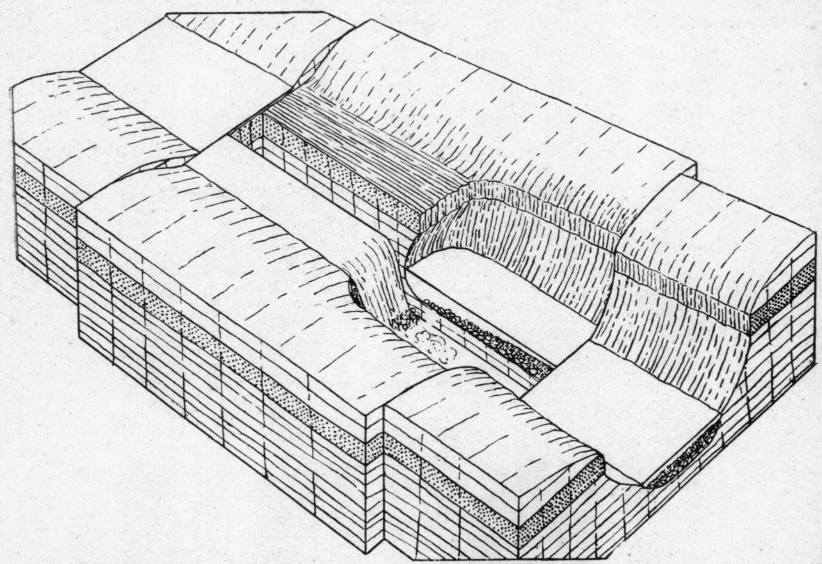

Fig. 52.— Diagram to illustrate the upstream retreat of falls in horizontal strata. The central block is shown as though cut in two longitudinally, with the halves separated so that the profile at the edge of the fall may be seen; on the farther half the water above the fall is not shown. Note the development of the trench below the fall.

Fig. 53.—Trench below the Wairua Falls, New Zealand, which have retreated headward. The fall-maker is the upper layer of a thick lava sheet. Note the jointed lava beneath it, which has been excavated by plunge-pool erosion.

C. A. Cotton, photo.

excavated by the splash and swirl of water in the *plunge pool* (fig. 52), which the descending stream digs out beneath the fall (*plunge-pool erosion*). As this goes on, the edge of the fall-maker is left overhanging, and from time to time blocks of it fall away, so that the edge of the fall, being constantly renewed, is kept always fresh

Fig. 54—The Whangarei Falls, North Auckland, New Zealand. Plunge-pool erosion is breaking up jointed lava in the deeper part of a thick sheet which is the fall-maker.

C. A. Cotton, photo.

and sharp. A fall of this kind retreats rapidly upstream (or *head-ward*), leaving a canyon or trench below the fall, the cross profile of which generally contrasts strongly with an open valley of the stream above the fall (figs. 52, 53).

As a general rule the rate of retreat (*headward migration*) of such a fall is enormously rapid as compared with the rate at which the same stream could cut down through the hard stratum by vertical corrasion, and so the majority of young valleys in horizontal strata with interbedded hard layers have been formed as falls have retreated rapidly upstream. The outcropping edges of the fall-

Fig. 55.—Cascade over the outcrop of a hard sandstone layer which dips downstream and is interbedded with mudstone strata, Clarence Valley, New Zealand.

C. A. Cotton, photo.

making strata may be seen on the walls of the canyons below the falls.

In some cases in New Zealand (figs. 53, 54), falls are migrating headward across thick horizontal lava sheets. Here the upper layer of the lava is the fall-maker and the deeper part of the same lava sheet is weakened very considerably owing to development of shrinkage joints, which separate columns.

Resistant inclined layers dipping at moderate angles upstream form falls similar to those made by horizontal strata; but in this case the falls can be worn back only a short distance, as they diminish rapidly in height, soon giving place to short rapids and then disappearing. Resistant strata dipping downstream form rapids rather than falls, unless the dip is very steep. In this case cascades will be formed (fig. 55), which are afterwards worn back into rapids.

Fig. 56.—Waikaremoana, a lake occupying a branching valley system as the result of blocking of a gorge (in distance at left) by a rock slide.

N.Z. Tourist Department, photo.

Lakes.—Lakes formed by natural agencies have been classified by Davis as: warped-valley lakes; fault-basin lakes; landslide lakes; glacial lakes; volcanic lakes; river-made lakes; and lake-like bays and lagoons.

Landslide lakes have been already mentioned in Chapter III. They are generally very short-lived (p. 26), but an exception to this rule is found in the large and beautiful New Zealand lake Waikaremoana (fig. 56). It is held up by a great rock slide through which water leaks, though little overflows. Lakes in the other categories mentioned will be explained more fully in later chapters, in which "special" processes, geomorphic "accidents," and features produced by diverse movements affecting already eroded landscapes will be dealt with.

All lakes are more or less ephemeral and must be considered features of young landscapes. Also, if regarded as expansions of the channels of the rivers which enter and leave them they make breaks in the continuously-descending valley-floor slopes which all rivers are striving to cut or build for themselves. Until they have succeeded in smoothing out all such irregularities the rivers are still young.

Initially undrained hollows may be expected to be present on a slightly uneven or irregularly uplifted surface in a first cycle. They are extremely abundant also on land surfaces which prior to the very recent initiation of the current cycle of normal erosion have been shaped by glaciers of the Ice Age. Water collects in initial

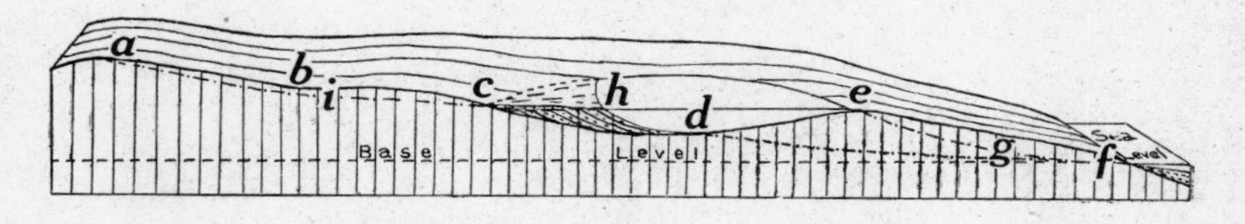

Fig. 57.—The draining and filling-in of a consequent lake. Initial profile, *abcdef;* initial lake, *ce.*

hollows of whatever origin and forms lakes which are *consequent* on the initial form of the surface (fig. 57, *ce*). Generally lakes are short-lived, and most of those formed on an irregularly uplifted first-cycle surface are particularly so. This is true especially of lakes high above sea-level. In the steeper parts of the course of the consequent rivers (*ef,* fig. 57) formed by the overflow from lakes of this kind deep trenches (*egf*) are soon cut. The heads of such canyons work upstream (from *e* to *d*) if the stream gradients are steep, and so the outlet of a lake is cut down as a notch, and the lake-level is gradually lowered until the lake is drained off.

At the same time corrasion is proceeding along the stream or streams (*abc*) which supply water to a lake, at first in the steeper parts of their courses and perhaps later throughout their whole length (*aic*). As a result the streams carry abundant waste, all the coarser and much of the finer part of which is dropped in the lake, for there the water loses its velocity and hence its transporting power (fig. 57, *chd,* where the lake is represented as partly filled before lowering of the outlet begins). The water leaving a lake at its outlet is nearly always clear, having been, as it were, strained free of sediment. Abundant waste is thus deposited in the lake and built up above lake-level by the inflowing streams, and so the lake is reduced in size.

Lakes, whatever their origin, eventually suffer the same fate. Low-lying lakes may disappear as a result of filling only; but in most cases filling and lowering of the outlet go together. The size of most of the large lakes of New Zealand—e.g., Wakatipu and Taupo—has clearly been reduced in both these ways. The Kawarau and Waikato Rivers, which drain these two lakes, leave them as crystal-clear streams, free from sediment. The same is true of the Rhone, where it leaves the Lake of Geneva.

CHAPTER V

MATURITY OF RIVERS AND LANDSCAPES

Base-level and grade. Maturity of rivers. Graded reaches. Dissection of the upland. Development of master streams. Coastal plains. Insequent streams. The law of equal declivities.

Base-level and Grade.—In the foregoing account of the activity of young streams it has been assumed that the rivers flow initially at a considerable height above the sea, under which condition their average slopes and velocities are high and they cut downward energetically. There is, however, a sharp downward limit to active down-cutting. As a stream cuts down so as to approach *base-level* (an imaginary extension of sea-level under the land,[1] fig. 57) the rate of deepening rapidly decreases, for the level of the stream, though it approaches base-level, can never quite reach it except where it enters the sea. In order that the water of a river shall flow its surface must have a certain slope down to the mouth, which, in the case of rivers flowing into the sea, is at base-level (sea-level). Every part of the channel of the stream must therefore remain at such a height that there will be a slope sufficiently steep to carry off the water. The necessary slope is steeper for waste-laden water than it is for clear water.

The minimum necessary slope varies not only in different streams and at different times, but also in the same stream and at the same time with varying conditions, chief among which is distance from the mouth. The necessary slope becomes steeper with increasing distance from the mouth, chiefly because towards the source the quantity of water in the stream is less.[2]

A stream that has attained the minimum slope under existing conditions is said to have reached *grade*, or to be *graded* (fig. 58). The longitudinal profile of a graded stream approximates to a hyperbolic curve. There are always, however, small departures from the ideal curve, and these are due largely to irregularity in the

---

[1] As defined by Powell and Davis.

[2] "*Ceteris paribus*, declivity bears an inverse ratio to quantity of water" (Gilbert).

increase of stream volume downstream, this increase resulting in part from the junction of tributaries of various sizes at irregular intervals.

Fig. 58.—Longitudinal profile of a graded river, showing the relation of grade to base-level.

A factor that influences the steepness of the graded slope at any particular place and time is the amount of waste being supplied farther upstream. This material has to be transported, and the fact that the profile is graded at any place implies that the supply of waste to the stream by tributaries and by rock streams and soil creep on valley sides is exactly equal to the amount the stream can carry past that place. If the supply were greater the surplus would be deposited farther upstream in the river channel, which would thus be steepened, giving the flowing water progressively higher velocity and transporting power until it was able to carry the whole of the waste supplied to it. If, on the other hand, the supply were less than the stream could dispose of, its bed would be swept clear of waste and it would farther deepen its channel, reducing the slope and so decreasing its own velocity and transporting capacity. The graded condition, therefore, represents equilibrium between the amount of waste supplied and the transporting capacity of the stream, and also between the processes of downward cutting and deposition in the stream channel.

When, owing to excess of transporting power over waste supply, a stream cuts downward to establish or maintain grade, it is said to *degrade;* and the process is termed *degradation.* When, on the other hand, owing to excess of waste supply over transporting power, a stream deposits in and so builds up its channel to establish or maintain grade, it is said to *aggrade;* and the process is termed *aggradation.*

In streams that are not yet graded degradation is rapid, as is shown by the trench-like valleys of young streams. When grade is established downward cutting becomes infinitely slower, but does not altogether cease. Afterwards the slope of the graded profile will generally be reduced gradually in steepness, but only with extreme slowness, as the supply of waste falls off owing to the gradual reduction of the relief of the whole region.

Maturity of Rivers.—It is obvious that, when a river is graded, falls, rapids, and lakes, which are irregularities in the profile, have disappeared. The stage of youth is then at an end, and the establishment of grade marks the passage of a river from youth to *maturity,* the next stage of the cycle.

Rivers become graded and therefore mature earliest close to their mouths, where their volume is greatest; and the mature, graded valley extends gradually upstream. The last statement is true only

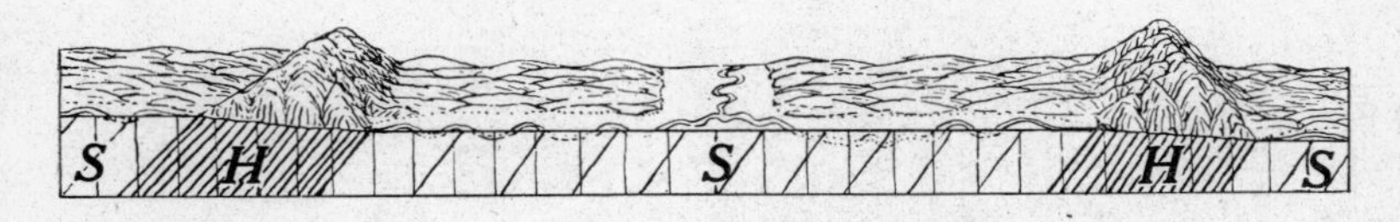

Fig. 59.—Diagram of graded reaches. The longitudinal valley-profile of a transverse stream crossing the outcrops of resistant (*H*) and weak strata (*S*) is shown by the front edge of the block. The river is graded on the weak but not on the resistant rocks.

in a general way, however. It takes no account of differences in the hardness of the rocks over which the river flows.

Graded Reaches.—A river crossing the outcrops of alternating weak and resistant rocks will very early develop *graded reaches* across the outcrops of weak rocks, while the profile remains for a long time irregular and steep across the resistant rocks, where falls and rapids survive, as shown in fig. 59.

In the ideally simple case of streams eroding the gently warped strata underlying a newly emerged sea-floor such an alternation of weak and resistant rocks as is shown in fig. 59 could not occur, but where the initial form at the beginning of the cycle is an older land surface this type of structure is not uncommon. It may be present also beneath a thin layer of newly spread sediment on a land newly emerged from the sea, in which case it would be quickly exposed by downward-cutting streams.

Graded reaches may be high above the *general,* or *permanent,* base-level, which is sea-level, but each is governed by a *local,* or *temporary,* base-level, which is the level of the first outcropping ledge of the next resistant rock downstream. The wearing away of this resistant rock takes place so slowly as to be practically negligible in comparison with the rate at which the adjacent weak rock can be degraded. Thus, though a temporary base-level of this kind is always being lowered, grade is maintained meanwhile across the weak rock next upstream. In course of time grade is established across the resistant rocks also, the graded reaches are joined together, and the stream becomes graded and mature for a great part of its length.

Fig. 60.—Graded reach in the Makara Stream, Wellington, New Zealand.
C. A. Cotton, photo.

Dissection of the Upland.—The initial uplifted surface is in course of time all destroyed. The beginning of this process is seen in the early excavation of narrow young valleys. During the course of a cycle the surface as a whole, as distinguished from the river channels, goes through stages of youth, maturity, and old age.

During the stage of youth the general outlines of the relief are determined by the form of the initial surface, which still survives in large or small areas on the *interfluves* (spaces between rivers), which are termed *doabs* if flat. The actual sides of the young valleys of down-cutting streams are entirely the work of erosion in the new cycle, but while young these valleys are narrow, and if widely spaced they occupy only a part, perhaps a small proportion, of the total area. Often consequent streams, including tributaries, are rather wide apart, and in an early stage of the cycle streams of other kinds have not yet been formed. In an aerial view, therefore, the newly cut ravines may scarcely be seen at all, and the initial surface may appear but little modified over large areas. In detail however, the surface will now resemble more or less closely the dissected plateau of the Gouland Downs shown in fig. 61, though in this particular instance the plateau is not really the initial surface but a flat floor of resistant rock some small depth below it, from

Fig. 61.—Young stage of dissection, Gouland Downs plateau, Nelson, New Zealand.
C. A. Cotton, photo.

which some layers of very much weaker rock have been washed and dissolved away (Chapter XII).

The destruction of the initial surface of the land by the action of streams is termed *dissection*. While considerable areas remain undissected the landscape is still in the stage of youth; but when dissection is complete, the sloping sides of newly-cut valleys intersect one another to form well-defined divides, and no trace of the initial form remains, the surface is *mature*.[1] Dissection may be so incomplete that the landscape is still young even though the dissecting

[1] Considerable latitude must be allowed in the application of this definition, and the transition between youth and maturity is sometimes otherwise defined.

streams have themselves reached the stage of maturity; while, on the other hand, a district may be maturely dissected by streams which are still young. Mature dissection is *coarse* or *fine* in *texture* according as stream lines are widely or closely spaced (fig. 62).

Plains uplifted bodily without deformation require a much longer time for their complete dissection than do districts of which the initial relief is diversified either on account of inheritance of relief from an earlier period of erosion or as a result of deformation accompanying uplift. In the case of diversified initial relief the

Fig. 62.—Mature landscape, Wellington, New Zealand; texture of dissection, rather fine. *C. A. Cotton, photo.*

streams on the uplifted surface are numerous and closely spaced. Many of them may run at first down steep slopes, and such streams will at once begin the work of dissection. When all the closely spaced valleys are incised to some depth the sloping sides of adjacent valleys intersect and the surface is maturely dissected—that is to say, no remnants of the initial form survive on the interfluves. Such dissection takes place with extreme rapidity if the superficial material is unconsolidated (fig. 64). Hence parts of the former sea-floor that are strongly deformed as well as uplifted are practically unknown in the young stage. On a uniformly uplifted plain on the other hand most of the precipitation sinks immediately into the ground, or gathers in pools to soak gradually away or to be dried up by evaporation; and any temporary streams formed on the horizontal surface as a result of unusually heavy showers are so sluggish that their corrading power is negligible. Thus considerable areas of such surfaces may survive for a long time, even though built of soft material.

Development of Master Streams.—On inclined surfaces the run-off is considerable, and there may be a large number of closely spaced consequent streams. These deepen their valleys side by side, and soon the initial surface on the portions of the interfluves separating the deepest (middle) parts of the young ravines is cut away, and the sides of adjacent ravines intersect, forming sharp ridges (fig. 63, block *A*). If the streams cut deeply, some of them,

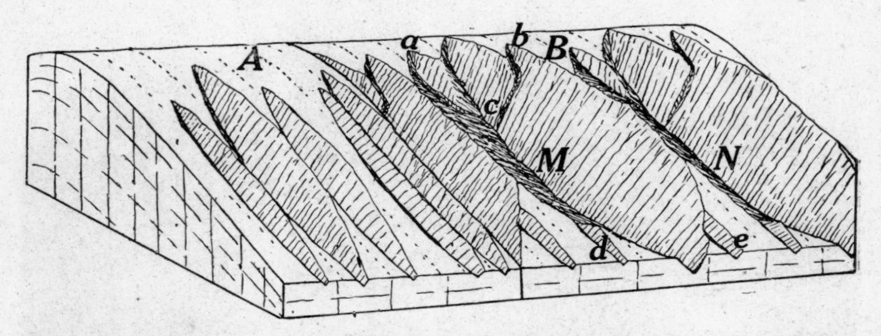

Fig. 63.—Diagram illustrating dissection by consequent streams and development of master streams in bottle-necked valleys.

favoured by draining initially larger areas, by having slightly softer material to excavate, or by some other circumstance, cut larger ravines than the others. These become *master streams* (*M, N,* fig. 63, block *B*), and as their ravines become deeper the sides are worn back until the ridges dividing them from the smaller, higher-level streams at either side are cut through, and the latter are compelled to run down into the valleys of the master streams and become their tributaries. (Thus *ac* and *bc* join the master stream *M*.) A few master streams may soon receive practically the whole of the drainage of the surface, though, near the foot of the slope, where the master valleys are shallower and therefore narrower, or *bottle-necked,* diminutive beheaded remnants (*d, e*) of some or all of the other original consequent streams will still remain. This process, termed *abstraction,* has been called also "the struggle for existence" among streams.

This competition among streams is well illustrated on the mud-covered hill-slopes in the vicinity of Lake Rotomahana, New Zealand, where showers of mud and fragments of pumice ejected from the basin of Lake Rotomahana by the volcanic explosion of 1886 formed a layer over the former topography, down the slopes of which innumerable consequent streams began at once to flow during every shower and to excavate ravines. Fig. 64, photographed in 1921, shows an advanced stage in the struggle for existence, in

Fig. 64.—Consequent drainage and abstraction on the mud ejected from Lake Rotomahana in 1886, photographed in 1921. Compare with fig. 63.
C. A. Cotton, photo.

which a great reduction in the number of ravines has taken place owing to abstraction of the smaller streams by the masters.

Coastal Plains—When a portion of the sea-floor emerges to become land, the uplifted portion is commonly a strip, narrow or broad, termed a *coastal plain,* bordering a pre-existing land (*hinterland*), which has been uplifted along with it. The uplift of a coastal plain may or may not be accompanied by deformation. A coastal plain of simple structure—that is, uplifted without notable deformation, though perhaps gently tilted seaward—serves as an example in connection with which may be considered the dissection of a flat area with very little slope.

In fig. 65 strip *B* shows the initial form of a coastal plain exposed by withdrawal of the sea; but contemporaneously with the uplift or very shortly after it the form shown in strip *C* will be assumed.

The majority of the rivers on a newly emerged coastal plain are the rivers of the old land extended across the newly uplifted sea-floor and seeking the sea by the easiest (consequent) paths. These are *extended* rivers. In the simplest case their courses are straight, parallel with one another, and at right angles to the shoreline; but, obviously, even small irregularities of the initial surface will

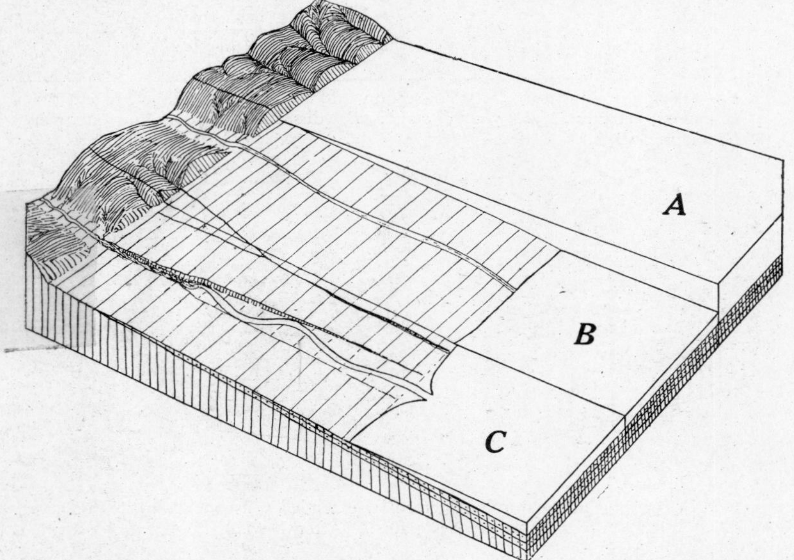

Fig. 65.—Diagram of a coastal plain of simple structure. Block *A* shows the hinterland before uplift, block *B* the newly emergent coastal plain, and block *C* the same after extended rivers have become graded in the soft coastal-plain sediments.

cause the rivers to take less direct courses, and two or more may unite before reaching the sea. These extended rivers, carrying as they do a considerable volume of water when they leave the hinterland, cut down and grade their courses very quickly in the weak sedimentary rocks of the coastal plain. Broad areas (doabs) of the flat interfluves may, however, long remain undissected. A coastal plain with a somewhat complicated history borders the eastern and Gulf coasts of the United States. Western and southern Australia also are bordered by extensive coastal plains.

Insequent Streams.—As consequent rivers in incised valleys (and in some cases rivers of other kinds) develop new tributaries, these start as steep ravines cut by concentrated rain-wash collected in hollows accidentally formed, perhaps as small slumps, on the steep sides of the main valleys. These gullies rapidly gnaw their

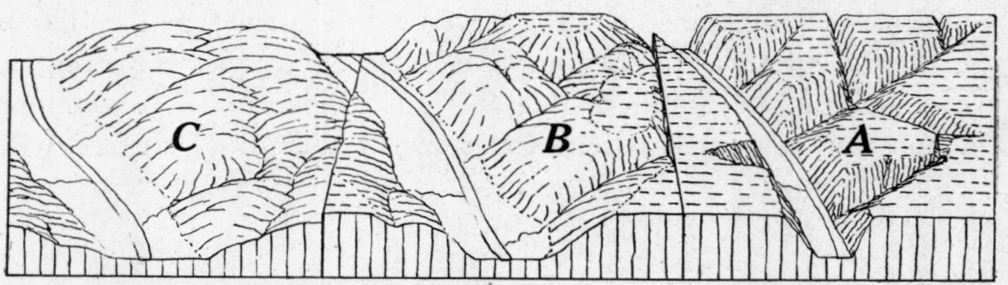

Fig. 66.—Diagram illustrating the dissection of an uplifted plain by insequent branching streams. *A,* young stage; *B,* dissection approaching maturity; *C,* mature stage.

Fig. 67.—A coastal plain maturely dissected by extended consequent, new consequent, and insequent streams. (After Davis.)

way back into the interfluves by *headward erosion.* As they grow deeper and are extended in length headward they receive an increasing amount of water both from surface run-off and from seepage of ground water along their steep banks. The positions and directions of streams that start in this way are purely accidental except in so far as they are determined by the side slopes of main valleys on which they originate and by a slight tendency of the gnawing head to turn towards the side best supplied by ground-water seepage—generally towards higher ground. They are termed *insequent* (figs. 66-68). They in their turn develop insequent tributaries, which also work their way back headward into the interfluves, so that the remaining area of undissected surface is reduced with increasing rapidity.

The pattern, as seen on a map, which is developed by insequent drainage has been likened to the branching of an apple tree, and has been termed *dendritic* (fig. 68).

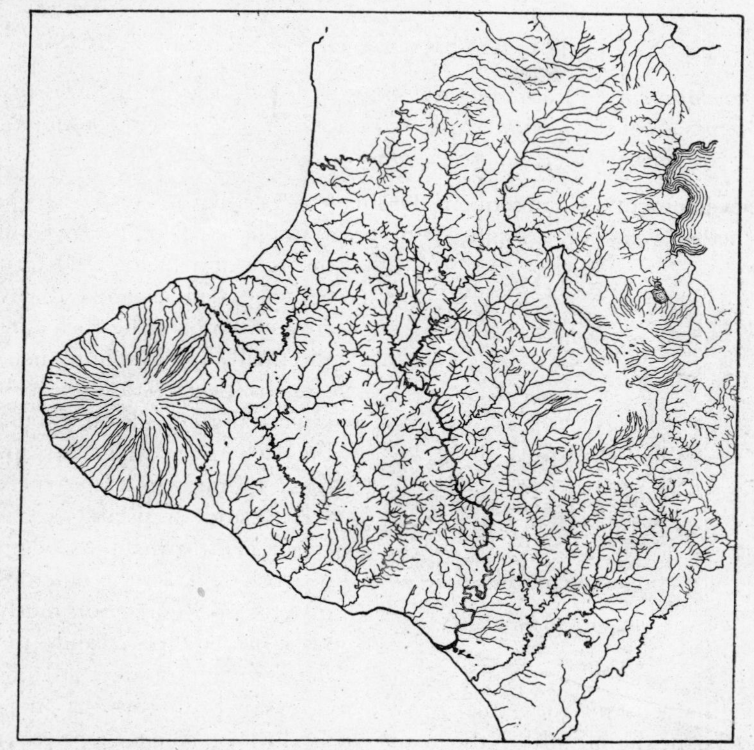

Fig. 68.—Dendritic drainage patterns of the Wanganui and other river systems of Taranaki and western Wellington, New Zealand. Compare this with the radial patterns of consequent streams on the volcanic mountains Egmont (West) and Ruapehu (east). (Map from Marshall's *Geology of New Zealand.*)

The Law of Equal Declivities.—Where homogeneous rocks are maturely dissected by consequent and insequent streams, the side slopes of the valleys which they cut—that is to say, all hillside slopes—tend to develop at the same slope angle, so that profiles of ridges, spurs, and valleys become symmetrical. This is Gilbert's *law of equal declivities.* The principle was originally stated as though the reduction of steepness of slopes took place entirely as a result of stream erosion, but it is true nevertheless as applied also to the effects of combined mass movements, as is indicated by the common occurrence of symmetry in landforms.

CHAPTER VI

SUBSEQUENT RIVERS AND RIVER DIVERSION

Development of subsequent drainage. Local base-levels. Shifting of divides. Capture, or "river piracy." Changes following capture. The Kaiwarra capture.

Development of Subsequent Drainage.—The nature of the rock, whether weak or resistant, is of great importance in determining the rate at which gullies can be extended headward by erosion. Where the rocks are all equally resistant insequent streams develop and branch impartially in all directions; but where a main stream crosses zones of alternately weak and resistant rocks tributary streams that begin to work back on the outcrops of weak rocks are enormously favoured thereby, and the development of new streams on the resistant rocks may take place so slowly in comparison as to be negligible. It is the tributaries which start on the weaker outcrops and are afterwards confined to and guided in the direction of their headward erosion by weaker zones of rock that are chiefly effective in dissecting the land surface. Such streams are called *subsequent streams* (*S,* fig. 69), and the divides between them are *subsequent divides.*

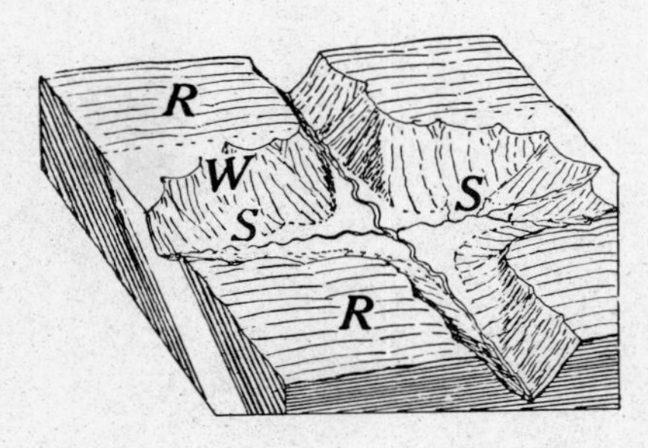

Fig. 69.—Diagram of the development of subsequent valleys. *R,* resistant formations; *W,* weak formation; *S,* subsequent streams.

Subsequent valleys that are guided by the outcrops of the weaker members of a series of stratified rocks (fig. 69) run parallel with the strike, and they are, therefore, longitudinal or *strike* valleys. The subsequent divides which separate them are also *strike* ridges. The subsequent longitudinal streams are generally developed as tributaries to transverse rivers, which are sometimes, though by no means always, of consequent origin. Some may be "superposed" (Chapter XII), others "antecedent" (Chapter XVII), and others merely "inherited" from an earlier cycle.

Local Base-levels.—As explained in Chapter V, the efforts of a young transverse stream to cut downward and attain grade are much impeded by the difficulty of cutting through the occasional strata of resistant rock that it crosses. By these the stream is literally "held up" for a relatively long period. Subsequent tributaries, which are eroded entirely along the outcrops of weak strata, have no such difficulties to contend with, and so they rapidly become graded (fig. 69), for the level of the main stream at the point of junction is for each side stream a local, or temporary, base-level (p. 60), which is being constantly lowered as long as the main stream below the junction is still degrading. In fact, the level of any point on a river may be regarded as a local base-level for the river above that point, with all its tributaries.

Shifting of Divides.—On the broad swells between the stream lines on a plain uplifted with very slight deformation, where such is the form of the initial surface, the divides are very poorly defined; whereas by the time the surface has been dissected to the mature stage the divides have been reduced to lines or narrow strips and are very well defined. Such well-defined divides do not, however, remain always in the positions in which they were first determined by the intersection of the slopes of the neighbouring valleys. A very obvious *shifting* of a divide takes place where one stream is abstracted by another in the manner already described. Here a great portion of the valley system drained by the abstracted stream is transferred and added in a moment to that of the master stream. This is an example of the sudden and radical transference of a divide from one position to another which is termed *leaping* of the divide.

There is a much slower, and hence less spectacular, shifting termed *creeping* constantly in progress from which no divide in a maturely dissected district is exempt. Wherever the heads of two streams are opposite to each other, one on each side of a more or less well-defined ridge, it is barely possible that the streams will degrade their channels at exactly the same rate so that when the divide has been lowered to some extent by erosion it will be immediately beneath its former position. Usually one of the streams will, on account of its greater steepness, its greater volume, or the weaker nature of the rock over which it flows, cut down more rapidly than the other, towards which the divide will be pushed. This is illustrated in fig. 70, in which possible differences in the resistance of the rocks are left out of account. The upper full line *ACB* represents the initial profile, and the lower full line *ACB* the

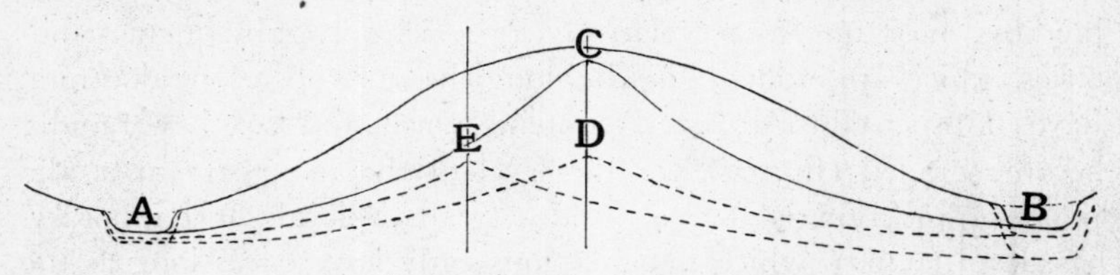

Fig. 70.—Profile of a shifting divide.

profile of the divide *C* after it has become sharply defined as a result of dissection by streams flowing as tributaries into the rivers *A* and *B*. As the surface is lowered, the divide may, at some later time, be at *D,* immediately below *C;* but it is much more likely to be at some point, such as *E,* to one side or the other of *C*. The shifting in this case might be brought about as a result of the more rapid deepening of the valley *B* than of *A*.

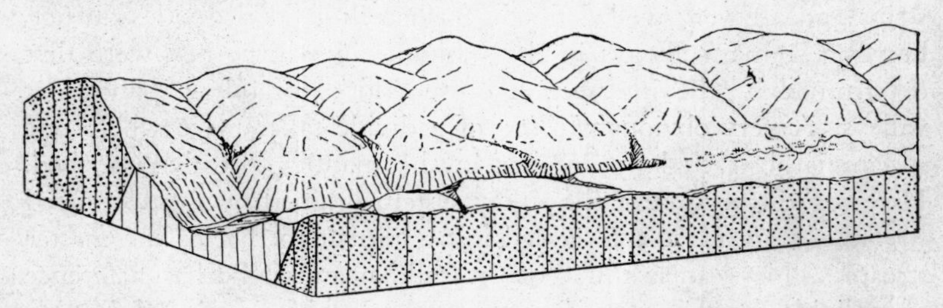

Fig. 71.—Diagram of a shifting divide in a subsequent depression. Remnants of the valley-bottom of the now shrunken stream on the right border the valley of the more vigorous stream on the left, which is rapidly pushing headward.

Shifting of this kind is most effective where the opposed streams are subsequents developed on the same weak formation (as in fig. 71), where proofs of rapid migration of the divide between their heads may sometimes be seen in the form of remnants of valley-floor deposits of the weaker stream, and portions of the valley floor itself may remain as terraces cut into by the narrower and steeper valley of the more vigorous stream, which flows in the direction opposite to the slope of the terraces. The weaker stream, having been robbed of part of its valley system, is of diminished volume. The valley bottom near the divide will probably be swampy, as it is no longer occupied by the full-sized stream which eroded it.

Capture, or "River Piracy."—In the struggle for existence among consequent streams (p. 63), in which a few streams assert their mastery in the manner already described, the headwaters of the minor streams which are abstracted and become tributaries to the master rivers may be said also to be *diverted,* or *captured,* and their diminished lower courses, if they survive at all, may be described as *beheaded*. Diversion of rivers into new courses takes place in various ways. Many diversions, producing drastic changes in river patterns, are effected by streams working headward under certain conditions so as to tap and lead off the water of others, as will now be described. To diversion of this type the term *capture,* or "river piracy," is applied.

Other conditions being similar, the channels of large rivers are deepened more rapidly than those of their smaller neighbours; and even when they are all graded the larger rivers flow in more gently sloping valleys than the smaller streams, and so at an equal distance from their mouths are more deeply incised. It frequently happens, therefore, that where two adjacent rivers cross the outcrop of a weak stratum, *W* (see fig. 72, *a*), the level of one, *A,* which is the local base-level for its tributaries, is considerably lower than that of the other, *B*. A subsequent tributary *a* of *A,* the more deeply entrenched river, working headward along the zone of weak rock, *W,* will, like all such streams, be graded for the greater part of its length, and may therefore be at a sufficiently low level at its head to tap the water of the higher-level transverse river *B,* which is led off to swell the volume of *A*.

The former upper course of *B,* which is now added to the valley system of *A,* is said to have been *captured,* while *B,* which has lost its headwaters and is thus much reduced in volume, is said to have been *beheaded*. The stream *a* is termed the *diverter*. The bend, *E,* in the course of the captured stream where it turns from the captured portion of its valley into the valley of the capturing subsequent stream is termed the *elbow of capture*.

Generally, before capture takes place, the river *B* will have a subsequent tributary *b*, heading opposite to the stream *a*; but during the process of capture the divide between the heads of the streams *a* and *b* will slowly creep towards the river *B* until the last remnant of the stream *b* is eliminated and the divide formerly at the head of the stream *a* leaps to a new position across the former course of

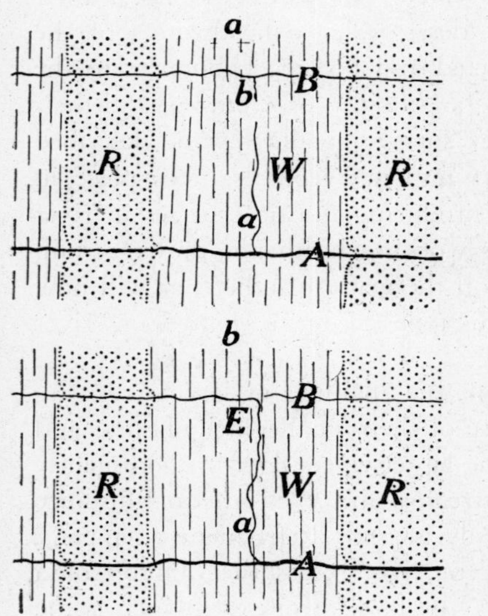

Fig. 72.—Diagrammatic maps illustrating the process of capture. *R*, outcrops of resistant rocks; *W*, of weak rocks. Map *a* represents the condition just before capture takes place; map *b*, just afterwards.

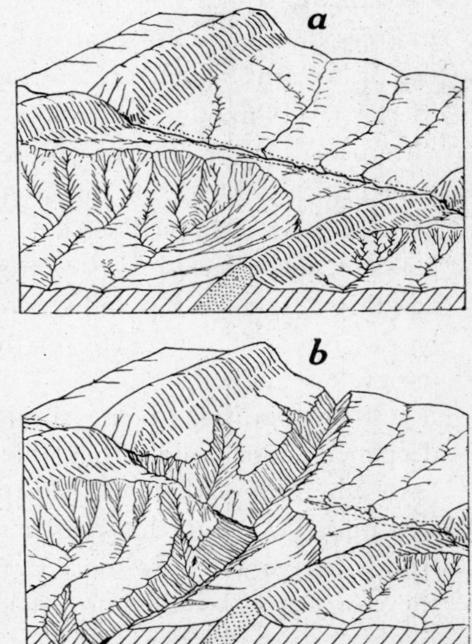

Fig. 73.—Diagrams illustrating capture of the headwaters of one transverse stream by the subsequent tributary of another. In the stage represented by diagram *a* capture is imminent; while in the stage represented by diagram *b* it has taken place. (After Davis.)

the river *B*, the headwaters of which are transferred to the valley system of the river *A*.

By the time the stage of imminent capture shown in fig. 73, *a*, is reached the headward erosion of the stream that is about to make the capture is hastened by an augmentation of its volume due to seepage of ground water leaking down through the bed of the threatened river.

Changes following Capture.—Immediately following capture there are important changes in stream profiles. The slope of the valley of the capturing stream, though graded, or nearly so, prior to the capture, is now much too steep, especially near the elbow of capture, for the largely increased volume of water it has to carry. Degradation at once becomes active, and the slope is reduced in steepness by the cutting of a trench. As this deepening steepens the slope down which the water from the captured stream flows, its valley also is correspondingly deepened. Thus the stream flows in a newly deepened trench around the elbow of capture. Tributary

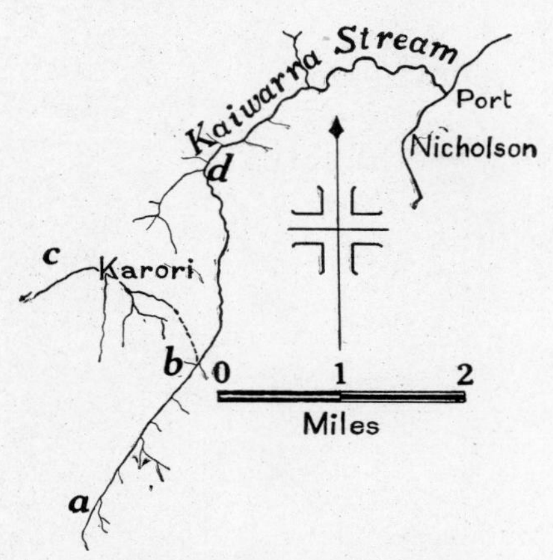

Fig. 74.—Map showing the Kaiwarra Stream, Wellington, New Zealand. Capture has taken place at *b*.

streams also become entrenched, on account of the lowering of the level of the main stream—their local base-level. As the depth of the trench around the elbow of capture increases, the new divide between the captured stream and the beheaded stream is pushed back so as to shorten the latter. It is probable, indeed, that by the growth of insequent tributaries from the newly deepened trenches, and by the general lowering of the land surface on the weak rocks which follows the lowering of the local base-levels, the new head of the beheaded stream will be gradually transferred to the outcrop of the next resistant stratum downstream. The former gorge, or water gap, through this stratum is now no longer traversed by a stream, and becomes an "air gap" (see Chapter VIII, fig. 108).

When the floors of the adjacent valleys have been farther lowered by erosion an air gap may be a mere notch in a subsequent ridge. In the early stages after capture the heads of the beheaded streams are poorly defined. Generally they rise in swampy flats which occupy parts of the floors of the valleys traversed by the streams before capture took place.

Capturing streams, though usually subsequent, do not necessarily belong to that class, for insequent streams working their heads

Fig. 75.—Sketch of the Kaiwarra capture. Captured stream (entrenched) on left; capturing stream on right; abandoned course through distant valley in centre.

back under favourable conditions are also obviously capable of effecting captures. Nor is a sharp turn in the course of a stream necessarily associated with capture. Many sharp turns are consequent on the irregular form of the initial surface, and, as will be explained in Chapter XIII, such irregularities are common in the courses of New Zealand rivers. In the Kaiwarra valley system, near Wellington, there is, on the other hand, a very instructive example of stream capture in which the capturing and captured streams are in the same straight line.

The Kaiwarra Capture.—The capturing stream, a tributary or the head of the Kaiwarra, has effected the capture by working back at first southward (from *d,* fig. 74), apparently as an insequent, and then south-westward as a subsequent along a belt of shattered and thus weakened rock (*shatter belt*) on the line of a fault, until at *b* it has led off the head (*ab*) of a stream which formerly followed the course *bc* (as the head of the Karori Stream). It would seem that the former course, *abc,* had originated by headward erosion of a stream at first insequent, *cb,* and then subsequent on the shatter-belt, *ba.* Fig. 75 is a sketch of this capture from a hill to the south-east, and fig. 76 is a photographic view from the south. This shows

Fig. 76.—View in the Kaiwarra valley, showing the abandoned valley of the beheaded stream, and the newly deepened valleys of the captured and the capturing stream, and (in the foreground) of a small tributary. (A lake in the main valley is artificially dammed.)

C. A. Cotton, photo.

that the captured stream is entrenched so that remnants of its former floor remain as a terrace which is continued by the floor of the abandoned valley of the beheaded stream (in distance, left of centre, fig. 76). The entrenchment of a tributary of the captured stream is seen in the foreground (compare fig. 73).

CHAPTER VII

MATURE LANDSCAPES: ADJUSTMENT TO STRUCTURE

Subsequent erosion on folded rocks. Adjustment to structure. The drainage of mountainous areas of folded rocks. Subsequent ridges in synclinal positions. Resequent drainage. Homoclinal ridges. Escarpments: their rapid retreat. Hogbacks. Cuestas. Homoclinal shifting. Mesas and buttes. Structural plateaux. Structural benches and terraces.

Subsequent Erosion on Folded Rocks.—In the preceding discussion of the development of subsequent streams it has not been assumed that the strata are steeply inclined. The structure may be homoclinal, and, when the surface has been worn down somewhat, consequent rivers may cross the outcrops of the successive rock formations. This is the case in a coastal plain of simple structure, where the beds of sediment of which it is built dip gently in the same direction as the general slope of the surface, and so the consequent streams flow in the same direction as the strata dip, or at right angles to their strike. On a terrain of closely folded strata, on the other hand, the larger of the consequent streams must follow courses corresponding to the axes of the synclines, for in these positions are the furrows of the initial surface (see fig. 77), and these streams are therefore longitudinal, or parallel to the general direction of the strike of the strata.

It is very rarely, however, that such consequent rivers surviving from a first cycle are found in existing landscapes. Where masses of closely folded strata have been upheaved as the initial forms of mountain ranges consequents must be replaced by other kinds of rivers very quickly even in the first cycle, and probably before the process of folding is complete. It is impossible to ignore in this case the erosion that accompanies uplift, for on the steep and varied slopes that will prevail over such initial mountains erosion must be exceptionally rapid on every kind of rock. Even if erosion were magically delayed until uplift was complete, the stage of youth would be hurried through almost in a flash, and when erosion during uplift is allowed for it becomes apparent that no such landscape is likely to be found in a youthful condition or even at the stage in which many rivers still follow synclinal consequent courses. In such a case the stage of youth is elided, and when such elision takes place a landscape is described as *mature-born*.

Fig. 77.—An initial surface on folded rocks. This is purely hypothetical.

In explanation of stream patterns and landscape forms in general which eventually are developed on closely folded rocks it is legitimate, however, to discuss a case in which it is postulated that erosion is delayed until uplift is complete, and thus to deduce the development of the mature landscape through hypothetical youthful forms.

Longitudinal, or *primary,* consequent rivers in the initial furrows will be fed by *secondary* consequent tributaries, which run, perhaps in minor transverse corrugations, down the flanks of the initial arches, and thus down the dip of the strata in the flanks of the anticlines. Such streams must degrade very rapidly, on account of the steepness of the slopes down which they flow. In their down-cutting they expose the outcrops of the weaker strata, and along these are developed other tributaries that are subsequent and longitudinal.

This process is shown in fig. 78, in which portions of an arch and of a trough are represented. Two resistant layers of rock are

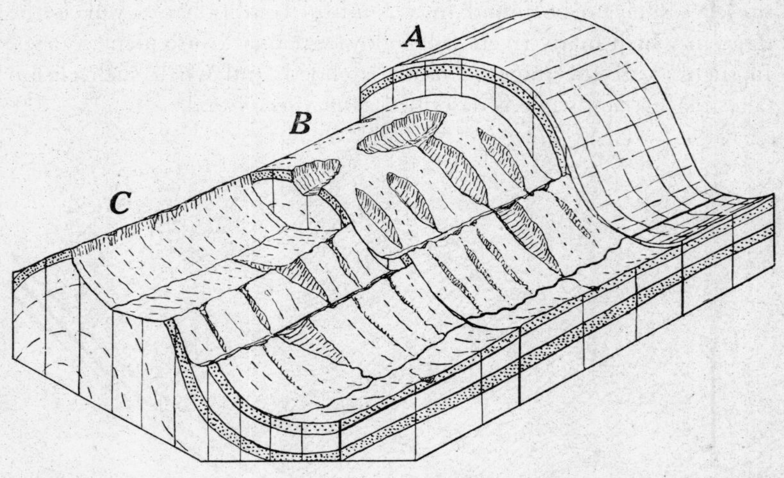

Fig. 78.—Development of subsequent river courses on a terrain of folded rocks.

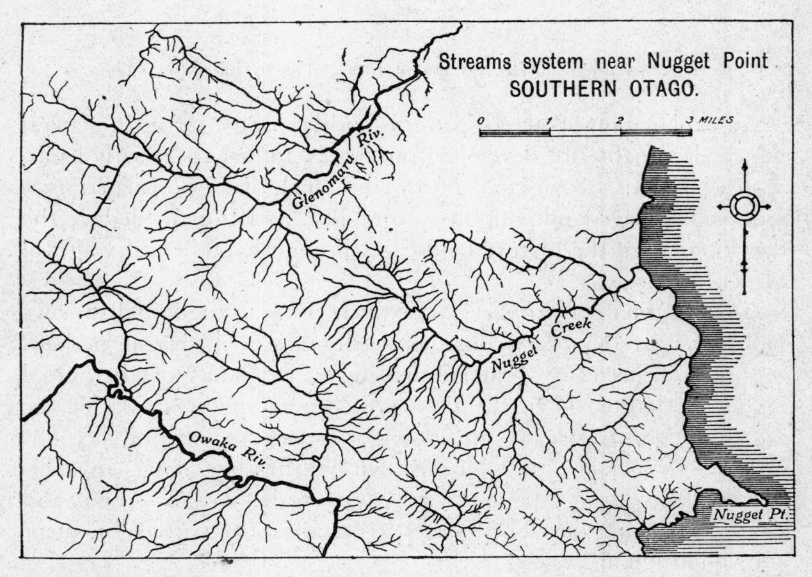

Fig. 79.—Map showing adjustment to structure near Nugget Point, Otago, New Zealand. There is a conspicuous development of subsequent ridges and valleys adjusted to the north-westerly strike of steeply dipping strata. (After Marshall.)

shown stippled, while the weaker formations are left blank. The streams consequent on the initial form (block *A*) are a river following a longitudinal course in the trough and a number of small tributaries running down the flank of the arch. In the stage represented by block *B* the highest resistant formation has been cut through and a subsequent valley has been developed on the weak underlying stratum. Some streams have cut through the second resistant formation also. Block *C* represents a more complete development of subsequent drainage, when the outcrops of both the resistant strata form subsequent strike ridges.

Adjustment to Structure. — The development of subsequent drainage, going on as it does in all regions of stratified rocks whether gently or closely folded, causes streams of types other than subsequent to shrink both in length and in volume, the subsequent streams meanwhile increasing in length and size as a result of headward erosion and the capture of earlier drainage. This general process, which results in the localisation of stream lines on weak zones, receives the name *adjustment to structure*. It begins in the stage of youth, but does not end with it; that is to say, adjustment is not completed but is going on continuously as the stage of youth is left behind.

The drainage pattern that results appears, on the map, as a system of subparallel stream lines following the strike of the rock formations and joined up by occasional transverse portions crossing the strike ridges in gorges some at least of which may be developed as shown in fig. 78. The rectangular drainage pattern so produced is described as *trellised*.

An example of very thorough adjustment of stream courses to structure is shown in fig. 79, and a well-marked parallel arrangement of ridges in the hilly district around Wellington, New Zealand, is assignable to the same cause (figs. 80A, 80B).

Though the type of structure most favourable to the conspicuous development of subsequent drainage is an alternation of contrastingly weak and resistant strata, adjustment to structure goes on in some measure practically everywhere. Even in massive rocks there are almost always lines or zones of weakness, such as fault lines, shatter belts, and even master joints, capable of guiding the headward erosion of streams. Occasionally such structures as these have a definite arrangement or pattern which allows the drainage guided by them to be recognised as subsequent. More often no such definite arrangement is recognisable, however, and the drainage pattern on massive rocks must generally be described as insequent, not because it is known that there is no structural control, but because structural control is not obvious. This is the case even in

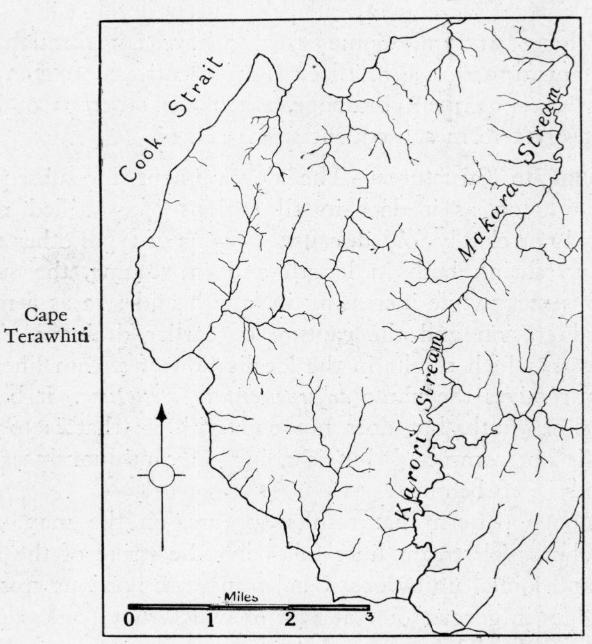

Fig. 80A.—Map of the western part of the Wellington Peninsula, showing the alignment of the streams in a north-north-east and south-south-west direction, and an approach to a "trellised" pattern. Compare fig. 80B.

some regions of sedimentary rocks where there are not notable differences in hardness between strata, as, for example, in many of the mountainous parts of New Zealand, where the drainage pattern is largely insequent, though among the larger streams consequents and subsequents may be suspected.

The Drainage of Mountainous Areas of Folded Rocks.—In strongly folded and uplifted districts the land surface as now found is generally far below the initial surface. In the early stages of the cycle introduced by the uplift with folding the great height above base-level together with the steepness of the initial slopes induces rapid erosion, and the streams have an excellent opportunity to seek out the weaker rocks and become adjusted to the structure. As the anticlinal ridges are initially high above the local base-levels and are flanked by steep slopes, their destruction goes on apace.

Fig. 80B.—Adjustment to structure as shown by parallel ridges of the Wellington Peninsula. Cape Terawhiti in foreground; compare fig. 80A.

V. C. Browne, photo.

Where they are formed of well bedded rocks with weak layers along which, when the rocks are waterlogged, landsliding may take place, the dip towards the valleys on either hand is conducive to mass movements on a large scale, which aid stream action in destroying the initial arch.

Subsequent Ridges in Synclinal Positions.—It has often been the subject of remark, and even a source of wonder, that the strata in some mountain ridges form synclinal folds, and that valleys occupy the axes of the adjacent anticlines. It is sometimes implied that this is a general rule in mountain ranges, and an explanation offered is that the rocks in symmetrical anticlines are stretched and broken and thus weakened during the process of folding, the rocks in the synclines being at the same time compressed and strengthened. If this were the case there would be a tendency towards the formation of subsequent valleys on the weakened rocks of the anticlines, between which would remain subsequent ridges on the strengthened rocks of the synclines. This hypothetical explanation is not necessary, however, for it is found that in the well-known and often cited examples of synclinal mountains the ridges or summits are formed of residuals of resistant rock overlying

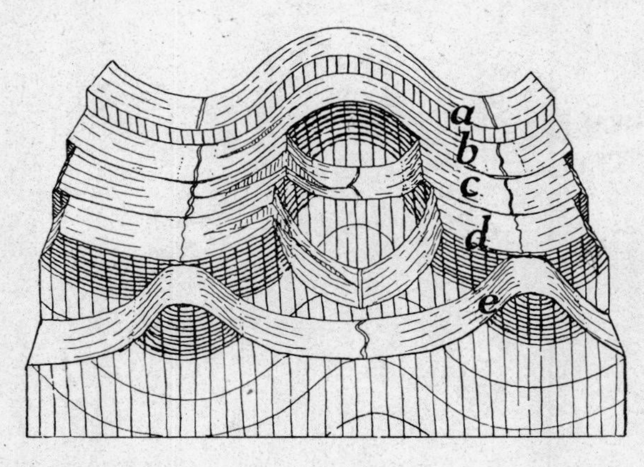

Fig. 81.—Diagram of the development of synclinal subsequent ridges. Successive stages are *a, b, c, d,* and *e.*

weaker strata (fig. 81), while the other parts of the resistant strata, which must have been at a greater height than the present mountains, have been removed by erosion.

In the development series *a-e* shown in fig. 81 it is almost necessary to assume that a general uplift of the land occurs between stages *c* and *d* to account for the great deepening of the subsequent valley which takes place; but it is conceivable that this deepening might be due to some other cause. The instability of initial arches that are not composed throughout of resistant materials is undoubted, but their very general non-survival is due rather to the fact that the great majority of rock folds are quite ancient as compared with the rate at which relief is destroyed by erosion—so ancient that the valleys and ridges now observable belong generally to a cycle of erosion later than that introduced by the uplift that accompanied the folding, the surface having been at least once in the interim planed off more or less completely by erosion. This might have been shown in fig. 81 by introducing after strip *c* another showing a peneplain developed at a level a little below that of the valley-bottoms at stage *c*.

The majority of subsequent ridges in mountainous regions are not in synclinal positions, but mark the outcrops of homoclines of the more resistant strata (see p. 84); and it is important to recognise in this connection that stream action is able, in the course of untold ages, to search out differences in the texture, the solubility, the closeness of jointing, and probably other properties of rock masses which we are incapable of observing.

Resequent Drainage.—With deep erosion in folded rocks, perhaps after a vast thickness of material has been removed during and after a succession of uplifts, as the strata forming subsequent ridges in the earlier stages of erosion are removed, the folding of the deeper-seated rocks now exposed may still be parallel in a general way with that of the original surface. This, is of course, likely to be the case only in districts of open, symmetrical folding. Where this type of structure occurs it may happen that a folded resistant stratum has such a relation to base-level that, although at the beginning of the cycle there is a subsequent drainage pattern inherited from an earlier period of erosion, as the rocks overlying the resistant stratum are eroded away the streams migrate down the slopes of its surface into synclinal positions, and stripped, unbroken anticlines form ridges between them (fig. 82, *A*). Synclinal valleys

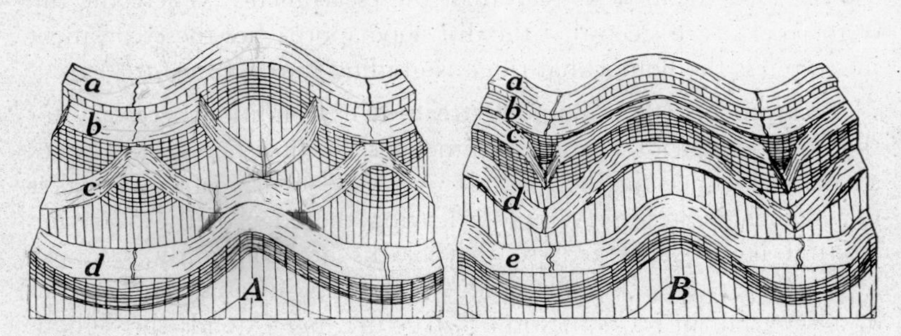

Fig. 82.—Diagrams contrasting resequent drainage, stage *d* in diagram *A*, developed from initial stage *a* through intermediate stages *b* and *c*, with consequent drainage, diagram *B*, persisting from initial stage *a* through successive stages *b*, *c*, *d*, and *e* during the removal of a great thickness of rocks.

and anticlinal ridges simulating consequent features but developed from a subsequent drainage pattern are termed *resequent.* Similar valleys and ridges which had remained in consequent synclinal and anticlinal positions since their initiation would not be termed resequent, but would still be consequent even after the removal of a great thickness of rock (fig. 82, *B*). Examples occur in the Jura Mountains. In the mountains of Cape Colony, which are formed of very ancient folded rocks, and have been exposed to erosion for a vast period, prominent anticlinal ridges and synclinal valleys occur for which a resequent origin has been suggested.

Homoclinal Ridges.—By the time that an area of stratified rocks is maturely dissected by subsequent streams the ridges and uplands forming the divides between these have generally taken definite forms determined by the attitudes of the resistant formations. In general they are not symmetrical, for, owing to difference in resistance of the rocks on the two sides of the crest-line divide, the law of equal declivities is not in operation. Various types of feature are developed according as the strata dip steeply, at a moderate angle, or gently. Where the inclination is moderate to steep the outcrops of the resistant formations stand out as *homoclinal ridges* (figs. 83, 84). The back of such a ridge is a *dip slope,* determined by the upper surface of the resistant rock only slightly lowered and reduced in steepness by erosion; while the front is an *escarpment* (figs. 84, 85), a steep slope, perhaps even a line of cliffs, which is *obsequent*—that is, faces in the direction opposite to the dip. As a general rule homoclinal ridges are asymmetrical, the dip slope being less steep than the escarpment. Where the dip of the rocks is so steep that the dip slope approaches the escarpment in steepness the homoclinal ridge is grading into a *hogback.*

Escarpments: their Rapid Retreat.—The condition necessary for the development of a true escarpment is the presence of a resistant stratum, inclined or horizontal, overlying conspicuously weaker rock which wastes away rapidly leaving the edge of the overlying stratum badly supported, so that blocks are constantly breaking away from a retreating sharp edge. This edge is analogous to that of a waterfall in rocks of similar structure, but extends throughout the length of outcrop characterised by this type of structure.

An escarpment is thus in rapid retreat, and this fact is generally made manifest by the presence of a sheet of coarse waste, some-

Fig. 83.—Homoclinal ridges, between the Ure and Clarence Valleys, New Zealand.
C. A. Cotton, photo.

Fig. 84.—Steep homoclinal ridge (almost a hogback), formed of a thick bed of limestone, Clarence Valley, New Zealand. The dip slope is towards the right, and the escarpment faces to the left.
C. A. Cotton, photo.

times thick enough to be a talus slope, derived from the edge of the resistant stratum and streaming down over the outcrop of the weaker rock below (figs. 85, 89, 91).

Hogbacks.—Ridges formed on the outcrops of vertical or steeply inclined resistant strata are termed *hogbacks*. They are more or less symmetrical. While the cycle of erosion is not yet far advanced they have, in general, and especially when developed on the outcrops of thin beds of hard rock, ragged, irregular crest-lines, resulting from the intersection of the steep upper parts of concave side slopes (figs. 86, 87). The steep sides merge below into gentler

Fig. 85.—Escarpment of a homoclinal ridge, the Chalk Range, Marlborough, New Zealand

C. A. Cotton, photo.

slopes on the neighbouring weaker formations, which may be more or less covered with fallen blocks from the ridge, forming talus slopes. Hogbacks developed on the outcrops of strata that are not vertical are less symmetrical, and the distinction between such asymmetrical hogbacks and homoclinal ridges is not well defined.

Cuestas.—In homoclinal ridges asymmetry becomes more pronounced as the dip of the beds diminishes; and when erosion lays bare the outcrop of a very gently dipping resistant formation the asymmetrical upland which results is given another name—*cuesta*.[1]

[1] Pronounced *questa*.

Fig. 86.—Serrate hogback ridge, Marlborough, New Zealand; one of many passed on the road from Kaikoura to Upper Waiau.

C. A. Cotton, photo.

Fig. 87.—Hogback formed by a nearly vertical bed of sandstone, Maunsell's Taipo, east Wellington, New Zealand.

C. A. Cotton, photo.

A cuesta naturally occupies a much larger area than does the ridge resulting from the baring of the outcrop of a more steeply dipping stratum. Its surface is a gently inclined dip slope which when followed downwards merges with the surface of the lowland developed on the overlying weak stratum, while upwards it is terminated by a sharp edge overlooking a steeper escarpment (figs. 88, 89) leading down to a lowland developed on the under-

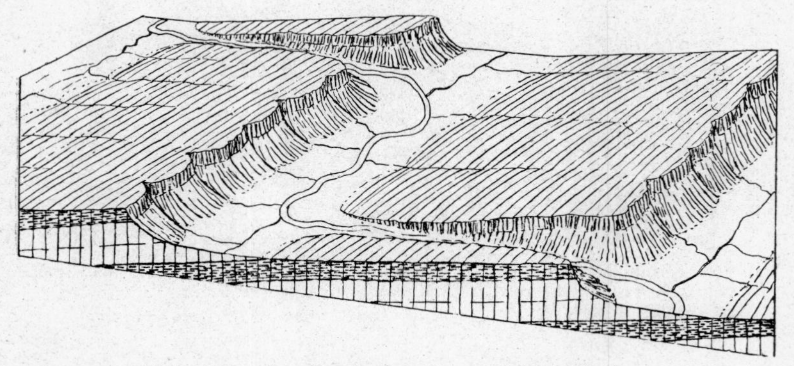

Fig. 88.—Diagram of cuestas separated by lowlands.

Fig. 89.—The escarpment of a cuesta, Oamaru, New Zealand.
A. C. Gifford, photo.

lying weaker formation. Such a lowland between two cuestas, together with the dip slope bounding it on one side and the escarpment on the other, is a *vale*. Cuestas are common features of dissected coastal plains of simple structure, which are described as *belted* when alternating cuestas and subsequent lowlands have been developed on them. The dip slopes of such cuestas are towards the sea, but where cuesta-making strata have been thrown by folding into gentle undulations, as is commonly the case in New Zealand, cuestas face in various directions.

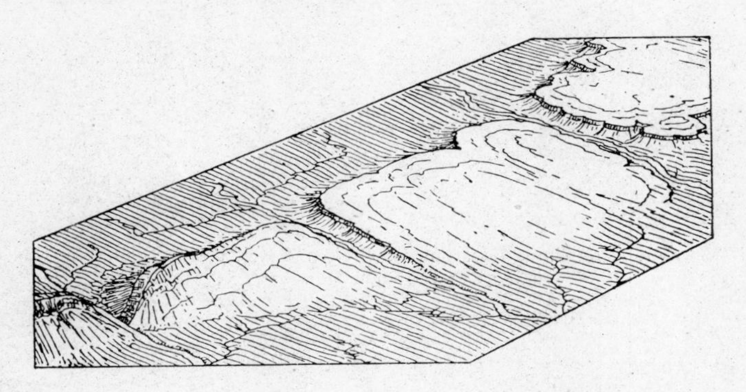

Fig. 90.—Transition from a hogback (left) through a homoclinal ridge and a cuesta to a mesa (right). (After Davis.)

Here and there most cuestas, and hogbacks and homoclinal ridges as well, are crossed by transverse streams in gorges, on the sides of which bare-rock outcrops occur and the dip and succession of the strata can be clearly seen (fig. 84).

Where cuestas are widely spaced, streams heading in their escarpments and joining as tributaries the subsequent streams in the adjacent vales may be of considerable size. These streams, the direction of flow of which, being opposite to the dip, is termed *obsequent,* cut back vigorously at their heads into the escarpment so that it may become crenulate instead of a straight line of cliffs (a "scalloped" escarpment).

Homoclinal Shifting.—Because of the lack of homogeneity of material in a cuesta or homoclinal ridge the law of equal declivities does not apply to its slopes. Erosion goes on very slowly on a dip slope of resistant rock but very much more rapidly on the steeper

Fig. 91—A rapidly retreating escarpment, Broken River basin, Canterbury, New Zealand.

C. A. Cotton, photo.

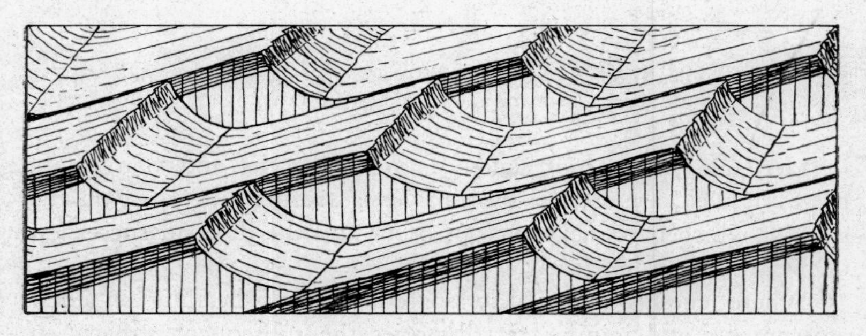

Fig. 92.—Homoclinal shifting. Ridges and valleys, divides and streams are shifting down the dip. Successive positions are shown in successive strips from back to front of the diagram.

obsequent slope, or escarpment (fig. 91). The divide formed by the crest-line of the cuesta or ridge is thus forced to migrate in the direction of dip, and as the general level of a landscape made up of homoclinal features is lowered the subsequent streams and the valley lowlands they have developed migrate also in the same direction (fig. 92). This is the process of *homoclinal shifting*. Obviously the rapidity and extent of horizontal migration are

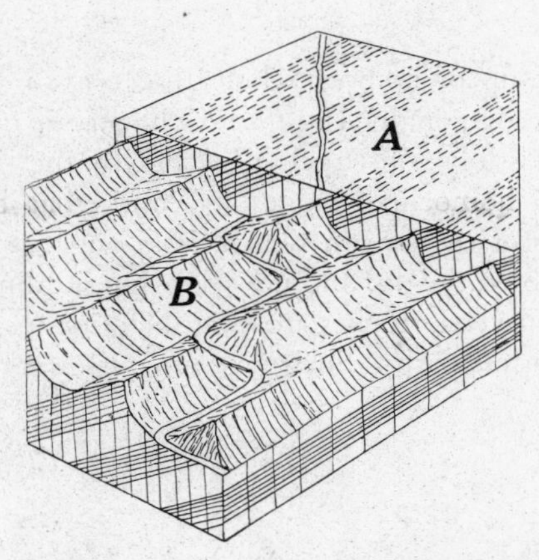

Fig. 93.—Development of a zigzag course as a result of homoclinal shifting of reaches.

Fig. 93A.—The Schlern (Sciliar) mesa, Dolomite Alps, South Tyrol.

greater in the case of gently inclined than in the case of steep strata.

A peculiar result of homoclinal shifting is seen where a stream crosses the strike diagonally (fig. 93). The stream may be straight at first (being possibly consequent), *A,* but by the time the surface is dissected into homoclinal ridges its course has become zigzag, *B,* as those parts of the stream which cross outcrops of weak rocks have migrated down the dip and now flow longitudinally. These are connected by transverse reaches crossing the outcrops of the resistant rocks by the shortest paths. Such zigzag courses are very common,

Fig. 94.—Butte of a hard volcanic stratum (ignimbrite), Mamaku, New Zealand. *C. A. Cotton, photo.*

and many have in all probability been developed thus, but a similar result might be attained under certain conditions by the joining-up of portions of successively captured transverse streams by subsequent reaches.

Mesas and Buttes.—Landforms closely related structurally to cuestas, though not developed in the same way by headward erosion of subsequent valleys, are formed where parts of horizontal resistant strata remain capping weaker materials. Large table-like forms are termed *mesas,* and small residuals are *buttes*[1] (figs. 90, 93A, 94). The level top of a mesa or butte is the upper surface of the

[1] Pronounced *may-sa* and *bewt.*

hard stratum generally stripped of its soft cover but itself little worn by erosion. The slopes on all sides are escarpments. The length and breadth of a butte are at the most not much greater than the height; but a mesa may be many miles in extent, its surface forming a plateau. Mesas are particularly well developed where horizontal sheets of volcanic or intrusive igneous rock lie over weak materials and the compound mass is in course of destruction by stream erosion and escarpment retreat. Mesas are reduced by erosion to buttes or clusters of buttes, which in their turn are destroyed.

Fig. 95.—Valley-side escarpment, Blue Mountains, New South Wales. *C. A. Cotton, photo.*

Structural Plateaux.—More extensive than mesas are *structural plateaux,* which are developed at the mature stage of erosion in terrains of horizontal strata some of which are particularly resistant to erosion. They are extensively developed in Africa and in the south-western interior of North America, and are stable (in the sense of long-enduring) landforms where the plateau-making strata are thick as well as resistant.

Main rivers may early entrench themselves in deep valleys below the level of plateau-making strata, but such valleys remain bounded by escarpments (fig. 95) and are widened but slowly. Dissection of the plateau margins is effected as falls at the heads of insequent streams and in the broken courses of other streams (which may be secondary consequents) gnaw slowly back in marginal embayments. These separate escarpment-bounded out-jutting points, which also slowly retreat or may be isolated to become dwindling mesas and buttes.

Structural Benches and Terraces—Successive resistant strata one below another may successively emerge as structural plateaux in the course of a cycle (fig. 96). As upper beds are reduced to mesas,

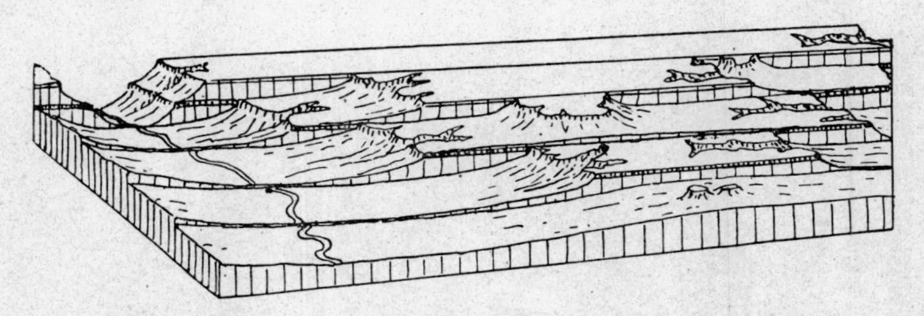

Fig. 96.—Dissection of a structural plateau (at rear) bordered by a structural terrace, which develops into a structural bench and lower-level plateau, in its turn to be destroyed by erosion (front strip). (After a diagram by Davis, redrawn.)

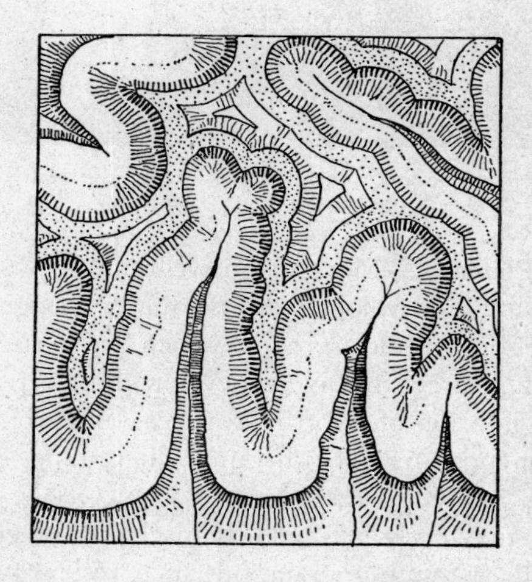

Fig. 97.—Dissection pattern of a plateau-margin escarpment, showing narrow-headed ravines dissecting a lower and amphitheatres scalloping an upper bench margin, Grand Canyon of the Colorado. (After Davis.)

the edges of others below them emerge as *structural benches,* or, where narrower strips are exposed on valley sides, *structural terraces,* and these may become summit plateaux when all beds above them have been stripped away.

The smaller streams in regions of structural plateaux remain long ungraded, descending over successive plateau-edges as falls and rapids in narrow and sharply-cut notches. They may flow in open valleys, however, which may be likened to graded reaches, where they cross broad benches. The edge of the bench serves for each such reach as a local base-level.

Between the out-jutting buttresses of a plateau-margin escarpment the embayments are either narrow-headed ravines or amphitheatres (fig. 97). The former are occupied by streams, but the latter are developed as a result of escarpment retreat where there is little or no drainage from above, though ground-water seepage may maintain a small stream in the embayment below the amphitheatre. Enlargement of adjacent amphitheatres may reduce formerly round-fronted buttresses between them to sharp cusps.

CHAPTER VIII

THE VALLEYS OF MATURE RIVERS

Lateral corrasion. Widening of valley floors. Valley plains and meanders. Cutting-off of meanders. Narrowed and cut-off spurs. Subsequent lowlands. Wide valley plains. Plains of lateral planation. Underfit rivers.

Lateral Corrasion. — As a river becomes mature and graded farther and farther upstream the cessation of rapid down-cutting is followed by a change in the cross profile of the valley. The valley becomes more widely opened, for the sides not only slope back more and more gently as interfluves are lowered, but at the same time the flat valley-bottom, or floor, also increases in width.

The widening of the floor, which contributes to the development of an open valley form, is due to cutting by the stream itself (*lateral corrasion*). Though a river is graded, and has therefore ceased to cut rapidly downward, it is as a rule not without energy. Where the current impinges against the valley side the bank is attacked and cut back, and thus the floor is widened.

In a perfectly straight stream the thread of fastest current would be in the centre, while at each side there would be almost still water fully loaded, or overloaded, with waste for the velocity at which it would flow, and incapable therefore of attacking the banks. There is no reason, however, to suppose that initial streams are ever perfectly straight, and if there is initial curvature, however slight, a stream will itself enlarge its curves. In a stream with a slightly curved course (as shown by the fine dotted lines in fig. 98) the thread of fastest current is thrown always by the momentum of the stream against the concave bank, which is thus attacked and cut back (strips 2-5 and 2′-5′). In this way the curvature is increased while deepening of the valley is still in progress, for the stream cuts obliquely outward on its curves as well as downward. Thus by the time a valley is graded it is also somewhat winding (as defined by the broken lines in fig. 98), and its V-shaped cross profile is asymmetrical (strips 5 and 5′), the slopes (*T, T′*) being steeper in the coves or amphitheatres against which the stream has cut

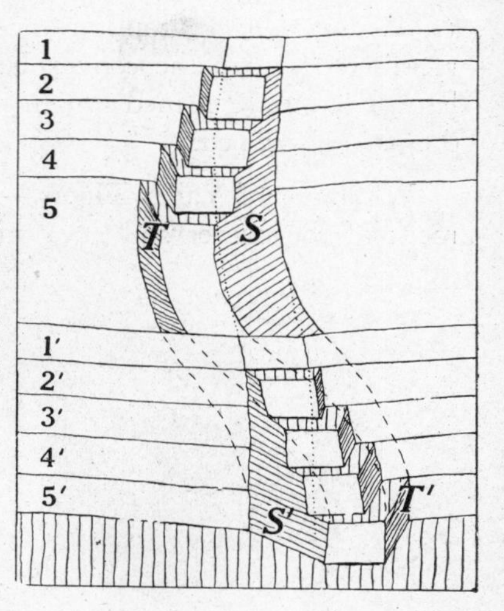

Fig. 98.—Diagram illustrating increasing curvature of a valley due to lateral corrasion accompanying downward cutting. Strips 1, 1′ show portions of the initial, slightly curved course; while strips 2-5 and 2′-5′ show progressive increase of curvature as the valley is deepened.

Fig. 99.—A young valley has developed windings during its entrenchment, and interlocking valley-side spurs now reach out into coves or amphitheatres enlarged by undercutting, near Wellington, New Zealand.

C. A. Cotton, photo.

(*undercut slopes*) than on the tapering and interlocking spurs running down to the convex banks (fig. 99). The slopes of the latter (*S, S′*) are termed *slip-off slopes* because of the way in which they are developed.

Widening of Valley Floors.—After a stream is graded, enlargement of the curves still goes on, but, since lateral cutting is not

Fig. 100.—Flood-plain scrolls on the narrow floor of the Kaiwarra valley, Wellington, New Zealand.
C. A. Cotton, photo.

now accompanied by vertical cutting, further enlargement of the curves results in widening of the valley floor. As the stream does not require the full width of the enlarged floor for its channel, it concentrates itself against the outer, or concave, banks of its winding valley, and deposits the coarser parts of its load along the inner, or convex, banks, where the current is sluggish, forming flat areas of new land which are covered only at times of flood. These are the beginnings of a *flood plain*. As they are at first short, crescentic, but slightly sinuous strips they are termed at that stage *flood-plain scrolls* (figs. 100, 101).

Fig. 101.—Flood-plain scrolls, Waimana River, Urewera, New Zealand. *G. Bourne, photo.*

The stream cuts not only outward on curves but also in a down-stream direction. It thus undercuts and eventually pares off the interlocking spurs which jut across its widening valley. They are first *trimmed* (fig. 102, stage 2), then *sharpened* (3), and later *blunted* (4). After this the sides of the valley are lines of rather steep *bluffs*, and the floor is flat, the flood plain being by this time continuous except where interrupted by the actual channel of the river.

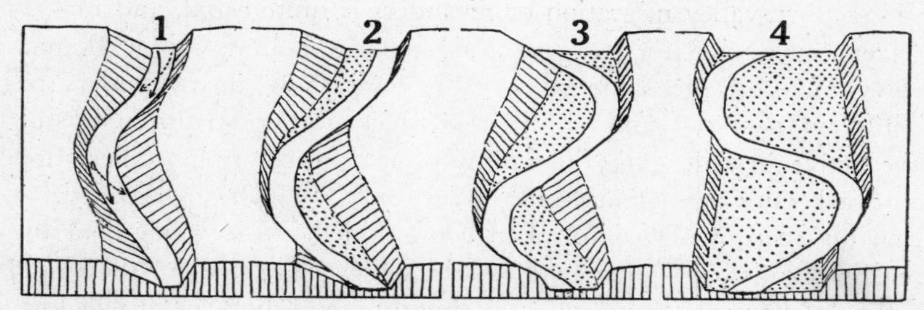

Fig. 102.—Diagram of widening of a valley floor. Stage 1, part of the course of a stream in which slight initial curvature has been increased during down-cutting; stages 2, 3, and 4, effects of lateral corrasion after down-cutting has ceased—trimming, sharpening, and blunting of spurs, and development of a flood plain.

Valley Plains and Meanders.—A continuous flood plain as it grows in breadth becomes a *valley plain*. During every flood the surface of such a plain has a layer of fine waste deposited on it, owing to the checking of the current by friction when the water is spread out over the plain in a thin sheet, the main flow of the stream taking place still (and with a velocity greater than usual) along the regular channel. It is the deposit of silt spread in this way that gives valley plains their fertility. The land is, as it were, top-dressed by every flood.

The development of curvature in the stream channel tends eventually towards the production of regular, flowing curves (termed *meanders*) which are of a size proportioned to the energy—that is, to the volume and velocity—of the stream. By the time valley-side spurs have been trimmed back and the flood plain has become continuous the curves of a river have generally developed into symmetrical meanders.

Widening of valleys as a result of lateral corrasion by streams does not cease when the originally interlocking spurs have been trimmed off, but continues while the hill slopes are being graded and their steepness is being reduced. Let it be assumed that the flat floor bounded by simple lines tangent to the convex curves of the stream is just wide enough to allow these curves to be developed into symmetrical meanders of full size corresponding to the size of the stream. The tendency of the curves to shift downstream is no longer checked by barriers of solid rock. Having only the loose alluvium of the flood plain to corrade, they sweep bodily down the valley, rebuilding the flood plain behind them as they go (fig. 102). This down-valley migration of meanders is quite rapid, and makes rivers unsuitable for geographical or farm boundaries. Old and new maps of the same river valley will show the meanders in different positions and of different shapes. The stream will still be active in enlarging the radius of its curves, and so these are pressed outward against the valley sides, which are eroded, a narrow strip of new flood plain being added to the valley floor by each meander as it travels down the valley. The foot of the slope of the valley side is cut away in this process, leaving at first a low cliff, which is worn back by slumping, rain-wash, and creep to a gentler slope after the meander has passed by, the whole valley-side slope retreating slightly each time this occurs (fig. 110A).

Cutting-off of Meanders.—When meanders approach the maximum size appropriate to the size of the stream—small in small streams, large in large rivers—their outward cutting and enlargement still continue, but, as the curves are now S-shaped ("dovetail" meanders), the concave banks of adjacent meanders towards the same side of the valley approach each other and ultimately intersect (fig. 103). As the water in the downstream meander is at

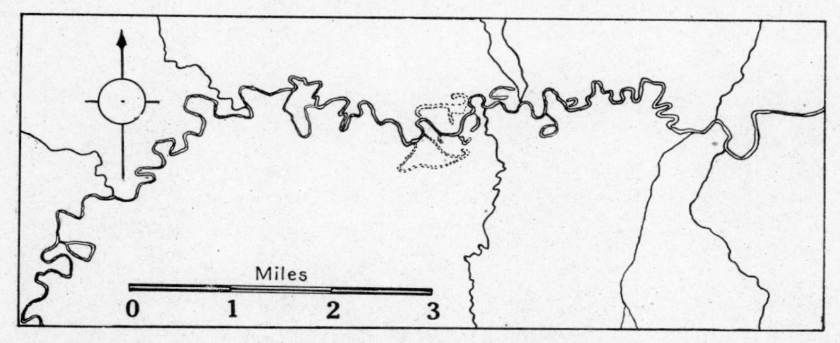

Fig. 103.—Map showing meanders and cut-off meanders in the course of the Taieri River through the Upper Taieri Plain, New Zealand.

a lower level than that in its upstream neighbour, when intersection of the curves results in the cutting-away of the neck of flood plain between them the stream takes a new course across the intersection. (Or, without actual intersection of the banks, at time of flood the stream may break across and scour out a channel through the narrow neck between adjacent meanders.) The former roundabout course, which is a meander towards the opposite side of the valley, is abandoned or *cut off*. It is in this way that the size of meanders is limited. Those that have overgrown the maximum size set by the volume and gradient of the stream are cut off, and a portion of the stream course is for a time relatively straight; but the development of new meanders begins at once. *Cut-off meanders* are common features of valley plains. At first they form horseshoe-shaped, or *ox-bow,* lakes or ponds (fig. 103), which later become swamps owing to accumulation of silt and growth of vegetation.

Narrowed and Cut-off Spurs.—Even while streams are still cutting vigorously downward—that is, before even the beginnings of a flood plain have been formed—the development of curvature may lead to the narrowing and finally to the cutting-off of the spurs between adjacent curves in a way analogous to the cutting-off of meanders on a flood plain. This takes place in small streams which are compelled to cut deeply to attain grade. In these the limiting size of curves is small compared with the depth of the incised valley. As adjacent curves approach each other the crest-line of the spur between them is lowered, and a *narrowed spur* results (fig. 104). When intersection takes place, with the develop-

Fig. 104.—Narrowed spur, Wellington, New Zealand. The narrow neck of the spur is at the right.

C. A. Cotton, photo.

ment of a new stream course across the neck of the spur and the abandonment of that around the end of it, a *cut-off spur* is formed (fig. 105), which stands as an isolated hill.

Exceptionally, in rocks that are free from joints, vigorous lateral corrasion may undercut cliffs so that they become vertical or even overhang (fig. 106), and so the neck of a narrowed spur may be cut through below but yet remain intact above, forming a *natural*

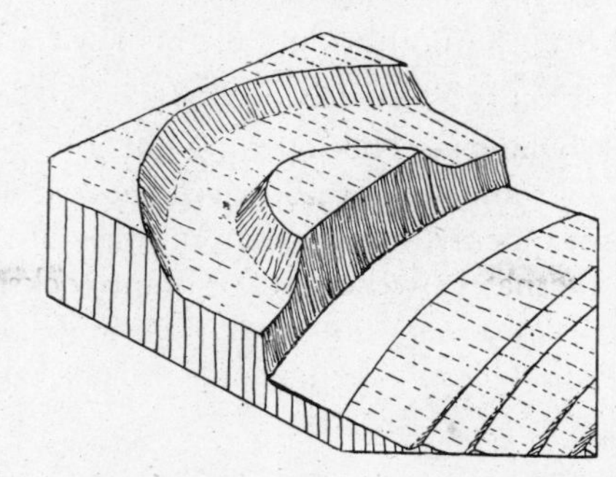

Fig. 105.—Diagrammatic sketch of the remnant of a cut-off spur in the Awatere Valley, New Zealand. The river, now at a level lower than that at which it flowed around the spur, is again cutting outward and destroying the cut-off spur.

Fig. 106.—An overhanging cliff developed by lateral corrasion of a stream cutting down and enlarging a curve, the "Dress Circle," Pipiriki, New Zealand.

F. G. Radcliffe, photo.

bridge, as in fig. 107. Natural bridges of this kind are less common than those developed by solution in limestone (Chapter X).

Subsequent Lowlands.—The opening-out of valleys both by widening of the floor and wearing-down of the side slopes naturally goes on much more quickly in weak than in resistant rocks (fig. 108). On a terrain of alternately weak and resistant rocks, therefore, the subsequent valleys along zones of weak rock and those portions of transverse valleys that cross weak zones are not only mature but

Fig. 107.—The Rainbow Natural Bridge, Utah.
H. E. Gregory, photo.

are broadly opened and reduced to lowlands while the transverse streams are still cutting through the resistant rock strata in young, steep-sided, rock-walled gorges. Gorges of this kind, cutting through strike ridges, are termed *water gaps* (fig. 108). Sometimes a river that has been cutting a water gap is diverted by capture while the general lowering of the land surface is in progress. The abandoned gorge remains as a notch in the crest of a ridge, and is termed an *air gap,* or *wind gap* (*a, a′,* fig. 108). The air gap is deep (*a*) or shallow (*a′*), according to the amount of general lowering of the surface that has taken place since the notch was

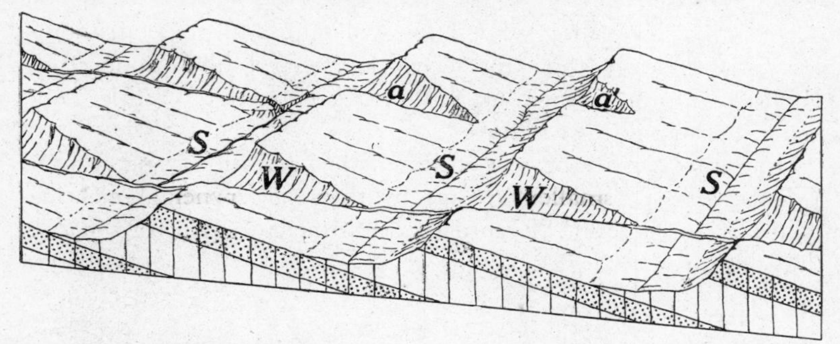

Fig. 108.—Subsequent lowlands, water gaps, and air gaps. *S,* subsequent lowlands; *W,* water gaps, *a, a′,* air gaps.

Fig. 109.—Subsequent lowland, flanked by a homoclinal ridge of strong relief, Coverham, Marlborough, New Zealand.

C. A. Cotton, photo.

abandoned. Development of subsequent lowlands is an example of *differential erosion* (fig. 109).

Wide Valley Plains.—After the limit of size has been reached for curves, these being now fully developed meanders, the width of the valley floors is greater than that of the belt (*meander belt*) between lines tangent to the outer curves of the meanders (fig. 110B). Not every meander is now cutting against the valley side. The meander belt is not constant in position, however—it swings from side to side; and occasionally the stream impinges against and undercuts a portion of the valley side. Thus widening still goes on, though less systematically than formerly, the steep bluffs produced by lateral corrasion fading out and being replaced by gentle slopes before another slice is removed.

Interfluves may be cut through by corrasion, and capture (*abstraction*) of smaller streams by their larger neighbours may take place as a result. Eventually adjustment to structure may be thus destroyed.

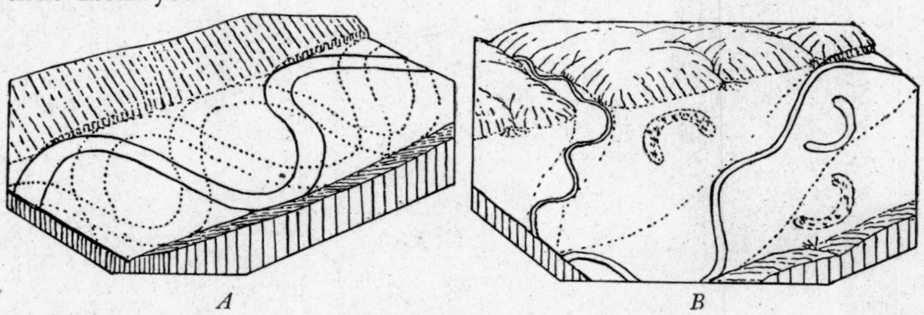

Fig. 110.—*A*: Down-valley migration of meanders results in widening a valley floor. Direction of stream-flow and migration of meanders, right to left.
B: a valley widened by planation. The valley plain is now very much wider than the meander belt.

Plains of Lateral Planation.—Wide valley plains cut by a continuation of this process, now termed *lateral planation,* are observed to be slightly convex; and such broadly conical plains, or *rock fans,* developing side by side coalesce at the margins when interfluves have been cut through and finally destroyed. This has sometimes happened to the extent of developing sloping piedmont (mountain-fringing) *plains of lateral planation* where extensive belts of soft rock have been crossed by steep-graded, vigorous, debris-laden streams from mountains at the rear. Smooth apron-like slopes of this origin fringe the bases of great escarpments in the south-western United States—notably the Book Cliffs escarpment, in Utah. Another example is the Maniototo Plain, in New Zealand, some three hundred square miles in extent, which slopes southward into Central Otago from the hard-rock frontal scarp of the northern highland (figs. 111A, 111B). Such plains have been termed also "pediments" and regarded as more or less closely related to those in mountainous deserts (Chapter XIX).

Underfit Rivers.—Mature valleys, especially those which are aligned on subsequent lowlands, may be of such ample dimensions as to convey an impression that the rivers flowing in them are too

Fig. 111A.—The Maniototo Plain, New Zealand. (After Benson.)

Fig. 111B.—The Maniototo Plain, New Zealand, largely a plain of lateral planation.
C. A. Cotton, photo.

small to have been capable of carrying away the vast amount of rock material which has obviously been removed in the process of differential erosion. One may be tempted to imagine a rapid scouring-out of a wide valley by some vastly larger river in a past age; but an examination of the land slopes and stream gradients on valley sides and floor generally shows them to be so closely in accordance with the river now flowing in the valley that they clearly have been produced by its agelong patient labour.

Where by some chance, on the other hand, a vigorous river has been diverted and has abandoned the valley it has excavated, features of the valley floor will indicate the *underfit* character of the diminished (perhaps beheaded) stream now flowing on it. Underfit rivers are incapable of carrying away all the debris descending from their valley sides and brought in by small side streams. Fig. 112 shows such accumulation of valley-side waste, which clogs the formerly clean-cut flood plain, converting it into swampy flats; and over what is left of the valley floor between encroaching tongues of debris the diminutive underfit river winds in numerous

Fig. 112.—Beheaded valley of the Karori Stream (compare figs. 74-76), Wellington, New Zealand, which is occupied now by an underfit rivulet.

C. A. Cotton, photo.

meanders of small radius which may be now imposed as minor contortions on the sweeping curves of the abandoned course of the former larger river (fig. 113).

A slightly underfit condition may be developed in some mature valleys as a result of diminution of stream volume owing to underflow through alluvial gravel which may build up flood plains to some extent in cases where the supply of waste from headwater dissection goes on increasing for a time after rivers have become mature. This can be no more than a transient phase in the history of a valley, however, for as the cycle progresses and the land surface generally is lowered the flood plain will be further worn down

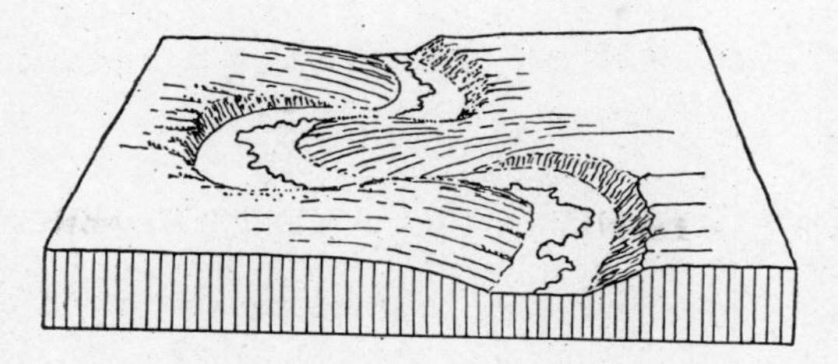

Fig. 113.—An underfit river. The valley of the Schmiecha. (After W. M. Davis.)

and the layer of alluvium on it will be reduced again to a thin veneer. Underflow in gravel is unlikely to deplete a river of water to the extent of rendering it incapable of carrying its load of waste and thus setting in train a cumulative process of aggradation.[1] It is rarely, therefore, that a strongly underfit relation of river to valley can be attributed to the operation of a spontaneous and cumulative process, and an extraneous cause such as beheading by capture must generally be looked for.

---

[1] "This might be a cumulative process were it not that the rapid gain of carrying power due to increase of velocity will soon make up for the slower loss of carrying power due to loss of volume." (W. M. Davis.)

CHAPTER IX

SUBDUED LANDSCAPES AND "SOIL EROSION"

Grading of slopes. Serrate and subdued summit forms. Convex and concave summit and slope profiles. Accelerated soil erosion. The soil-erosion problem. Soil-depleting processes. Wind erosion. Secondary effects of accelerated erosion. The remedy for accelerated erosion.

Grading of Slopes.—On the sides of young valleys and gorges and on escarpments, where, owing to steepness of the slopes, removal of waste goes on as rapidly as the waste is produced by weathering, outcrops of bare rock occur, of jagged and irregular form, so that the slope is not only steep but uneven (fig. 113A). Such slopes are analogous to the uneven profiles of young rivers and, like them, may be described as not yet graded. Later, owing to cessation of down-cutting by streams, and to continued weathering and streaming down of waste on the slopes, these are worn back to gentler gradients. During this process outcrops of bare rock, which at first are almost continuous, are gradually replaced by slopes of waste. These are at first short, discontinuous, and broken by rock outcrops, but, as the outcrops are worn down, the waste slopes become *graded* in a manner analogous to the grading of a water stream, though the graded slope of a waste stream is necessarily very much steeper than that of a water stream on account of the inferior mobility of the material of which it is composed. In this way are developed the smooth hill slopes so prominent in the majority of familiar landscapes.

Serrate and Subdued Summit Forms.—At the beginning of the stage of mature dissection the crest-lines of ridges and spurs are formed by the intersection of the slopes of valley sides, which are as a general rule still steep, so that the ridges are sharp and uneven. The topography may be described as *serrate*. Later, however, summits become rounded off, earliest in areas of moderate relief and on the flanks and among the foothills of mountain ranges, but eventually also among the mountain peaks. This is a result partly of

Fig. 113A.—Ungraded land slopes, Dunstan Gorge of the Clutha River, New Zealand.
C. A. Cotton, photo.

Fig. 114.—Summit convexity in a mature landscape, Wangamoa Hill, Nelson, New Zealand.
V. C. Browne, photo.

reduction of steepness due to the grading of land slopes and of the headwaters of streams.

When slopes have become moderately gentle in a district of coarse-textured dissection broadly rounded convex hills or mountains are produced, which are described as *subdued*. By the time that the stage of late maturity has been reached in the cycle of erosion of the land surface most of the salient forms are subdued.

Convex and Concave Summit and Slope Profiles.—The action of streams and the grading of land slopes in a manner analogous to that which results in the faintly concave profile of a graded water stream cannot be called upon to explain the convexity of hilltops (fig. 114), for the intersections of concave slopes, however gentle they may be, are angular. Convexity of divides may be explained as the result of wasting-away of the surface under the dominant or perhaps even unaided action of creep, though this can be effective only when there is a layer of soil. Some very thinly soil-covered summits may be lowered, it has been suggested, mainly by the removal of finely weathered particles in sluggish off-flowing films of water at times when the ground has become saturated by heavy rain. This is a process which is termed *sheet erosion* by soil geologists when it becomes important as a factor in the accelerated removal of soil which follows depletion of natural vegetation.

During the removal of a thin surface layer of uniform thickness from the crest of a ridge by soil creep or sheet erosion the amount of soil passing a given point increases progressively with the distance of the point from the divide. Hence for the removal of the layer a slope increasing in steepness with distance from the divide is required. Farther down the hillside, where rain-wash comes more into play and becomes increasingly important in the removal of waste there is a point of inversion between the upper convex and a lower concave graded slope.

The lower parts of concave valley-side slopes become extremely gentle in late-mature landscapes and merge imperceptibly into the margins of the true valley plains which have been cut by the rivers as flood plains.

The concavity of the slope in the lower valley-side strip (or *valley-floor side-strip*) is explained as a result of the progressively increasing fineness of texture of the soil on it, those particles near the foot of the slope having been long in transit and long subject to weathering. Where the declivity becomes scarcely perceptible only the finest particles can be moved forward by rain-wash.

Accelerated Soil Erosion.—On subdued landscape forms and on graded slopes generally, where the waste mantle consists of weathered material not streaming but slowly creeping downhill, vegetation flourishes. In fact, the stability of slopes depends largely on the natural vegetation. A slope may be steep and yet the soil may

Fig. 115.—Gullying, accompanied by accumulation of the eroded debris in the form of a fan, such as takes place when a naturally grass-clothed graded slope has become subject to accelerated erosion owing to depletion of the vegetation, Marlborough, New Zealand.

F. H. Clift, photo.

be so bound and protected by the vegetation, forest perhaps, that streaming is prevented and only creep permitted, so that there is a state of balance between the rate of removal of waste and the rate of supply by weathering.

When the natural vegetation, whether forest or grass, is interfered with, re-dissection may begin on a previously graded surface (fig. 115). Clearing or burning the forest from many slopes has seriously disturbed the state of balance between the rates of

Fig. 116.—Here gullying, accompanied by reversion of graded to ungraded slopes, is taking place after forest has been cleared, Wellington, New Zealand.

C. A. Cotton, photo.

Fig. 117.—Some of the beech forest still survives, which has long protected and maintained the stability of a graded slope, South Island, New Zealand.

N.Z. State Forest Service, photo.

weathering on them and of removal of the waste (fig. 116). Removal of weathered waste becomes more rapid owing to exposure to rain-wash and to the absence of binding roots. The upper soil may be entirely removed, actual streaming of loose waste derived from the subsoil may begin, and the formerly soil-covered hillside may become a loose talus slope, broken by ragged outcrops of exposed rock (figs. 117, 118). It thus appears that there is a critical slope above which it is a great mistake to clear forest from hillsides. This critical slope varies with the nature of the rocks and also with the climate. It may be discovered in any particular district only by experience. Good turf protects slopes nearly though not quite as

Fig. 118.—A slope similar to that shown in fig. 117. Here sheet erosion has already removed much soil since the forest covering has been destroyed. Gullying and streaming of talus are in progress.
N.Z. State Forest Service, photo.

well as forest, and in many parts of New Zealand rather steep slopes have been cleared and grassed successfully, the grass becoming established before the binding effect of tree roots is lost through their decay.

In some parts of the world great quantities of soil have been lost and large areas rendered barren by cultivation of slopes that are too steep, the critical slope for tillage being much gentler than for pasture land. In some countries slopes are terraced at great expense to save the soil, and some loss may be obviated by contour ploughing. On the other hand, attempts to check the further development of newly eroded ravines by choking them with stones and brushwood are futile unless well planned.

The Soil-erosion Problem.—In parts of most "new" countries a "soil-erosion" problem is now acute. Cumulative damage is done by accelerated erosion in districts where because of abundant rainfall the primitive vegetation has been forest; but loss of soil has seriously impoverished also semi-arid grassland districts that have been subjected to frequent burning and to overstocking with grazing animals. In New Zealand in particular, where there were no herbivorous mammals under primitive conditions and the balance of vegetation was adjusted in their absence, there has been great depletion of natural grassland vegetation by sheep and rabbits. Even in inaccessible forest areas in New Zealand, which have not suffered by the hand of man, the depredations of imported deer threaten the existence of the forest trees.

"Soil erosion" as popularly understood is accelerated erosion affecting previously graded slopes. Such acceleration of erosion may occur under natural conditions only if desiccation of climate reduces rainfall below the critical amount necessary to maintain the existing vegetation that protects the soil. Obviously man's attempts to replace a protective by a non-protective vegetation produce similar results without climatic change.

A continuation of erosion at the former rate would obviously neither deplete the soil nor destroy the smoothly graded surface. The stability of the latter "depends largely on the natural vegetation, which may so bind together and protect the soil that surface wash is prevented and only creep and a certain amount of mass movement permitted. A state of balance between the rate of removal of waste and the rate of supply of new waste by weathering of the underlying rocks is thus attained, but this holds good only for the particular type of vegetation covering it. Under these conditions erosion proceeds at its normal steady rate and soil-forming processes have time to convert the weathered rock materials into topsoils and subsoils which are the soil resource of agriculture and forestry.

"When, however, land is cleared of its natural vegetation and the soil either bared to the direct attack of wind and rain or else covered with a vegetation that protects it less effectively than did the natural cover, erosion of an entirely different order is induced. The processes that previously operated slowly are now speeded up enormously. Erosion . . . . proceeds far in excess of soil-formation. This means gradual soil-destruction."[1]

Soil-depleting Processes.—Graded slopes are robbed of fine soil particles by sheet erosion (p. 112), the effects of which are accelerated by exposure and parching of the soil; while soil creep and slumping are simultaneously accelerated as the soil and subsoil layers are disintegrated by seasonal cracking and swelling which result from alternate drying and wetting.

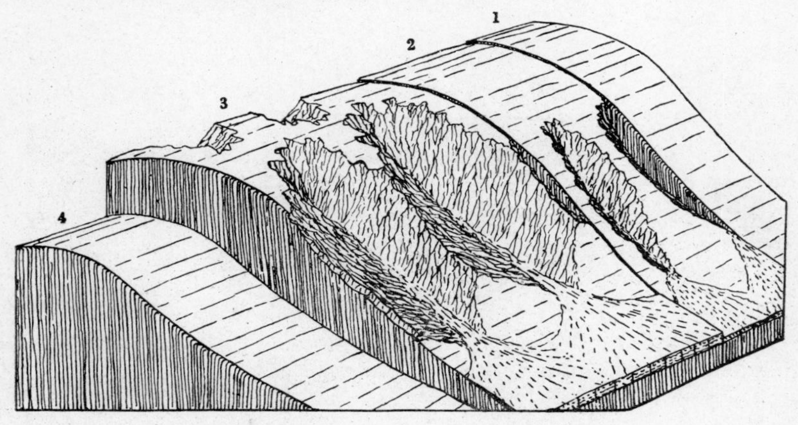

Fig. 119.—The cycle of gully erosion. Extreme effects of gullying where erosion has been accelerated; followed eventually by a regrading of the land surface.

Movement of the soil towards the valleys results in steepening of upper slopes, in which bare rock becomes exposed, resulting in further increase in the run-off.

"Where the soil is underlain by rocks that weather slowly and are low in plant foods, the steeper and more unbalanced slopes tend to become more and more infertile. Each time a slip occurs some bare rock is exposed and much of the surrounding soil is left in a shallow and infertile condition."[2]

Loss of superficial soil may be followed by the development of ravines ("gully erosion") as a result of increased run-off. This takes place where consequent rills running down the steepest

[1] Maintenance of Vegetation Cover in New Zealand. . . . (Report of Committee of Inquiry), *Dep. Sci. and Ind. Res. Bull.*, No. 77, p. 8, 1939.
[2] *Loc. cit.*, p. 18.

slopes develop into rivulets. The consequent ravines, confined at first to a zone on the steepest part of a hillside, gnaw back later by headward erosion towards convex summits (fig. 119, stages 1, 2, 3). Thus formerly smooth and graded slopes enter on a new cycle of erosion in which they may be deeply and maturely dissected in badland fashion. Eventually—in the far distant future—if the processes of nature are left to take their course, re-grading must result in the production of a new smooth soil-covered slope of gentler declivity than that formerly prevailing (fig. 119, 4). Hill

Fig. 120.—Lag gravel in a "man-made desert" on a formerly grass-protected terrace, Tarras, Otago, New Zealand.

L. Cockayne, photo.

summits, meanwhile, will have been lowered somewhat and river gradients readjusted to allow of the transportation of a vast bulk of waste; and eventually on a new and stable surface natural vegetation may be re-established. Man's life is too short, however, for him to await such a natural solution of the problem.

Minor landsliding (slumping) plays an important part in slope-grading, especially on the steeper slopes that are kept stable by forest growth. Here creep and minor slumping work hand in hand. Though a normal process, slumping is one that is particularly prone to acceleration by the interference of man.

"Everywhere throughout the forest hill lands arcuate scars indicate the sites of former slips," but "ground bared by slips has time to be invaded by vegetation before another slip appears; bare rock has time to weather" (N. H. Taylor). Not so, however, on cleared ground. Thus large areas of the North Island of New Zealand are now disfigured by a network of innumerable slump scars, which expose infertile subsoils and sterile bare-rock surfaces on the steeper slopes though these were formerly graded and soil-covered.

Wind Erosion.—Wind becomes effective as a process of soil depletion in some dry districts when the surface loses the natural protection of steppe or grassland vegetation. It removes fine particles as the soil is dried up and crumbles, so as to leave nothing of topsoil or subsoil but a "lag gravel" (fig. 120). Obviously this may take place on plains as well as on slopes.

Secondary Effects of Accelerated Erosion.—Accelerated erosion going on in headwater regions produces serious effects far down river valleys. The supply of waste to streams is increased to such an extent that they become overloaded and are caused to aggrade, filling up and reducing the capacity of their channels so that they become subject to frequent floods, and also depositing coarse gravel over what may have been very fertile valley plains. The tendency to flood is also increased by a rise in the proportion of the precipitation that runs off immediately from the surface, stream volumes thus fluctuating much more than formerly. This is owing to loss from the hill slopes of the waste mantle, which has, when present, a great capacity for absorbing rain-water and storing it as ground water.

Obviously little can be done in lower valleys to prevent damage caused by an over-supply of waste from upstream. The remedy is prevention of an undue amount of erosion at the headwaters.

The Remedy for Accelerated Erosion.—The symptoms having been stated, it may be as well to outline a treatment. The best remedy for "soil erosion" is prevention. It would be too drastic, however, as well as too late, to recommend that the forests of new lands should be left entirely in their primitive condition. It is too late also, after damage has been done, to delimit areas in which forest clearing has been and will be comparatively innocuous in its effects on the landscape and those where it has proved disastrous in its consequences. It is not too late, however, to advocate a policy of wisely-controlled reafforestation and the reservation of some headwater, or stream-catchment, areas and the protection of these from fire and the depredations of deer, so that a second growth of natural vegetation may be encouraged, which in time may check erosion and the excessive transportation of unwelcome waste to lower valleys.

CHAPTER X

LIMESTONE LANDSCAPES

Rock solubility: erosion by underground water. Sinkholes, caves, and natural bridges. Hums. Travertine falls and dams. The karst or limestone cycle.

Rock Solubility: Erosion by Underground Water — Chemical weathering results in the removal of part of the waste in solution from all wasting surfaces. During the young and early-mature stages of the cycle of erosion mechanical erosion is so much more active on most rocks that it overshadows the purely chemical effects of solution, and it is not until the stage of old age is reached, when mechanical erosion has become relatively feeble, that more than a negligible proportion of the lowering of the surface is due to this cause. In districts consisting largely of soluble rocks, such as limestone, however, the effects of solution are important in the earlier stages of the cycle also, and as long as the surface retains pronounced relief striking topographic effects are produced as a result of the enlargement of fissures by percolating water. Limestone and the closely related dolomite rock and magnesian limestone are the only soluble rocks that occur commonly in sufficiently large masses to allow solution to produce important topographic effects.

A general result of the enlargement of fissures by solution is a reduction of the run-off from the surface, as a great part of the precipitation sinks immediately into the ground and runs away into underground channels. When fissures are enlarged so as to form open passages (fig. 121) they offer infinitely less resistance to the flow of water than do the minute passages in relatively insoluble rocks. There is thus far less heaping of water under elevations. In other words, the water-table becomes nearly horizontal, and lies at a considerable depth beneath the surface except at the bottoms of rather deep valleys, where the ground water flows out from caverns or wells up as springs to join permanent surface streams. Smaller surface streams become rare, though in some valleys streams flow intermittently, being absent except after unusually heavy rains when the ground-water level is unusually high. Thus mechanical erosion

Fig. 121.—Stream flowing from a solution tunnel, Broken River Basin, New Zealand.
Photograph from Professor R. Speight.

Fig. 122.—Minor relief features on a limestone terrain, which result mainly from pitting due to development of underground drainage in solution channels, Ruakokopatuna, New Zealand.
C. A. Cotton, photo.

comes to play a relatively small part in the lowering of the surface. A feature, therefore, of limestone regions is the coarse texture of the dissection, or, rather, the wide spacing of the stream-cut valleys, for minor irregularities due to pitting by solution may make the surface of the interfluves very uneven (fig. 122).

Sinkholes, Caves, and Natural Bridges.—Some landforms that are of very common occurrence on limestone terrains are the direct results of the opening of underground channels by solution (fig. 123). Basin-shaped hollows (fig. 124) and steep-sided pits (fig. 125)

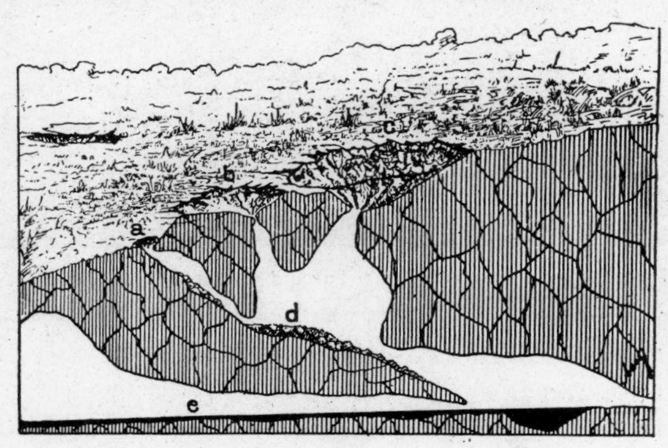

Fig. 123.—Relation of sinkholes (*a, b, c*) to caverns and underground water-channels (*d, e*) in limestone. (After Cvijic, by courtesy of the *Geographical Review*.)

may mark the upper ends of enlarged fissures. These do not as a rule remain as open pits, but are more or less choked by fallen blocks of rock and by finer waste washed in from the surface. The funnel-like hollows and pits are termed *sinkholes* or *dolines*. The water that collects in them and may stand for a time after rain does not overflow but drains downward to join the ground water.

Some sinkholes may be formed by the collapse of portions of the roofs of galleries dissolved out by water flowing along horizontal fissures. Such caverns are extremely common in limestone areas (fig. 28). Occasionally underground rivers flow in them (fig. 121), some of which are surface streams that take a short underground course and emerge again upon the surface. In other cases water no longer flows through the caverns, the streams that enlarged them having been led off to lower levels as neighbouring valleys have been deepened.

Fig. 124.—Sinkholes in the Pareora district, New Zealand.
M. C. Gudex, photo.

Fig. 125.—Sinkhole, Southern Wairarapa, New Zealand.
C. A. Cotton, photo.

When enlargement of a cave by solution ceases owing to the sinking of ground water to a level below its floor, deposition of carbonate of lime begins on the roof and floor, the substance being brought in in solution by water percolating through the roof. Water can hold carbonate of lime in solution only when charged with dissolved carbon dioxide. A drop of the solution hanging from the roof evaporates slightly and loses some carbon dioxide. It can no longer hold the whole of its dissolved carbonate of lime, but

Fig. 126.—Stalactites and stalagmites, Waitomo Caves, New Zealand.
F. G. Radcliffe, photo.

deposits some as a tiny ring on the roof. Drop after drop hanging from the same point deposits layer after layer, so that the ring grows into a pendent tube which later becomes thickened by a deposit on the outside until it is a typical *stalactite*. The drops when they fall on the floor lose more carbon dioxide and deposit more carbonate of lime in layers which build a stool-shaped *stalagmite*. Thus stalactites and stalagmites are characteristic of limestone caves (fig. 126).

Where a spring emerges from an underground channel to form a full-sized surface stream, the valley of the latter, though perhaps deeply cut, is enclosed at the head by steep, perhaps precipitous, walls. Some valleys ("blind" valleys) end downstream in a similar way at a point where drainage disappears underground.

The greater part of the roof of an underground river-channel may fall in, leaving only a small arch, or *natural bridge* (fig. 127). A natural bridge may also be formed by a stream abandoning its course over a fall to flow along and enlarge a fissure so as to emerge below the former edge of the fall. Natural bridges developed by solution in limestone are of much more common occurrence than those cut under exceptional conditions by lateral stream corrasion (p. 102).

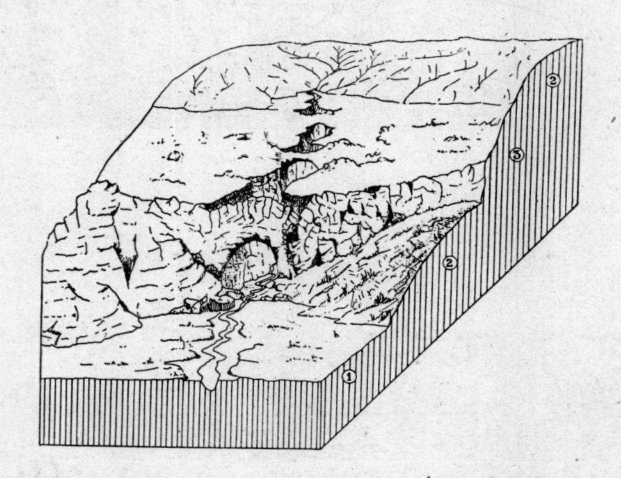

Fig. 127.—Natural bridges result from collapse of parts of the roof of a cavern in Serbia. (After Cvijic, by courtesy of the *Geographical Review*.)

Owing to the prevalence of underground drainage the continuous valleys characteristic of normally eroded regions may be replaced by strings of bowl-like hollows (fig. 128) connected by tunnels.

The residual soil is easily washed off a limestone surface when the natural vegetation is disturbed. Partly owing to loss of soil in this way, and partly to dryness at the surface due to the great depth to which the ground water sinks, upland plateaux and mountains of limestone are generally deserts. The naked surface of the limestone is often carved by the solvent action of rain-water into innumerable pinnacles or narrow ridges separated by deep and narrow trenches. It is then a *karrenfeld* (fig. 129).

Fig. 128.—One of an aligned series of sinkholes connected by tunnels of an underground stream-course, Nelson, New Zealand.

C. A. Cotton, photo.

Fig. 129.—A locally-developed karrenfeld, Punakaiki, New Zealand.

M. C. Lysons, photo.

Hums.—Mesas, buttes, and smaller outcrops of bare limestone that are wasting away are fluted by lapiés (figs. 19, 130) and may be carved into fantastic "architectural" forms by the enlargement of joints or other separation planes in the rock (fig. 131).

Fig. 130.—Lapiés on the Pikikiruna Range, New Zealand.
C. A. Cotton, photo.

The last remnants of a limestone sheet overlying other rocks may survive as cavern-riddled small outliers, which are termed *hums*. They are well developed on hard-rock plateaux in the Nelson district of New Zealand, where, being bush-covered, they stand out prominently from a barren surrounding landscape (figs. 132, 152).

Travertine Falls and Dams.—Water that has become a saturated solution of calcium carbonate when flowing in an underground course is ready to deposit some of this when it emerges at the surface and loses some carbon dioxide. At Tivoli, near Rome, and at many places in the limestone region east of the Adriatic Sea there are "constructive" waterfalls, where crystalline calcium carbonate is being deposited as a compact material ("travertine") in river channels; and a lake may be impounded in a river valley where a travertine dam is built at the emergence of a large tributary from an underground course. Constructive travertine falls are

Fig. 131.—A limestone mesa, or hum, carved by rain-water solution into "architectural" forms, near Whangarei, New Zealand.

C. A. Cotton, photo.

Fig. 132.—Cavern-riddled hum of limestone on the Gouland Downs plateau, New Zealand.

C. A. Cotton, photo.

present in the course of the Gregory River in northern Australia. On a smaller scale mounds of less compact "calcareous tufa" mark the points of emergence of many small springs of lime-saturated water.

The Karst or Limestone Cycle.—In early stages of a geomorphic cycle a landscape on limestone terrain may be dissected normally by surface streams, for the opening up of solution channels underground may not yet have proceeded far enough, or major valleys may not yet have been sufficiently deepened, to allow of ground water being drained away to a deep level. A mature landscape developed in this way, or a structural plateau exposed where weaker strata overlying a thick limestone formation have been stripped

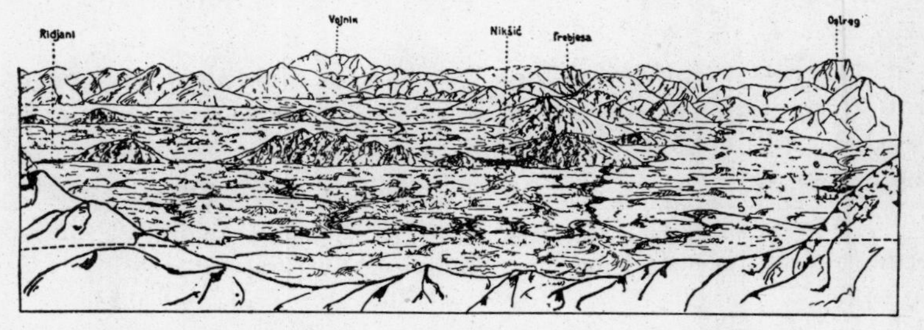

Fig. 133.—A polje in Montenegro. (After Cvijic, by courtesy of the *Geographical Review*.)

away, may provide an initial form on which a special limestone or *karst* cycle (named from the Karst region of the Dinaric Alps) develops. In the former case valleys are abandoned as "dry" valleys, no longer subject to enlargement by stream erosion, when the ground-water level sinks; and in all cases a new pitted relief diversifies the surface. Sinkholes develop, both small and large, perhaps becoming laterally confluent and forming collapsed areas of basin shape (*uvalas*) as solution wastes the limestone away. Caving-in of cavern roofs may convert the caverns into trench-like blind valleys.

The few major streams which, as they are not above ground-water level, flow permanently and continue to deepen their valleys by mechanical corrasion will be confined between the precipitous walls of trenches, perhaps of great depth, for limestone is a resistant rock.

Such a surface, very different from the integrated system of valleys that results from normal mechanical erosion, and now largely obliterating any such system that may have been present under former conditions, may be considered the mature landscape of the karst cycle. An old-age form may be developed if wasting of the limestone by solution continues down to the ground-water level, which as a local base-level may control such levelling. In horizontally sheeted formations an impermeable stratum under the limestone may in its turn control the ground-water level over a considerable area. This stage has been reached on the floors of some of the remarkable enclosed basins termed *poljes* (fig. 133) in the Dinaric region of karst landscapes. Scattered residuals (hums) are all that remain of thick limestone formations wasted away by solution.

Poljes have no surface outlets, but are drained through underground channels. Some may have been formed in the course of the karst cycle entirely by solution; but most of them appear to be tectonic basins enlarged and greatly modified by karst erosion. In other terrains such basins would overflow and be drained eventually through open valleys. Only on a limestone terrain can they become true poljes drained by underground rivers.

In the Dinaric region the ground-water level sinks during the dry summer season and rises during the winter, when the deeper parts of poljes are converted into seasonal or intermittent lakes. The floors of some large dolines have been lowered to a level which is below that of the ground-water surface at all seasons, so that the dolines have become the bowl-shaped basins of permanent small lakes. On the lake floors and rather generally over the floors of poljes silt is deposited which has been carried down by intermittent streams from the margins of the surrounding plateau. This material has been washed from the red earth (*terra rossa*), which is the residual clay resulting from weathering of the limestone and is derived from its small quota of insoluble mineral constituents.

CHAPTER XI

PENEPLAINS

Destruction of relief. Peneplains and monadnocks. Old-from-birth peneplains. Dissected peneplains. Accordance of summit levels.

Destruction of Relief.—In late maturity summits are gradually lowered and valley-floor side-strips (p. 112) become more and more extensive even along the valleys of secondary and minor tributary streams and little is left of the relief of a region. Valley plains where they have been somewhat built up by aggradation during a phase of maturity are eventually cut down again, and in late maturity graded streams in general are degraded to levels much lower than those of early maturity owing to the fact that gentler gradients suffice for transportation of the greatly diminished supply of waste to the rivers after the relief of interfluves has been destroyed or much reduced. Such lowering of valley floors takes place so slowly, however, that widening and extension of valley lowlands is not interrupted by it, but goes on continuously.

Peneplains and Monadnocks.—With the disappearance of all strong relief over large areas the *old-age* or *senile* stage of the geomorphic cycle is attained, and the senile surface—not quite a plain—is a *peneplain.* A few isolated groups of hills or even subdued mountains rise generally above the nearly level surface of a peneplain. These remnants, or residuals, of a former relief are termed *monadnocks,* from a prominent example, Mount Monadnock, in New Hampshire (fig. 134). They are what remain of dividing ridges or of the mountain masses where several divides meet, and are composed of the most resistant rocks of the region, for on the outcrops of these the divides have become fixed at an earlier stage of the cycle.

Unlike a valley plain, which is a true plain produced by lateral corrasion, a peneplain is not an approximately plane surface throughout. It consists in part of broad valley plains of rivers, but in part also of intervening areas of low undulating forms with very gently graded slopes and no rock outcrops. Such areas are shown in outline, but without surface detail in fig. 135.

For the development of a peneplain in a region of resistant, or mixed weak and resistant, rocks an enormous period is required—certainly millions of years, and perhaps many millions. The time required for the change from mature relief to senile relief must be many times greater than that taken for the development of mature dissection. The amount of material removed from the surface

Fig. 134.—A monadnock standing above a peneplain, Mt. Monadnock, New Hampshire.

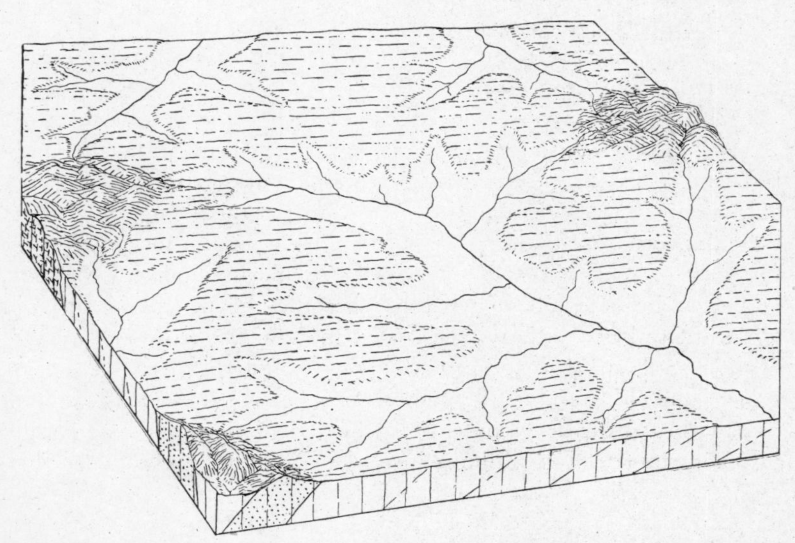

Fig. 135.—A peneplain, with monadnocks surviving on the outcrops of the most resistant rocks.

during the latter half of the cycle may be no greater than during the earlier half, but the rate of removal from slopes becomes exceedingly slow as these slopes become gentle. So slow does the mechanical removal of waste from the gentle slopes become that chemical erosion, relatively unimportant in the earlier stages of the cycle when mechanical erosion was more active, is now responsible for a great part of the lowering of the surface, the material being removed in solution.

Old-from-birth Peneplains.—It has been suggested that peneplains have not necessarily resulted from the wearing down of the relief of mature landscapes. Something may be said in favour of the argument that uplift is not necessarily always confined to the introductory phase or initiation of a geomorphic cycle, such as has been outlined in foregoing chapters. On the contrary, it may go on with extreme slowness throughout a vast period, accompanied by progressive erosion of an upheaved surface. On the surface of a terrain of extremely weak rock material upheaved thus slowly it may readily be imagined that vertical corrasion may fail ever to outpace valley-side grading and the general wearing-down of the surface, so that no young, and perhaps even no mature, landscape features can be developed. Once a peneplain always a peneplain is the rule under such conditions. Youth and maturity are elided from the cycle and the landscape which results has been described as *old from birth*.

When an attempt is made to apply such a theory of origin to a peneplain on a terrain of resistant or even mixed weak and resistant rocks the fact of the extreme slowness of down-wearing and every phase of erosion on a senile surface raises an insuperable difficulty. In order to account for the removal of the rock materials formerly present with a thickness measurable in thousands of feet and even in miles above what has become the peneplain surface one must call upon the immeasurably more active erosive processes of early cycle-stages to perform a great part of the work. On this ground the old-from-birth hypothesis must be ruled out as a general explanation of the development of peneplains unless one is prepared to allow hundreds of millions instead of millions of years for the duration of the process.

A much less extravagant demand on time is made by a variant of this hypothesis which postulates upheaval at such an appropriate steady pace that it is accompanied throughout by maintenance on the upheaved surface of mature landscape forms with sufficiently strong relief to ensure that erosion of the surface will be rather rapid. There may be some such landscapes, the peneplanation of which is prevented by the continuance of upheaval. Some of them may belong to the mature-born class (p. 77).

Fig. 136.—Uplifted and dissected peneplain, Southern Tableland, New South Wales. *Eric Merton, photo.*

Dissected Peneplains.—There have been so many earth movements in comparatively recent times that the cycle of erosion at present in progress has hardly anywhere advanced beyond the stage of full maturity, except locally on exceptionally weak rocks; but, though young and mature forms are the rule in the current cycle, peneplains developed in earlier cycles have not been entirely obliterated. Some have been uplifted, with the result that they have formed the initial surfaces upon which erosion began to cut the forms of

Fig. 137.—Peneplain remnant on a ridge crest in a deeply dissected landscape, Wellington, New Zealand.

C. A. Cotton, photo.

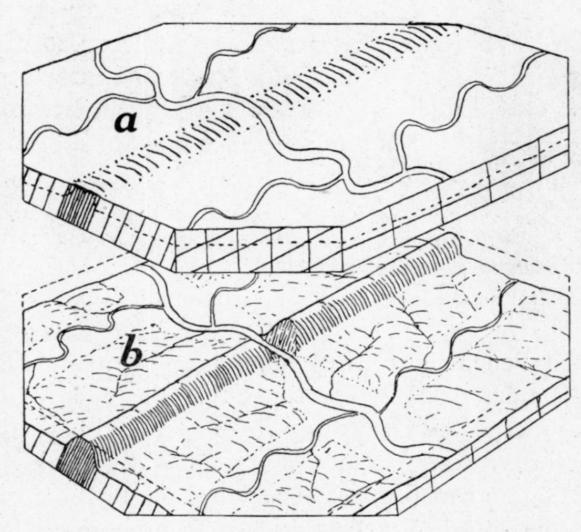

Fig. 138.—Even-crested ridge on the outcrop of a resistant stratum preserving a remnant of the peneplain *a* at a later period, *b*, when weaker formations have been worn down to lowlands.

the present cycle. Others have been submerged at various times during the earth's long past history, and preserved beneath masses of sediment.

Dissection of a peneplain may generally be ascribed to uplift or an equivalent sinking of sea-level. Sometimes, however, it may be due to subsidence of the neighbouring land.

Fig. 139.—Accordance of summit levels in south-western New Zealand. View northward from Lake Te Anau.

V. C. Browne, photo.

Portions of many dissected peneplains still survive as plateaux, more or less thoroughly dissected (fig. 136), or as occasional flat-topped mountains and ridges in maturely dissected regions (figs. 137, 138). In such cases the peneplain surface may be restored by the imagination by joining up the flat remnants. The restoration thus made may show that, instead of remaining horizontal, the peneplain as it was uplifted suffered deformation, being perhaps irregularly warped or else uplifted as a more or less elongated dome.

Peneplain surfaces survive longest on the hardest rocks, and so even-crested, flat-topped ridges of resistant rock are sometimes found separating low-lying areas of small relief on belts of weaker rock, where the reduction to lowlands of a later cycle is far advanced (fig. 138). On the very even crested ridges which survive on the hardest of the steeply-inclined strata in the Appalachian ridges of the eastern United States remnants are preserved of an ancient and perfectly developed peneplain.

Accordance of Summit Levels.—Where no flat remnants of a peneplain actually survive, *accordance of summit levels* (fig. 139) may indicate that a peneplain has been destroyed by erosion, a number of peaks still reaching to about a common level, though the top of each peak must be some little distance below the position of the former surface.

Accordance of summit levels does not indicate with certainty the destruction of an uplifted plain, but the former existence of such a surface may usually be inferred with a fair degree of confidence where accordance is well marked with a restored surface either plane or domed. Occasional summits that are much above the common level may mark the sites of monadnocks (fig. 139).

Where folded or diverse structures occur in the terrain there is no danger of confusion of peneplains or their dissected remains with structural plateaux or with the stripped roofs of large bodies of intrusive granite. There has been sometimes difference of opinion, however, whether an ancient plain now uplifted has been a peneplain or a plain of marine erosion cut by the waves as the sea has encroached on the land (Chapter XXX). The origin of the level summits on mountains in Wales is thus in doubt.

CHAPTER XII

SUPERPOSED RIVERS AND RESURRECTED LANDSCAPES

Erosion on compound structures. Superposed river courses. Resurrected fossil plains. Tests of fossil-plain origin. Intersecting peneplains. Dissection of an undermass by superposed rivers.

Erosion on Compound Structures.—Beneath superficial covering strata the rocks of an undermass (p. 42) may be present at a sufficiently shallow depth to ensure that they will be exposed by erosion in the course of a cycle—that is, considerably above the general base-level. In such a case river courses from the cover may be incised through it into the undermass, and later the cover may be entirely removed from the areas separated by these rivers so that the undermass rocks are the only part of the terrain then remaining.

When this has taken place, stripping-away of the cover may expose the buried surface of the undermass over considerable areas in the form in which it was worn by erosion prior to the accumulation of the cover over it. The floor, that is to say, on which the cover was spread is *resurrected*. This floor, having been previously an erosion surface—commonly such as is developed in a normal geomorphic cycle, which may have reached the stage of youth, maturity, or old age before its burial—may either before or after it is exhumed be described as a *fossil* erosion surface. It is a *fossil peneplain* if it had attained a senile condition of development. In some cases recognisable ancient soils and land deposits form the basal beds of the cover overlying a fossil plain or peneplain; but elsewhere marine sedimentary covering strata rest directly on the worn surface of the undermass, which is then not weathered like the residue on an ancient peneplain but consists of fresh rock evidently planed at the margin of an advancing sea. Even in such cases, however, the land surface prior to a marine submergence was quite probably a peneplain, for if submergence took place gradually, though not necessarily very slowly, the waves of the sea would stir up and remove the soil and the whole of the waste mantle from such a surface, grind residual boulders into gravel, and expose and plane the bedrock.

Quite obviously re-exposure of such a floor that has been buried can take place only where the undermass rocks are strongly resistant to erosion, whereas the cover must be relatively very weak—when it may be cleanly stripped away "as mud is washed from a board."

Where there is not so great a contrast between the resistance to erosion offered by undermass and cover such floors or fossil land surfaces can be seen only in profile sections at chance intersections by sea or river-cut cliffs or by artificial cuts. In these fossil surfaces geologists see strong "unconformity"—that is, a chronological break in the sequence of formations recording a period of upheaval and exposure in which the fossil erosion-surface was cut or worn down by erosion.

Superposed River Courses.—Whether a cover is or is not markedly different in its resistance to erosion, but differs in structure, from an undermass neither the surface form nor the structure of the undermass can in any way influence the directions that will be taken by courses of streams on the cover. Streams consequent on the slopes of the surface and beds of the cover or subsequents adjusted to its structure will, as a general rule, have courses that are entirely out of adjustment with the rocks, and perhaps also with the form of the surface, of the undermass. So long as the undermass remains entirely buried there is no apparent anomaly, its surface form and its structures being either unknown or having been revealed only by boring or by mining. With deeper erosion, while considerable areas of the cover still survive, even though the deeper valleys have been cut down through it into the undermass, the relation of stream courses to the cover is still obvious.

Stream courses that have been cut down through the rocks on which they were developed into rocks of different structure, to the stratification and other structures of which they can have neither a consequent nor a subsequent relation, are termed *superposed.* In general they are superposed from an unconformable cover on to the rocks and rock structures across which they now flow. Those that were consequents before they became superposed are now *superposed consequents,* but subsequents that have been adjusted to the structures of the cover may be present also, and are now *superposed subsequents.*

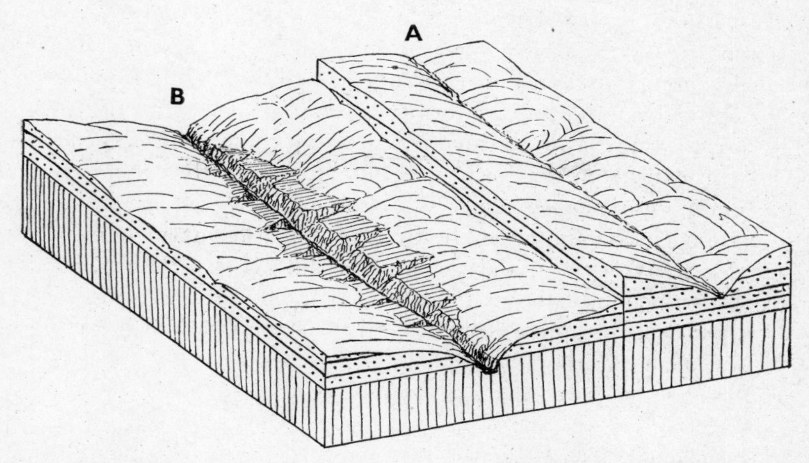

Fig. 140.—On a terrain of compound structure a consequent river (*A*) becomes superposed (*B*).

Streams superposed on an undermass and incised in it by further valley-deepening are thereby fixed in position, just as are consequents incised beneath an itital surface (fig. 140). As local base-levels sink beneath the surface of the undermass complete removal of the cover from the adjacent area will follow in the course of the erosion cycle, and as this proceeds all the streams, small as well as large, will become superposed. Thus the entire drainage pattern from the cover is stencilled on the undermass, while the cover itself disappears.

Systems of valleys with definite patterns resulting from superposition are rather common. Systems of parallel valleys cutting

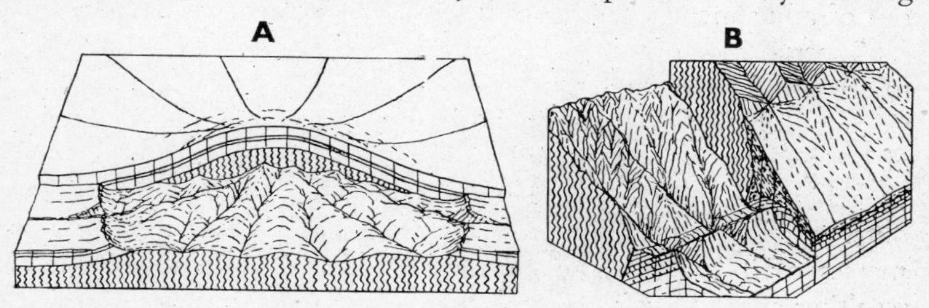

Fig. 141.—Diagrams of superposed drainage. *A,* radially arranged superposed consequents; *B,* transverse streams superposed from courses guided by the slope of a temporary accumulation of waste. In both diagrams the early drainage pattern, before the removal of the cover, is also shown.

transversely or diagonally across the strike of the rocks may be superposed subsequents, while a not uncommon grouping of superposed consequents is a radial arrangement indicating the presence of a dome-shaped uplift of a former cover[1] (see fig. 141, *A*).

Streams may also be superposed from courses, in a general way consequent on the form of the uplift, which they take down the apron of waste (Chapter XV) accumulating along the base of a young mountain-range, the front of which forms an unusually steep declivity of the initial surface (see fig. 141, *B*). When, later, general reduction of the uplifted surface by erosion is accompanied by removal of the apron of waste, and the stream pattern from it is

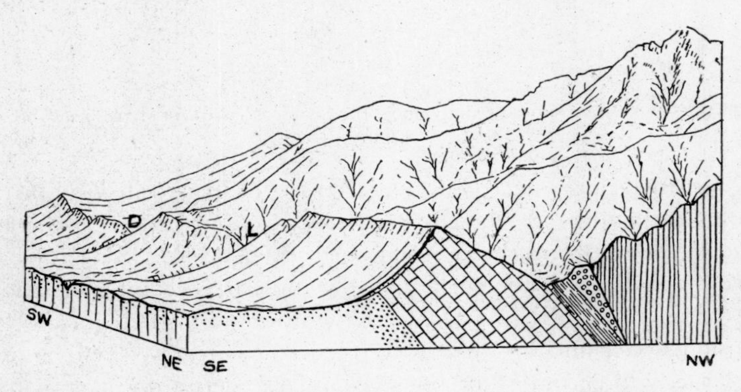

Fig. 142.—The south-eastern slope of the Kaikoura Range, showing the gorges (D and L) of two transverse streams (probably superposed) through the homoclinal ridge along the base of the range. Compare fig. 141, *B*.

stencilled on the underlying rocks, the streams are generally quite out of adjustment with the rock structures across which they flow.

Superposition of this latter kind may perhaps correctly be invoked to account for the numerous transverse streams across a homoclinal ridge which lies close along the base of the Kaikoura Mountains of New Zealand on their south-eastern side (fig. 142). The peculiar branching of some of these streams, which takes place upon the outcrop of the thick limestone of the ridge, isolating island-like masses of it between the branches (fig. 143), is a phenomenon resulting apparently from some cause other than headward erosion, and points to superposition probably of this kind (see also fig. 84).

[1] E.g., in the Lake District of Cumberland (England).

Several south-westward-flowing streams which join to form the Spey, a tributary of the Conway River, in New Zealand, seem to be of superposed subsequent origin (fig. 144). Some superposed subsequents in the eastern United States have been adjusted as subsequents to the homoclinal structure of coastal-plain strata, and when these have been removed remain stencilled on the undermass.

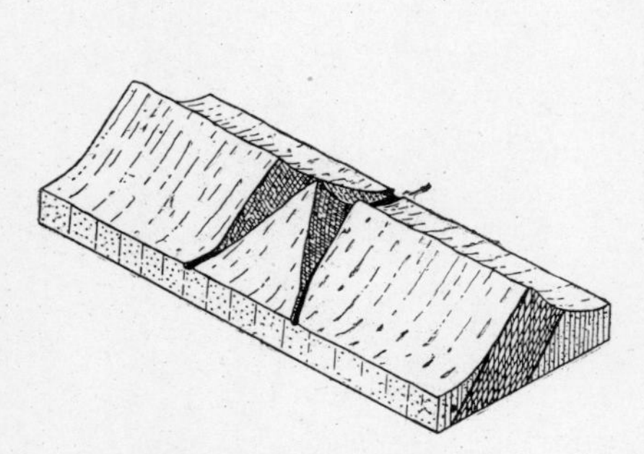

Fig. 143.—Diagram of the fork of a stream superposed on a homoclinal ridge.

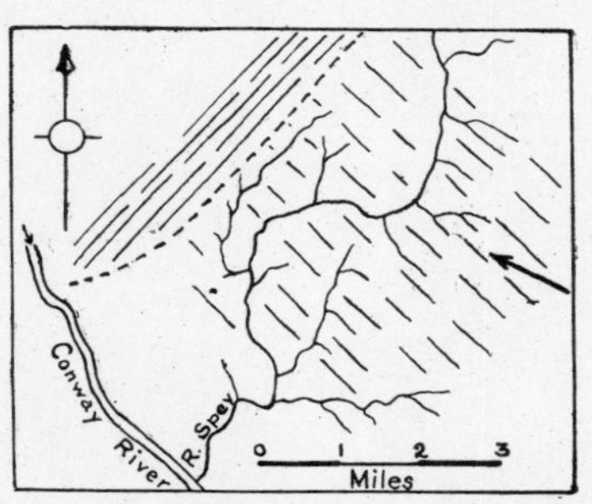

Fig. 144.—The streams of the Spey system, which are probably superposed subsequents. The strike of cover where preserved nearby is indicated (north-west corner) and that of the undermass in the centre. The arrow indicates regional slope.

Since superposed stream courses result from the removal of beds differing in structure from those below and generally unconformable to them, it follows that they are often associated with fossil plains. This association is not, however, a necessary one, for superposition of streams does not require that the undermass shall be any more resistant to erosion than the cover. Where they are about equally resistant, or the cover is more resistant than the undermass, the latter will be thoroughly dissected by the time the former is all removed.

Resurrected Fossil Plains.—The stripping of the cover from fossil plains and the survival of the surfaces to form prominent features of a landscape depend, above all, on the relative resistance offered to erosion by the undermass and the cover. Stripping is favoured by the tilting of strips or blocks of country, but survival of the fossil plain may be expected only where the angles at which they are tilted are moderate, the permissible slope being steeper in a dry than in a wet climate.

Extensive fossil plains are known that have been uplifted bodily so that they retain their original horizontal attitude scarcely modified; but it will simplify this discussion to consider the case in which tilting has taken place to a moderate extent (fig. 145).

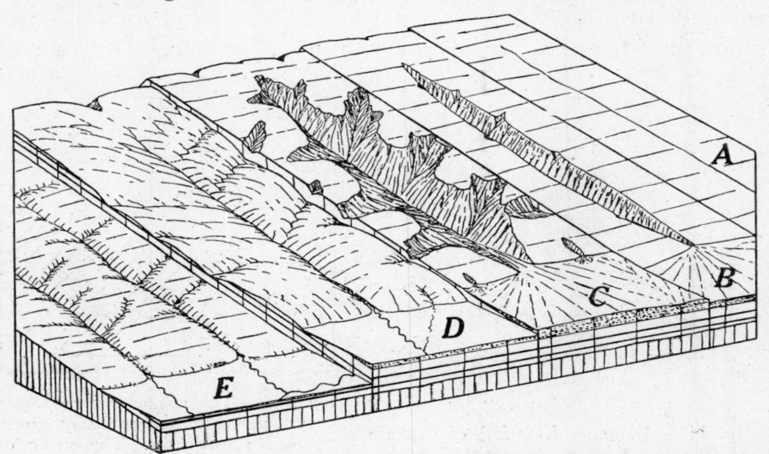

Fig. 145.—Diagram of the development of the surface of a gently tilted area with a relatively weak cover and resistant undermass. *A,* initial form; *B, C,* and *D,* early sequential forms; *E,* stage at which the fossil plain is exposed.

On such a surface, when first uplifted, numerous consequent streams will come into existence, and these will be approximately parallel if the tilting is uniform. They will soon be actively engaged in grading their courses. In streams such as these, with initially steep declivities, this process involves simultaneous corrasion throughout their length, but the lower courses will, on account of the greater volume of the streams, be deepened first, and when the graded condition is approached the maximum valley-depth will be found in the middle courses.

From the rapidly deepened consequent valleys some insequent tributaries will be developed, and perhaps also subsequents. Thus, since the spacing of the consequents alone may be close and the texture of dissection becomes finer when other new streams have been developed, deep entrenchment of the whole system beneath the sloping surface of the weak covering strata must rapidly take place. Maturity of dissection will be rapidly attained, first in the middle part of the slope, and later over the whole area of the surface.

The consequent and other streams of the sloping upland, when they cut through the cover and become superposed on the resistant undermass, will receive a check, and the rate of farther downward cutting will become comparatively slow. Before this stage is reached the measure of the relief has been increasing progressively with downward cutting, and even after this stage it may still increase, though very slightly, if maturity of dissection of the surface is still to be attained. After the attainment of maturity reduction in height

Fig. 146.—Partly-dissected stripped fossil plain, near St. Bathans, Central Otago, New Zealand. *C. A. Cotton, photo.*

of the interfluvial areas of weak covering strata may go on more rapidly than vertical stream corrasion on the resistant underlying rocks, and the measure of the relief may be thus reduced. Even if the streams had attained grade without cutting through the cover in the early stages of dissection, after the cover has been largely removed from the neighbourhood of their headwaters they will be forced to cut deeper and will eventually become superposed. Later, when the covering strata have been largely or wholly removed from the whole sloping surface, all the streams will be incised to some extent in the undermass. Owing to the resistant nature of the rocks of the undermass, however, the ravines in it will for long remain narrow, *simulating* youth, while on the interfluves inclined flat areas will survive where the ancient eroded floor has been stripped of its cover (fig. 145, *E*; also fig. 146). This stage will be attained earliest at the middle parts of evenly sloping surfaces, for half-way down the slopes stream corrasion has resulted in the greatest valley-deepening and the greatest development of tributaries. Farther down the slopes, owing to smaller depth of corrasion, undissected interfluvial areas are likely to be larger; and farther up, as the general inclination is not steep, there will be little concentrated wash. So in both these positions remnants of the cover may be expected to survive longer than in the middle of the slopes.

This is the stage of erosion that has been reached on large areas of upland surfaces in various parts of New Zealand. They are now

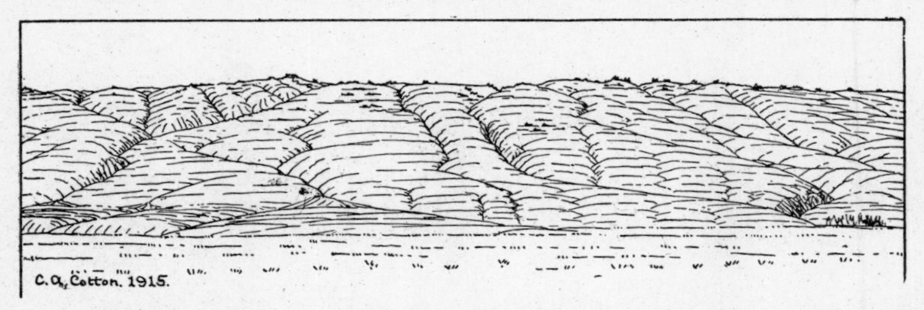

Fig. 147.—A north-westward-sloping stripped fossil plain forming part of Rough Ridge, New Zealand, which descends in the foreground beneath covering strata.

sloping fossil plains almost entirely stripped of their cover, and crossed by many steep-sided, generally superposed consequent ravines, which increase rapidly in depth as followed upstream from their debouchures, with rare salients formed by remnants of the covering strata relieving the otherwise nearly plane interfluvial strips. Among the most perfect examples are those forming the back slopes of some of the "block mountains" of the South Island—e.g., the western slope of Rough Ridge (fig. 147); a long north-easterly slope from the broken plateaux of Central Otago to the depression followed by the Shag River (fig. 165); a similar slope, though rather more deeply dissected, descending south-eastward to the Taieri Plain (fig. 148); and the westward slopes of the Hunter's Hills

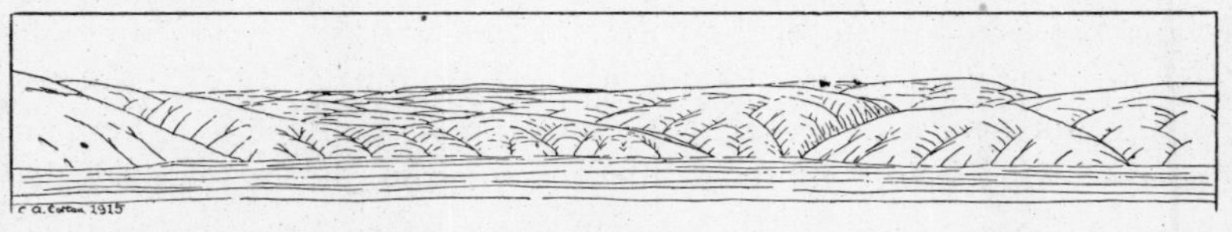

Fig. 148.—Undulating plateau—at least in part a fossil plain—descending towards the Taieri Plain, from the interior of Otago, New Zealand.

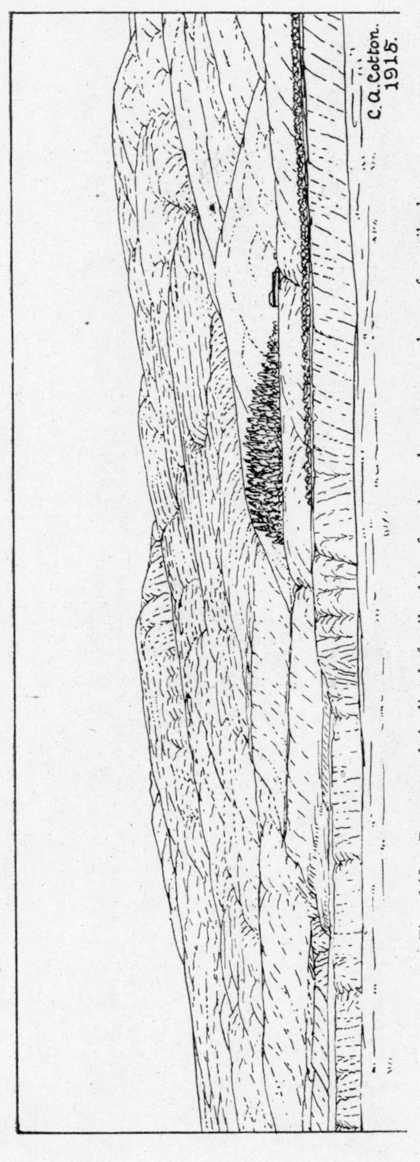

Fig. 149.—Re-exposed inclined fossil plain forming the western slope of a tilted tectonic block that forms the southern end of the Hunter's Hills range, Canterbury, New Zealand. In the middle distance the surface descends beneath similarly-inclined marine covering strata which rest upon it as a floor.

Fig. 150.—Dissected margin (at Hillend) of the interior plateau of Otago, New Zealand.

C. A. Cotton, photo.

Fig. 151.—Horizontally preserved peneplain or fossil plain, Barewood, Otago, New Zealand, traversed by the Taieri River.

C. A. Cotton, photo.

range (fig. 149). A very extensive undulating plateau which is the dominant feature of the landscape of eastern Otago has been described as, and is in parts, a true peneplain; but some areas of this land surface also must be regarded as portions of the more ancient buried peneplain which have been recently resurrected (figs. 150, 151).

Other extensive plateaux of this origin which remain approximately level and are but little dissected (being on a terrain of very resistant rocks) survive in north-west Nelson, notably on Mount Arthur and the Gouland Downs (fig. 152). The planation of the fossil surfaces now re-exposed in various parts of the New Zealand region was not completed simultaneously. They were submerged and buried, indeed, at very different periods from the late

Fig. 152.—The Gouland Downs plateau, New Zealand, a resurrected fossil plain. A few residual hums of a limestone cover, which carry bush, contrast with the bare plateau.

C. A. Cotton, photo.

Cretaceous to the middle Tertiary in the South Island, while in the North Island similar fossil plains are of upper Tertiary age.

In Europe—notably in France, but rather widely in north-western Europe also—considerable portions of extensive plateaux and level upland surfaces formerly considered true peneplains are now known to be resurrected fossil surfaces.

Tests of Fossil-plain Origin.—In the case of some of the examples cited the cover has consisted of marine formations; elsewhere parts of fossil plains are buried beneath terrestrial—mainly river-laid—deposits; and presumably parts of the same great plains (or peneplains) escaped burial. Such parts have not an equal chance of preservation in an undissected condition, however, unless they have remained low-lying until very recently. Evidence of the "fossil" nature of surfaces is available where they slope down and their downward continuation still remains buried beneath covering strata, or where, on higher ground, resistant outliers of the cover stand above the plateau surface. Where such outliers have been destroyed by erosion with the exception of some residual boulders derived from an exceptionally hard layer, these if conspicuous are *sarsen stones*. The fragments, though dwindling in size as the result of long continued weathering, still litter the surface of the undermass. On the Otago plateaux in New Zealand (already described) small examples of such residual boulders, consisting of hard-cemented quartz grit and conglomerate, are widespread; and in a few places these are large enough to make conspicuous sarsen stones (fig. 153).

Fig. 153.—Sarsen stones on the partly-dissected, sloping fossil plain of Rough Ridge, Otago, New Zealand.

J. Park, photo.

Though they may testify to the former existence of covering strata, sarsen stones do not prove that a surface on which they lie is the actual floor on which the cover was deposited. Some of those shown in fig. 153 lie on such a nearly-plane (sloping) surface, whereas others have descended into a ravine which dissects that surface.

Intersecting Peneplains.—Resurrected fossil plains which are in a tilted attitude may be cut across obliquely by peneplains which have never been buried and which have more nearly retained their original horizontal attitude. These latter have originated in a cycle of later date than the period in which the covering strata were deposited but older than that in which they have been stripped from now exposed parts of the fossil plain they formerly buried (fig. 154). Such *intersecting peneplains* are known to combine, for example, to form the Otago plateaux, in New Zealand (p. 148). It is possible for the younger as well as the older of two intersecting surfaces to be "fossil," at least in part.

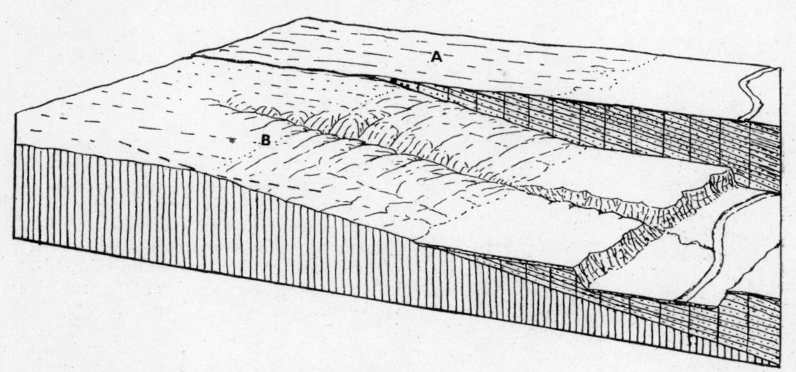

Fig. 154.—Intersection (*B*) of a fossil peneplain with a peneplain (*A*) of more recent development, which remains (in this case) horizontal.

Dissection of an Undermass by Superposed Rivers.—Where there is such an adjustment of the slope of the surface to the volume of the streams that the latter are graded while not deeply incised, stripped fossil plains traversed by ravines of moderate depth will escape dissection and will survive for a long time. In a region of small rainfall an initial slope of 5° or even 10° may have resulted in the development of small consequent streams none of which has become a master, and thus a large number of subequal, graded, but still shallow ravines occupied by intermittent streams will traverse the surface. These will destroy the continuity of the surface to some extent, but, unless the stream spacing is very close indeed, the plateau remnants on the interfluvial areas will then be relatively stable (fig. 145, *E*).

As the ravine-sides become graded by soil creep the sharp shoulders which will at first bound the plateau remnants will early disappear. The interfluvial areas will thus be reduced to broadly convex, subdued forms; but their summits will still be accordant with one another, allowing the eye to reconstruct the destroyed tangent surface of the undermass. These are the conditions obtaining in low-rainfall districts of the South Island of New Zealand, where such surfaces are common because they are stable (long-enduring) forms, wasting away very slowly as a whole instead of suffering dissection (figs. 146-149).

Under other conditions irregularly uplifted plains, whether of fossil-plain, peneplain, or other origin, are relatively short-lived.

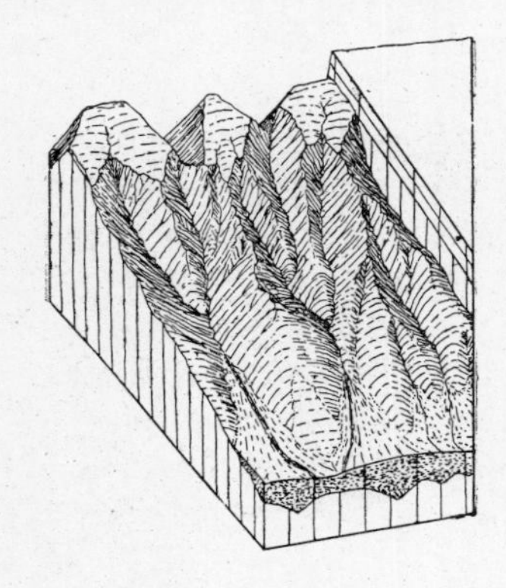

Fig. 155.—Dissection of a somewhat steeply tilted tectonic block by vigorous streams. The initial surface of a weak cover lying on a resistant undermass is shown at the right. A strip of fossil plain survives at the top of the slope, where only shallow dissection is possible at the stage depicted, but this strip is threatened with destruction as a result of headward erosion by streams descending the steep far slope of the initial landscape.

Fig. 156.—Profile view of dissected tectonic slopes (towards the right) which still exhibit accordance. The major tectonic features shown are (from left to right): Seaward Kaikoura Range, Clarence Valley, Kaikoura Range, Awatere Valley. View looking south-west across Cook Strait.

J. W. Jones, photo.

If, owing to abundant rainfall, to steepness of initial slope (fig. 155), or to initial irregularities of surface which have resulted in concentration of consequent drainage into a few streams, the graded profile for the dissecting streams lies far below the uplifted surface, the remnants of this will be attacked on all sides owing to the deepening and widening of consequent, insequent, and perhaps also subsequent ravines, and to their headward erosion. A fossil plain thus attacked may be destroyed progressively as it is exposed by the removal of the cover, and where these conditions are extreme a stage will early be reached at which dissection is deep and mature. Lower slopes will be less deeply dissected. Here the number of ravines will be reduced in the struggle for existence (p. 63), and between those that survive the ridge crests will descend with a more or less even slope, so that a general rough accordance of their summit levels with the sloping surface that has been destroyed is still traceable. Tectonic slopes in this stage of dissection are not uncommon in New Zealand. As examples may be cited the deeply cut north-western slopes of the resurrected undermass surface in the recently upheaved Kaikoura and Seaward Kaikoura mountain ranges, shown in fig. 156.

CHAPTER XIII

BLOCK STRUCTURE

Faults and their effects. Fault scarps. Fault blocks and block mountains. Cycle initiated by block-faulting movements. Earthquakes related to faults. Scarplets. Reverse scarplets. Horizontal fault movement.

Faults and their Effects.—In order to simplify the presentation of the concept of the geomorphic cycle the assumption was tacitly made in the foregoing chapters that faulting (p. 9) had no part in the production of such irregularities of surface as were formed during the uplift that initiated the cycle, upswelling and arching of the surface and of the underlying rocks taking place by bending (*warping*) without breaking. In addition to such deformation by warping, however, some actual breaking (*faulting*) generally occurs when differential movement of adjoining areas takes place. The movement along faults may be quite subordinate to warping and folding; but, on the other hand, it predominates in some cases over all other kinds of deformation, producing very striking effects. In this chapter and that which follows, therefore, the results of the presence of faults will be discussed—not only faults formed during the movements that initiate the current cycle, but also more ancient faults, for these, if present, equally complicate the structure of the terrain and affect the course of differential erosion in a characteristic manner.

Fault Scarps.—Where faulting has just taken place, actual breaks of the surface occur—abrupt descents from the high-standing to the low-lying sides of the faults. These are *fault scarps.* They form striking landscape features in the early stages of the cycle introduced by the movements associated with the faulting. In soft material, such as that immediately underlying a newly uplifted first-cycle surface, they are very rapidly destroyed by erosion; but they are longer-enduring in cycles introduced by the uplift and deformation of pre-existing land (generally on terrains of more resistant rocks) and also where newly uplifted sea-bottom or alluvial accumulations (forming the cover in a terrain of compound structure) are thin and rest on a resistant undermass, the latter being exposed in the initial fault scarps. This is a common case in New Zealand (fig. 157).

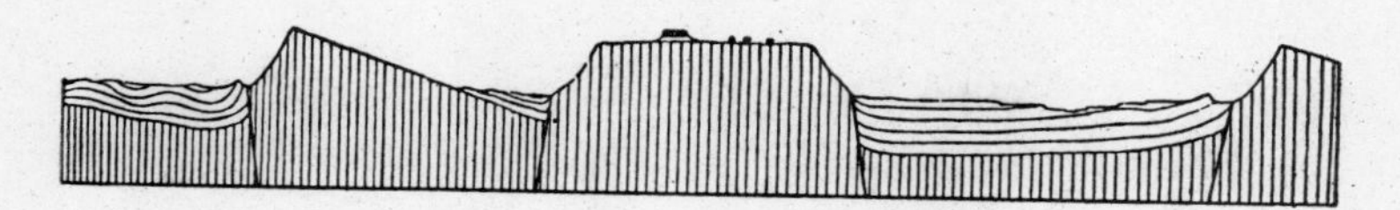

Fig. 157.—Cross-section of range-and-basin structure of the New Zealand type, in which faulting varied by warping and monoclinal flexure has broken up a terrain of compound structure. The cover is in course of removal from a fossil plain on the high-standing blocks.

Fault Blocks and Block Mountains.—Faults of large displacement generally occur in roughly parallel systems; or there may be two such systems intersecting each other so as to define quadrangular *blocks* which have moved up or down or have been tilted independently of their neighbours. Where there is only one prominent system of faults it determines the trend of elongated blocks, which are terminated by warped surfaces instead of cross faults (fig. 158, and southern part of fig. 159).

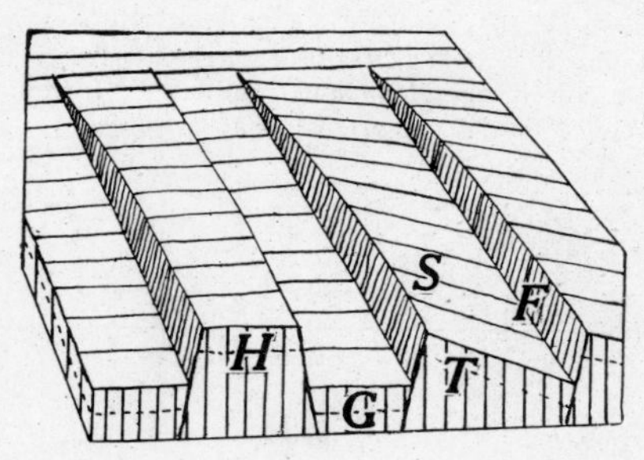

Fig. 158.—Elongated fault blocks,

The movement of a block may be uniform throughout a particular cross-section (or nearly so) the block having simply sunk or risen, forming in the one case a trough or *graben* (*G,* fig. 158; *Mo,* fig. 159) and in the other a *horst* (*H,* fig. 158; *RP,* fig. 159; also figs. 160-162) bounded on opposite sides by fault scarps.

In contrast with horsts some blocks are strongly tilted or rotated on a hinge-line so that one side of a block is relatively uplifted and the other depressed (*T,* fig. 158; also figs. 163, 164). Such a *tilted block* is bounded by a fault scarp only on the relatively uplifted

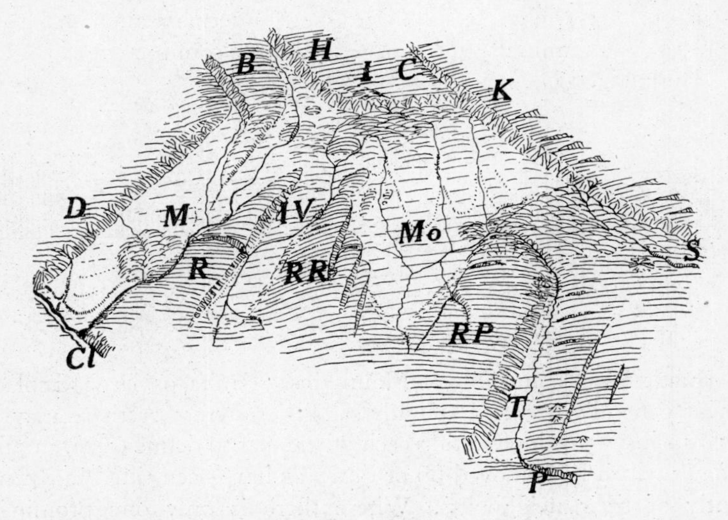

Fig. 159.—Generalised diagram of Central Otago, New Zealand, showing ranges that originated as block mountains and are separated by relatively depressed intermont basins. The rivers are mainly consequent. Fault scarps have been somewhat dissected, and upland surfaces have been reduced to resurrected fossil plains by stripping-away of soft cover. *D,* Dunstan Mountains; *M,* Manuherikia Valley; *R,* Raggedy Range; *IV,* Ida Valley; *RR,* Rough Ridge; *Mo,* Maniototo Plain; *RP,* Rock and Pillar Range; *T,* Strath Taieri and Taieri River; *P,* Barewood Plateau; *B,* St. Bathans Range; *H,* Hawkdun Range; *I,* Mount Ida; *K,* Kakanui Range; *S,* Shag Valley and River; *Cl,* Clutha River.

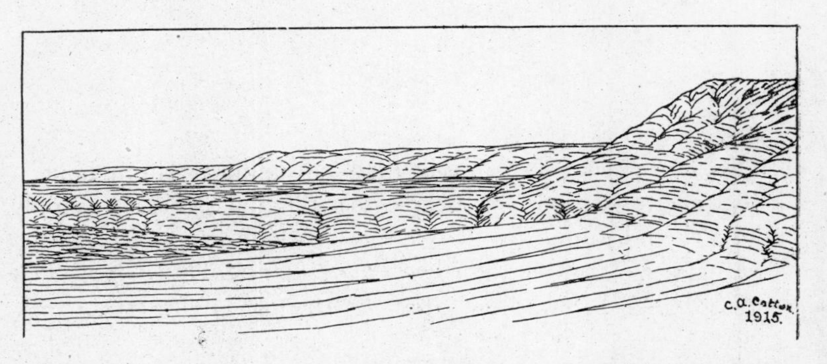

Fig. 160.—Mountain blocks standing as horsts above the eastern Otago plateau in New Zealand. (Rock and Pillar, Lammerlaw, and Lammermoor Ranges.)

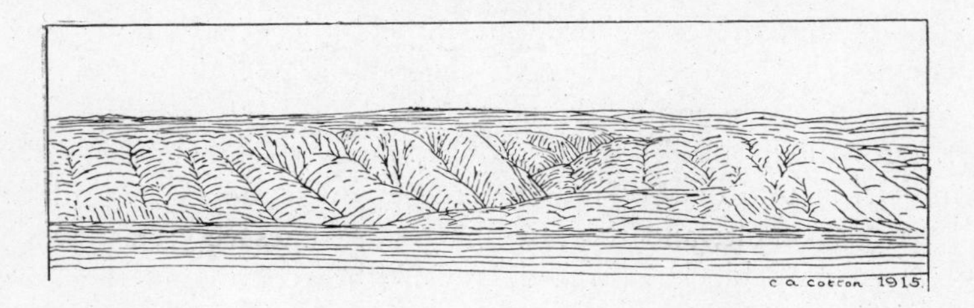

Fig. 161.—Distant view of the horst that forms the Rock and Pillar Range, Otago, New Zealand, from the west. (Relief, 3,000 feet.)

Fig. 162.—Mount Pisa horst, Otago, New Zealand, as seen from the Upper Clutha graben.

C. A. Cotton, photo.

C. A. Cotton 1916

Fig. 163.—Scarp at left and back slope (right) of a small tilted-block mountain near Kurow, New Zealand. (Relief, 1,000 feet.)

side, and from the crest-line at the top of this scarp an inclined *back slope* (*S*) descends, and ends generally in a *fault angle* at the base of the scarp bounding the next upland block (*F*; also figs. 163, 164). A tilted block thus shows some resemblance to an asymmetrical fold of the land surface of which the steeper side is replaced by a fault; and the resemblance becomes very close when the crown of a block is arched, as is rather commonly the case.

Fig. 164.—Tilted blocks: view across a fault angle and up the back slope of a distant tilted block from a view-point above the scarp-edge of a foreground block; broken plateau east of Strath Taieri, New Zealand (*T*, in fig. 159).

C. A. Cotton, photo.

Resemblance of block structure to arched or domed structure is emphasised also where a fault is in part replaced by a sharp local warping termed a *monoclinal flexure* (p. 174). Ranges carved by erosion from large uplifted blocks bounded on one or more sides by fault scarps are termed *block mountains* (figs. 159-165). These and the depressions or basins between and among them, which equally owe their initiation to earth movements of a differential character, are among the major landscape forms described as "tectonic" (p. 38). Together they make up a *range-and-basin* landscape (fig. 159).

Cycle initiated by Block-faulting Movements.—In a cycle initiated by rapid movements in which faulting is prominent the inequalities of the initial surface so produced will give rise to the usual features characteristic of youth, such as, for example, consequent lakes (in tectonic basins) and consequent falls (where

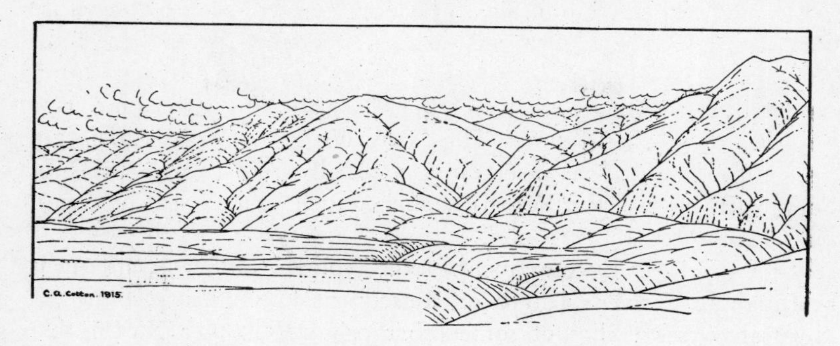

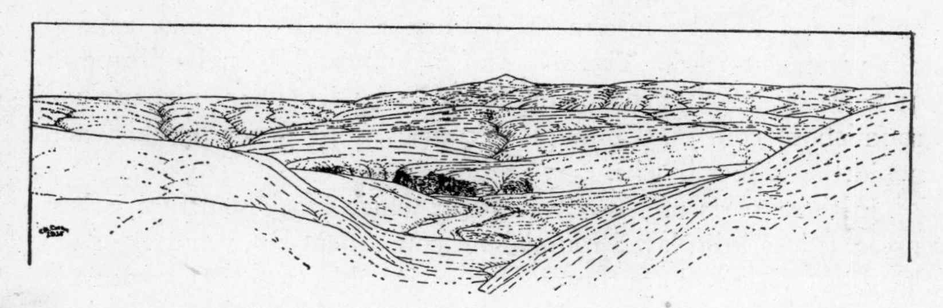

Fig. 165.—Two views across the fault-angle valley of the Shag River, New Zealand (*S*, in fig. 159). Above: View showing the Kakanui Range fault scarp. Below: View from the fault scarp, showing the down-tilted Otago plateau, with the Shag River, a consequent, in the fault angle.

consequent streams descend fault scarps). Draining of the lakes and grading of the broken stream courses and of the surface generally proceed on much the same lines as in cases already discussed.

If the deformation takes place more slowly—that is, not so rapidly that it may be considered instantaneous from a geological point of view—there will be a smaller initial development of lakes, or perhaps none at all will be formed, for the outlets from enclosed basins will be cut down to some extent by the streams that drain them as the enclosing blocks rise across their paths. Erosion also will be very active on the rising blocks, supplying much waste to be deposited, temporarily at least, in the depressions, so that deposits of alluvium forming *basin plains* (Chapter XVII) may entirely or almost entirely take the place of consequent lakes.

Where deformation goes on slowly, however, it may be irregular, now one area being upheaved and now another. Thus rivers that are strictly consequent in relation to the landforms produced in the *first* writhing of the land surface may not flow out from intermont basins through what are *eventually* the lowest tectonic gaps or sags in the basin rims. They may now be enclosed in gorges cut through what have become eventually rather high parts of mountain blocks. Further discussion of such courses will be found in Chapter XVII.

The principal consequent river courses—either consequent throughout a river's length or consequent in segments connected by transverse reaches of some other origin (Chapter XVII) that cross high blocks in gorges—traverse and occupy grabens, fault angles, and broader intermont[1] basins, in which they may expand (in youth) as lakes. The rivers of a range-and-basin landscape of tectonic origin thus normally follow very irregular, zigzag, and roundabout courses. Consequent courses must generally skirt and avoid the higher blocks.

In those parts of New Zealand in which block structure is best preserved and displayed roundabout consequent river courses of the kind just described are commonly recognisable (fig. 159)—especially so in the northern and southern districts of the South Island, where the areas of typical range-and-basin tectonic landscape are most extensive.[2]

River courses established on a block-faulted landscape will eventually become graded throughout. Across basins initially very deep the rivers may still meander in their late maturity and old age on wide plains of lateral planation worn down on the gravel filling hurriedly accumulated in the basins in the stage of youth or while differential earth movements were still going on. The surface will be degraded far below the original constructional surface, however; and the floors of shallower basins will be degraded to a sufficient depth to remove all such filling material and re-expose bedrock.

---

[1] Intermont: surrounded by mountains.

[2] Notable examples are the courses of the Aorere, Takaka, Awatere, Clarence, Waitaki, Taieri, Oreti, and Waiau Rivers.

In youth the surfaces of blocks that stand high enough above local base-levels will be rapidly eroded; and the blocks will be worn down eventually (and their margins worn back) by erosion, so that when the stage of full landscape maturity is attained the initial forms and outlines of block-mountain ranges may be inferred only rather uncertainly, and in old age even their outlines can only be guessed at.

Where of large area the upper surfaces of evenly uplifted blocks, and the back slopes of gently tilted blocks, may be thought of as passing through their geomorphic cycle as independent units. Initially they may be either eroded surfaces (young, mature, or old) of an earlier cycle, or may be plains of deposition or of lava accumulation. Where the upper surfaces are initially smooth or nearly so—being in such cases parts either of sedimentary or lava plains or of peneplains—the streams on them will be consequent on the slopes resulting from the uplift. In other cases, however, where a stronger initial relief is inherited from a former land surface, this will generally influence the courses of streams on block surfaces, as in the general case of two-cycle landscapes yet to be described (Chapter XVI). Insequent and subsequent streams may be developed as erosion proceeds, and the general course of the cycle will be similar in a broad way to that on regional surfaces as previously described.

As a special case must be noted the New Zealand range-and-basin type (fig. 157), in which the terrain that is broken into blocks has been of compound structure with a planed undermass of resistant rock covered rather thinly by weak strata. Here the removal of the cover leads to re-exposure of a fossil plain. This takes place in the early-mature stage of the cycle introduced by block faulting and before erosion has obscured the outlines of the initial blocks (figs. 159-166); and so at this stage the tectonic nature of the major relief is most clearly displayed.

Earthquakes Related to Faults.—Most great earthquakes are caused by movements along faults, and these commonly occur as readjustments of blocks in regions where the presence of range-and-basin landscape features of tectonic origin indicates that great displacements have already taken place. Many sudden, earthquake-making movements seem to be the results of either continuance or

Fig. 166.—Range-and-basin features, Otago, New Zealand. View across the Ida Valley basin (compare fig. 159) towards a northern block complex.

C. A. Cotton, photo.

Fig. 167.—Parallel scarplets in front of the base of the rejuvenated fault scarp of the Seaward Kaikoura Range, New Zealand.

H. E. Fyfe, photo.

recurrence of faulting and up-thrusting along lines that bound mountain blocks.

Scarplets.—Either along lines tracing the outcrops of these pre-existing faults or at what appear to be new breaks, low fault scarps

Fig. 168.—An overhanging fault scarplet dislocating the Murchison-Westport highway and the bed of the Buller River, New Zealand. (An inclined "deviation" joins the severed ends of the road.) *H. E. Fyfe, photo.*

(*scarplets*) suddenly appear, which vary in height from a few inches to 20 feet and even more. As these are formed simultaneously with earthquakes they are clearly related to the earthquakes either as cause or effect. True earthquake scarplets—as distinguished from the many irregular, short, curved slump scars which are also formed during earthquakes but are really earthquake effects—are long, nearly straight, and in some cases continuous for many miles. They must be the surface manifestations—i.e., the outcropping edges—of faults which cause the earthquakes or, if merely surface breaks related to deeper-seated movements of greater magnitude, cause at least part of the earthquake disturbance.

Scarplets related in origin to earthquakes which occurred in 1888 are shown in fig. 167. In 1929 a surface break thus produced by movement on a reversed (overhanging) fault crossed the Buller River (New Zealand) and the main highway beside it, which was dislocated in a 15-feet-high step (fig. 168); and in 1931 a similar

Fig. 169.—Fault scarplet (in part a monoclinal flexure of the surface) crossing an alluvial plain west of Hastings, New Zealand, and formed in 1931. View looking north-east.

C. A. Cotton, photo.

dislocation took place in the North Island of New Zealand along a line running north-eastward to the sea at a point just south of the port of Napier. Traceable as a scarp in places even across plains of unconsolidated alluvial gravel (fig. 169), this break separated an uplifted area north-west of it from stationary land to the south-east. At the Napier port and estuary (from which mudflats emerged to make permanent dry land) the uplift was about six feet, as became evident soon afterwards when new and old high-water marks on wharf piles could be compared (fig. 169A). The formation of similar new scarplets has been recorded in Japan and in Nevada, where especially they indicate that renewed uplift of mountain blocks has taken place.

Fig. 169A.—New and old high-water marks on the piles of a wharf at Napier, New Zealand, uplifted in 1931.

C. A. Cotton, photo.

Reverse Scarplets.—A peculiar kind of *reverse scarplet* as it may be termed—or, given its popular name, "earthquake rent"—is known from numerous conspicuous examples in the North and South Islands of New Zealand, but has not been observed elsewhere. In this case the movement, such as obviously must cause an earthquake, follows the line of a mountain base and quite clearly is

Fig. 170.—A reverse scarplet ("earthquake rent") on the line of the scarp which bounds the Seaward Kaikoura Range (New Zealand) on the south-eastern side. (Lottery Creek.)

W. A. McKay, photo.

a renewal of movement on a pre-existing fault. Either locally or for the whole length of the line it is a reversal of earlier movement, however, and produces a scarplet facing in towards the mountain slope and enclosing a trench (fig. 170), which may be reduced later by erosion to a less distinct terrace. One such trenchlike reverse scarplet may be traced along the north-west side of the Awatere Valley for about fifty miles; and examples have been

Fig. 170A.—A reverse scarplet ("earthquake rent") in the Ruahine Mountains, North Island, New Zealand. (After R. J. Waghorn.)

found in the Kaikoura and Ruahine Ranges (fig. 170A) and the Southern Alps.

Horizontal Fault Movement.—The San Francisco earthquake of 1906 was caused by, or was closely related in origin to, a horizontal movement of several feet along a vertical break hundreds of miles long—the San Andreas Rift. Traces of a similar movement in New Zealand, which caused dislocation and displacement of fences to the extent of 8 feet (fig. 171), have been observed for several miles along a more ancient fault line. This movement occurred along with, and must have been at least in part the cause of, a severe earthquake in 1888. According to the "elastic rebound" theory of earthquakes, horizontal movement goes on continuously in a direction parallel to a fracture, straining the rocks like bent springs until sufficient stress has accumulated to overcome friction along the fracture and make one wall of it move past the other, causing the shock. Such continuous movement has been observed in

Fig. 171.—Fence offset by a horizontal movement of the ground to the east (relatively) on the north side of a line of dislocation at Glenwye, Hope Valley, South Island, New Zealand.

W. A. McKay, photo.

California. In the case of recent earthquakes in New Zealand associated with vertical faulting, however, slow progressive upwarping prior to the earthquakes, such as the theory requires, has not taken place. Shoreline displacements have accompanied, but not preceded, the Napier earthquake of 1931, for example (p. 164).

CHAPTER XIV

FAULT SCARPS AND FAULT-LINE SCARPS

Dissection of fault scarps. Rejuvenated fault scarps. Monoclinal scarps. Distributed faults and fault splinters. Fault-line scarps. Composite fault scarps. Fault-line valleys. Recognition of fault scarps. The outcrops of strata displaced by faults.

Dissection of Fault Scarps.—The fault-scarp faces of fault-bounded tectonic blocks differ so much in their initial forms from any features of initial surfaces in landscapes as hitherto described that the stages of their dissection, transformation, and ultimate destruction by erosion call for special attention. The fault surface (loosely termed "fault plane") of which a fault scarp is the outcrop may be vertical, may slope back towards the upheaved block, or may be overhanging. In the case of a fault surface sloping back at a considerable angle from the vertical the initial landscape scarp formed by its outcrop may rise at the actual slope of the fault (fig. 172, *a*); such scarps are probably rare. In the case of a steeper, vertical, or overhanging fault a great quantity of rock debris will slump and slide away from the edge of the scarp as it emerges, and so the newly-formed scarp—in what may be termed its *infantile* condition—will have a moderate slope like that of the initial scarp in the first case (fig. 172, *b, c*).

An infantile scarp will be a continuous wall, either straight or gently curved[1] (fig. 173, stage *A*), but ravines will soon be cut by streams consequent on the initial slope (stage *B*).

In the case of a simply tilted block the drainage of the whole back slope is led away from the scarp, and so the streams forming on the scarp collect and carry away only the water actually falling upon it; but if the block surface above the scarp is simply uplifted, and especially if it is arched by the uplift, or if it is tilted in such a way that all or part of it slopes towards the scarp, the dissecting

---

[1] Faults, the forms of which are well known from their occurrence in innumerable natural sections and artificial cuttings, never trace jagged, irregular, or sharply curved lines. Though they are not generally quite straight, such curvature as they exhibit is so broad and open that fault-traces are described as "simple" lines.

streams of the scarp will be the lower courses of streams of considerable size, perhaps consequent on the tilting, that drain the upland surface. At the infantile stage they will traverse the scarp as falls or cascades. Examples of such streams, now incised in deep valleys, descend the western scarp of the Rock and Pillar horst

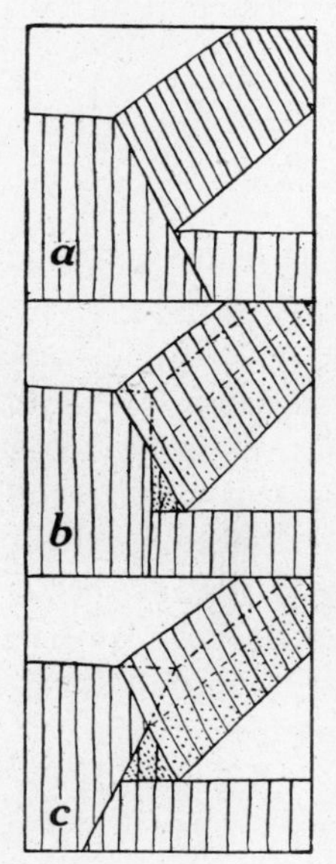

Fig. 172.—Initial and infantile forms of fault scarps formed by (*a*) backward-sloping, (*b*) vertical, and (*c*) overhanging faults.

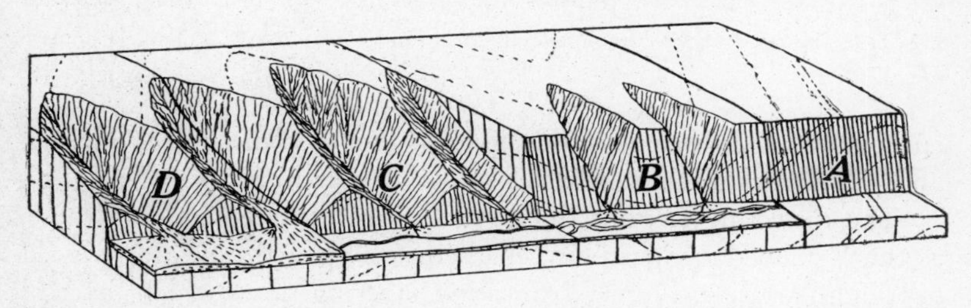

Fig. 173.—Dissection of a fault scarp. *A*, initial or infantile form; *B, C, D*, young sequential forms.

(figs. 159, 161), where the whole upland surface of the block slopes down towards this scarp, that on the other side of the range being, in contrast, undissected. The tilted block forming the Kakanui Range (fig. 165) seems to have been uplifted with an arched crown so that its crest-line divide was initially some distance back from the mountain front. This may be inferred from the fact that the scarp is now well dissected by streams of considerable size that have their heads far back in the range.

With variation in the size of the drainage areas of the dissecting streams the rate of dissection of scarps may vary considerably; but even the small streams originating on the slope of a scarp have much

Fig. 174.—Facets of the Wellington fault scarp, Hutt Valley, New Zealand. (Compare fig. 176.)

C. A. Cotton, photo.

energy, owing to their steep declivities; they become deeply incised, and then work back headward into the upland block.

The dissecting streams divide the scarp into sections, and these, as the V-shaped ravines between them are opened out, are reduced to triangular *facets* bluntly truncating tapering spurs which descend from the upland above the scarp (fig. 173, stage *C*, and figs. 174, 175). The bases of these facets of the fault scarp are situated approximately at the fault line, and so they trace a simple (straight or gently curved) line (figs. 175, 176).

At this stage the dissecting ravines may be aggraded near their mouths if alluvium is accumulating in the depression at the base of the scarp (fig. 173, *D*).

Fig. 175.—Facets of the western base of the Wasatch Range, Utah.
Douglas Johnson, photo.

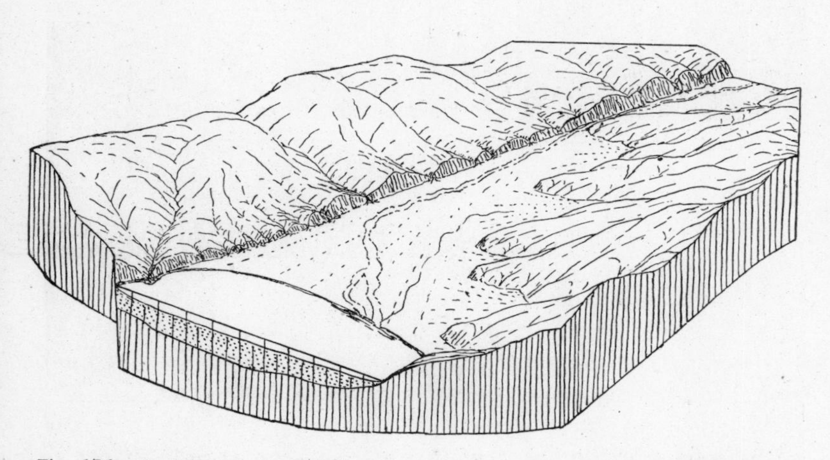

Fig. 176.—Straight base line of the valley-side slope formed by the Wellington fault scarp, Hutt Valley, New Zealand (north-west side). Contrast the valley-side spurs, half buried by alluvium, on the opposite side of the valley. (Generalised diagram.)

When the facets have been so reduced in size by the widening of the ravines between them, and their edges have been so rounded off by soil creep, that they no longer preserve the form of the infantile scarp, the dissection of the fault scarp is said to be mature

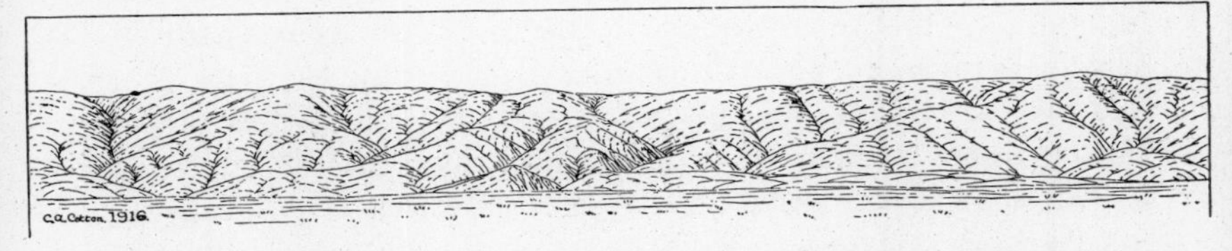

Fig. 177.—The Hawkdun fault scarp, Otago, New Zealand—a maturely dissected scarp facing southward and bounding the Hawkdun Range (see fig. 159).

(fig. 177). The ends of the spurs are still, at this stage, conspicuously ranged in line (fig. 178).

When the cycle of erosion is far advanced towards old age the spur ends may be worn back irregularly from the fault line, and so the even base line is to a great extent lost, and the scarp becomes obliterated.

Fig. 178.—Blunt-ended spurs of a dissected fault scarp ranged strictly in line, Wellington, New Zealand. (Compare fig. 179.)

C. A. Cotton, photo.

It has been assumed in the foregoing discussion that deformation and uplift are so rapid that they may be regarded as complete before erosion begins. It should be recognised, nevertheless, that much of the dissection of a fault scarp may take place while movement is still in progress, either very slowly and continuously or intermittently. While this is going on, the spur ends between the dissecting ravines are always newly emerged portions of the scarp, and, as they are being actively cut into by the ravines on both sides of them so that soil creep cannot round off the edges, they present conspicuous sharp-edged facets. Growing fault scarps have thus been recognised (fig. 175).

Fig. 179.—Full-face view of the scarp shown in fig. 178, Wellington, New Zealand.
J. W. Jones, photo.

Rejuvenated Fault Scarps.—Fault scarps freshened by renewed movement taking place after the first-formed scarps have been somewhat worn by erosion may be described as *rejuvenated*. Earthquake scarplets of recent origin along the base line are indications of rejuvenation (fig. 167); but relatively ancient scarps also may afford evidence of growth during successive episodes of fault movement separated by intervals which have allowed of mature dissection of the more ancient upper parts of the scarps. Below a definite line such a scarp is young and wall-like; and streams cross it in broken courses as falls or rapids. This is the case on the Wellington fault scarp (New Zealand), (fig. 179). A very similar effect will be produced, however, if the lower part of a scarp has been protected from erosion for a time by burial under a fringe of alluvial gravels, later removal of which resurrects the scarp.

Monoclinal Scarps.—Closely related to fault scarps are the scarps formed by monoclinal folds or flexures of the land surface, which is thus sharply bent down, instead of being dislocated by a fault, to form the boundary between a high-standing block and an adjacent tectonic basin. When maturely dissected these *monoclinal*

Fig. 180.—Monoclinal scarp (dissected by bottle-necked valleys) forming the east side of the Upper Clutha tectonic basin at Cromwell, New Zealand.

C. A. Cotton, photo.

scarps will generally be indistinguishable from fault scarps except in so far as their origin is indicated either by underlying rock structures or by their relation to the broader features of a deformed landscape. Where a fossil plain is resurrected, remnants of it may persist on a monoclinal scarp long after the cover has been stripped from it, though obviously it is more liable to dissection here than where it is less steeply inclined. Inclined strips of resurrected fossil plains in New Zealand (Chapter XII) pass in places into monoclinal scarps (figs. 180, 181). In a similar way a strongly (monoclinally) warped strip of a peneplain on resistant rocks may form a persistent scarp dissected (as is the case in the front of the Blue Mountains upwarped arch in New South Wales) by bottle-necked valleys into facets which may long survive on the ends of spurs.

Distributed Faults and Fault Splinters.—Faults are not always simple breaks. Sometimes the dislocating movement, instead of taking place along a single surface, is *distributed* throughout a zone of considerable width—a *shatter belt*—in which the rock is separated into many differentially moving slices, and is much crushed and shattered. The scarps of such faults must be initially somewhat

Fig. 181.—Monoclinal scarp, Gouland Downs, Nelson, New Zealand.
C. A. Cotton, photo.

ill-defined, especially if the shatter belt is wide, but when maturely dissected they will closely resemble the scarps of simple faults. Where the slices are wider, and escape complete shattering, the whole descent is broken into steps by *step faults,* which form at first separate scarps, and which leave their traces in the stage of maturity as jogs in the crest lines of the spurs that descend from the upland block. A simple fault, again, may branch once or many times, perhaps passing thus into a distributed fault.

Earthquake scarplets developed, as they commonly are, in alluvium that has been deposited along the base of a maturely dissected scarp indicate branching of faults (figs. 182, 183).

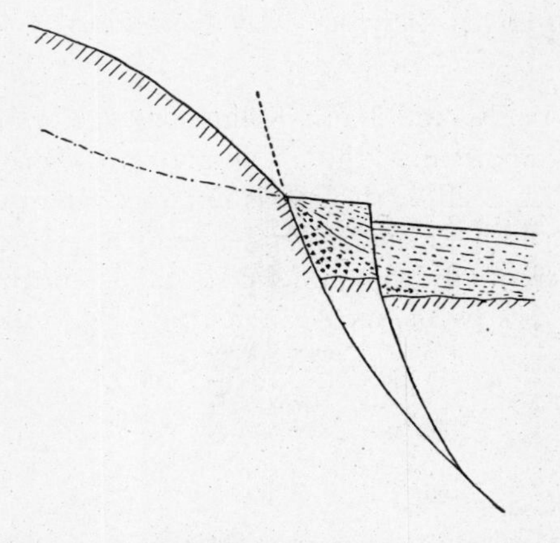

Fig. 182.—Movement on a branch fault has formed a scarplet in alluvium already deposited in front of a fault scarp.

Fig. 183.—Distributed or branching faults have made scarplets in alluvium, western base of the Wasatch tectonic block, Utah. (Compare fig. 182.)
U.S. Geol. Survey: G. K. Gilbert, photo.

A *splintered fault* differs from a distributed fault and from a branching fault in that, while the displacement on the whole fault system remains constant throughout its length or varies constantly in one direction or the other (as might the displacement on a single simple fault), dwindling displacement on one line (such as *ab,* fig.

184) is compensated by the development parallel to it of another line of fault (such as *cd*) with increasing displacement, and this may occur more than once (*ef*); so that discontinuous faults *en échelon*

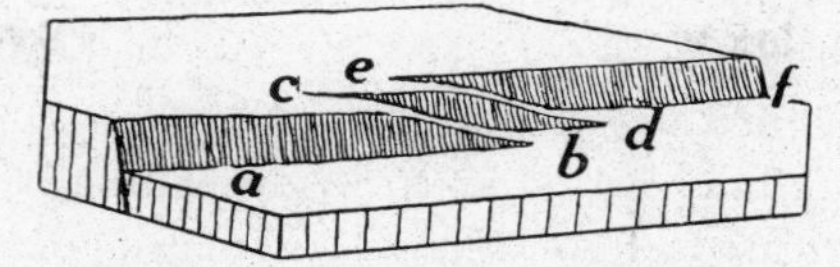

Fig. 184.—A splintered fault dislocating a plane surface.

separating successive splinters form the complex boundary between adjacent high and low-lying blocks.

The eastern side of the Rough Ridge block shown in fig. 159, is formed by the scarps of a splintered fault. Other splinters break the continuity of a fault scarp which forms the northern boundary of a complex graben which has become the valley of the Waitaki River (fig. 185).

Fig. 185.—A splinter from the fault scarp forming the northern wall of the Waitaki Valley, New Zealand. *C. A. Cotton, photo.*

Fault-line Scarps.—Faulting may have brought together weak and resistant rocks on opposite sides of a fault surface; and in such a case removal of the weak rock by rapid erosion leaves exposed a scarp at the edge of the more resistant terrain. Such a scarp persists until this terrain also is worn down by erosion, the accomplishment of which may be a slow process, giving the scarp a long life, during which it very gradually fades out of the landscape.

A scarp so formed is generally termed a *fault-line scarp,* though some prefer "fault-line erosion scarp" as making a better discrimination from fault scarps. Fault-line scarps may appear in the "first" cycle initiated by the deformation of which the faulting is a part.

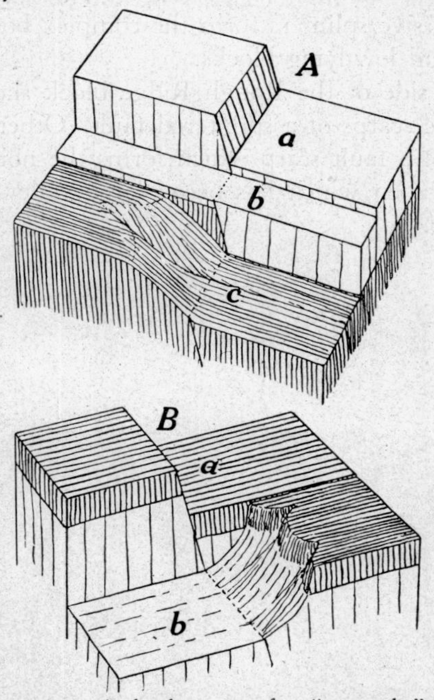

Fig. 186.—Fault-line scarps. *A,* development of a "two-cycle," resequent fault-line scarp; *B,* development of an obsequent fault-line scarp from a fault scarp in the "first" cycle.

In other cases, on the other hand, fault-line scarps are exposed by the erosion following a regional uplift that takes place long after the formation of the faults, and long after the true fault scarps marking the initial breaks at the surface have been obliterated by erosion (fig. 186, *A*).

Fault-line scarps are of two kinds, *resequent* and *obsequent,* according as they face in the same direction as the initial fault-scarp on the same line of fault or in the opposite direction. Thus a resequent fault-line scarp (fig. 186, *A*) faces, or descends towards, the structurally depressed (downthrown) side of the fault, while an obsequent scarp (*B*) descends towards the structurally uplifted (upthrown) side.

Fig. 187.—A resequent fault-line scarp bordering the valley of the Wairoa River, at Hunua, Auckland, New Zealand. (Since its first exposure this scarp has been partly buried under alluvium and later resurrected.)

J. A. Bartrum, photo.

Resequent fault-line scarps (fig. 187) are commoner than the obsequent variety, since it is true in a general way that the more deeply buried rocks, being older and having been subjected to greater pressure than those above them, are harder and more resistant to erosion. Exceptions to this general rule, are, however, quite frequent. A condition that may lead to the formation of an obsequent scarp even in a single cycle is the occurrence of a sheet of volcanic lava (a hard and resistant rock) overlying soft material. Faulting will produce a scarp—a fault scarp—facing towards the downthrown side; but when the lava on the high side has been worn off the faulted continuation of it at a lower level on the other side may still survive and determine an obsequent fault-line scarp. This condition is illustrated in fig. 186, *B,* which should be compared with diagram *A* of the same figure, representing the development of a resequent scarp. In the latter the strip *b* represents a stage of erosion at which all traces of the fault scarp have been obliterated; if this has occurred the change to stage *c,* in which the fault-line scarp appears, is unlikely to take place until a general uplift of the region makes renewed erosion possible.

Composite Fault Scarps.—On terrains of compound structure with an easily eroded cover the distinction between fault scarps proper and resequent fault-line scarps of first-cycle origin is difficult to make. There is some uncertainty, for example, in the identification as simple fault scarps of most of the New Zealand scarps cited in Chapter XIII; for in most cases a certain thickness of weak rock has been removed by erosion along the base since the initial emerg-

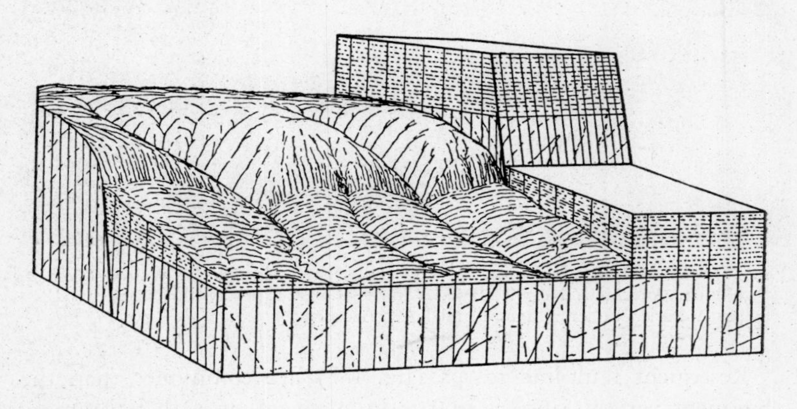

Fig. 188.—Development of a composite fault scarp (in its upper part a fault scarp and in its lower part a fault-line scarp) from the initial fault scarp shown at the right. If the covering strata were much thicker than they are here shown, a one-cycle fault-line scarp only would survive.

ence of the scarp, by which erosion a strip of the fault surface has been exposed that did not form part of the scarp initially. Such strips are one-cycle fault-line scarps by strict definition. If, however, the scarps as a whole as they exist at present are considerably higher than the probable thickness of soft material removed by erosion from the downthrown side, they must be inferred to be true fault scarps in their upper parts.

Strict accuracy requires recognition of the composite nature of many such scarps, however, and to indicate this they have been termed *composite fault scarps* (fig. 188).

Fig. 189.—A fault-line scarp or composite fault scarp forming the eastern face of the Hunter's Hills tilted block, South Canterbury, New Zealand.

C. A. Cotton, photo.

Fig. 190.—Maturely dissected fault-line scarp or composite fault scarp, Ruakokopatuna Valley, Wairarapa, New Zealand.

C. A. Cotton, photo.

The scarps shown in figs. 189, 190 may be entirely fault-line scarps; but this is by no means a certainty, and, therefore, since they are almost certainly one-cycle features, they are perhaps better classed as composite.

Fault-line Valleys.—Though a consequent river may be guided by a graben or a fault angle, and occupy it as a valley or excavate a valley on its floor, faults do not actually form true valleys.

The headward erosion of streams may, however, be guided by the shatter belts produced by distributed faulting (p. 175), either in the cycle introduced by the deformation of which the faulting is part or in some later cycle (Chapter XVI). The valleys so formed by headward erosion along fault lines are termed *fault-line valleys.* It makes for clearness to observe rigidly this distinction in nomenclature between "fault-line" features, whether valleys or scarps, which are developed by erosion along faults, possibly long after the faulting takes place, and "fault" features, which are directly consequent on the dislocation.

Lines of adjustment of streams to structure in stratified rocks (the "grain" of the terrain) and those of adjustment to shatter belts may cross obliquely; and this is the origin of some "barbed" stream junctions.[1] There are examples of these in the valley of the Hutt River, near Wellington, New Zealand, which follows the line of a diagonal fault; northward-flowing tributaries, which are adjusted to structure, join a main stream which flows south-west along the fault line.

A similar sharp bend in the course of the Wairoa River, near Auckland, has been described, where the river doubles back from a south-westward headwater course which is consequent on an ancient regional slope into a northward lower course along a fault angle of more recent origin.

Recognition of Fault Scarps.—Fault scarps give such a clear indication of the presence of dislocations in the underlying rocks that their recognition is a matter of geological importance. A landscape that displays fault scarps and tectonic block features preserves a record not only of the erosion but of the differential earth movements that have taken place in the latest chapter of the earth's history.

It would be a mistake to generalise from the observed absence of fault-made scarps in stable regions and conclude that fault move-

---

[1] Another cause of "barbed tributary junctions," or "boat-hook bends" as they have been called in eastern Australia, where they are characteristic features of the stream pattern, is reversal of flow of rivers by drainage changes which have caused migration of main divides.

ments are too deep-seated to affect surface forms or that they are all so slow that scarps are worn away progressively as they emerge. It is just as rash, however, to assume prematurely that any scarp or line of cliffs is a fault scarp; and it must be borne in mind that fault-made surface features are rare in, or entirely absent from, the landscapes of many regions and are comparatively rare in most.

Apart from the sometimes difficult question of deciding between a "fault" and a "fault-line" origin, it must be borne in mind that scarps otherwise made originate as:

(1) Lines of cliffs formed where marine erosion is cutting back a coast;
(2) The escarpments which bound mesas and cuestas;
(3) Valley-sides in early-mature valleys which have been cut back to steep slopes by lateral stream corrasion;
(4) The walls of glacier troughs which have been straightened and oversteepened by ice erosion.

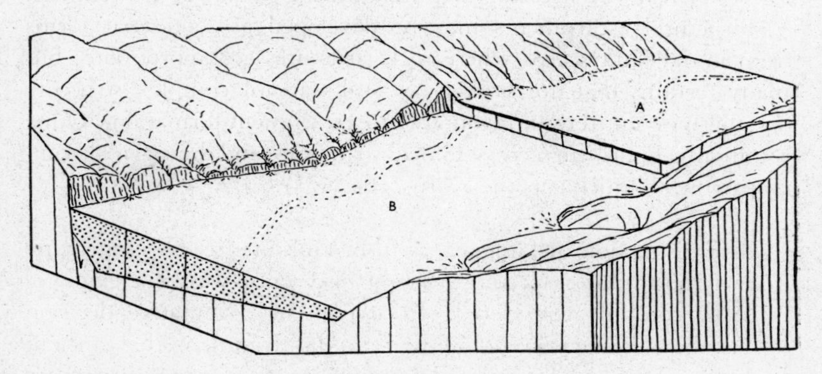

Fig. 191.—Suggested pre-faulting form (*A*) and present fault-angle profile (*B*) of the alluvium-floored Hutt Valley, Wellington, New Zealand. (The line of the pre-faulting valley was related to more ancient faulting.)

Except in the very exceptional case of fresh fault scarps (or of fault-line scarps) facing each other across a narrow graben, the distinction from (3) and (4) is easily made. In the ordinary case a fault scarp, unlike the wall of a stream-cut or glacial valley, is not confronted by a similar scarp. In the case of a fault-angle valley, which is bounded on one side by a fault scarp, this presents a striking contrast to the tilted surface forming the opposite side. In the Hutt Valley, New Zealand, which is a fault angle (figs. 176, 191) developed in a mature landscape, the tilted surface forming the valley side opposed to the scarp is embayed by alluvial filling in the valley, thus emphasising the contrast (see also fig. 213).

An important feature of fault scarps that descend below a lake or sea-level (fig. 192) and one which distinguishes them from wave-

Fig. 192.—The Wellington fault scarp (New Zealand) descends below sea-level. Though perceptibly trimmed, the fault-scarp facets have been worn back little by marine erosion, as is shown by complete absence of sea-level cut-rock platforms such as would be formed if long projecting spurs were cut back by the sea to this form.

cut cliffs is the absence of worn rock platforms at the base, such as are formed as a necessary accompaniment of marine cliff-cutting.

Structural escarpments may be developed as sequential forms from initial fault scarps where rock structures are appropriate; but many terrains that are broken by faults are of complex structure or otherwise entirely unfavourable to escarpment-formation. Quite commonly faults cut across folded structures and linear rock outcrops run obliquely up the scarps (fig. 173).

The distinction of fault scarps from fault-line scarps is in many cases by no means easy; and in doubtful cases all available evidence must be carefully considered. In arriving at a tentative decision it may be necessary even to resort to the argument that ancient faults (such as lead to the development of erosion scarps) are common, whereas faults so newly formed as to dislocate the landscape are comparatively rare and are almost confined to the earthquake regions, or "mobile belts."

The best evidence for the existence of a fault scarp (as distinguished from an erosion or fault-line scarp) is the matching of landscape forms on opposite sides of a line of surface dislocation (fig. 193). This is rarely available, however, owing either to post-faulting erosion on both sides of the fault line or (quite commonly) to complete burial of the landscape on the downthrown side under basin-floor deposits or river-laid alluvium. A river which flows in a consequent course along a fault angle is the most potent agent available for either the burial or destruction by erosion of a considerable area of a faulted landscape. Reasonably good matching of mature landscape forms is found on opposite sides of the Hutt Valley, New Zealand (figs. 176, 191). Here, however, the matching forms are partly buried and are referable to opposite sides of a valley which existed before the fault scarp was formed. (To this valley the recent fault break is parallel, both being controlled by an older dislocation.)

Fig. 193.—Ideal evidence of landscape faulting.

The Outcrops of Strata displaced by Faults.—The effects of ancient faults in displacing outcrops are frequently made apparent by erosion, especially where strong ridge-making strata are dislocated. It is unnecessary in describing these effects to take into consideration the transformation through which the initial fault scarps passed. The faults may be assumed to be much more ancient than the topography—as, indeed, the majority of known faults are.

Faults dislocating stratified formations may be divided into two classes according as they are transverse or parallel to the strike. The latter are called *strike faults,* while the former may be termed *transverse faults.*

In some faults the movement is horizontal and the effects on topography are simple. Ancient faults with a horizontal movement parallel with the strike do not affect topography, while transverse faults in which the movement is purely horizontal simply dislocate outcrops and strike ridges to the extent of the movement. More commonly there is either no horizontal movement along the fault-line, or movement in that direction is subsidiary to that which has taken place in a direction up or down the fault surface. This is the class of faults which when first formed produce conspicuous fault scarps at the surface, and which also determine the positions of the most prominent fault-line scarps.

When erosion has reduced the dislocated portions of the outcrop of a stratum on opposite sides of a transverse fault of this kind to a common level (fig. 194, *A,* stage *c*), they are not, as a rule, in the same straight line, but one is offset relatively to the other to a distance depending upon both the amount of displacement on the fault and the angle of dip of the stratum, the offset, or "heave," being

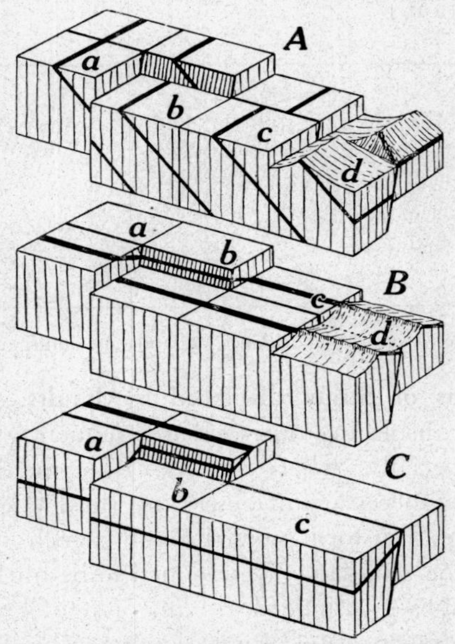

Fig. 194.—Diagrams showing displacement of strata by faulting. *A,* effect of a transverse fault; *B* and *C,* effects of strike faults. In each diagram *a* represents the stage before faulting takes place; *b,* the stage immediately after faulting; *c,* the outcrops if the surface is reduced to the same level on each side of the fault; and, in diagrams *A* and *B, d* shows relief etched out by subsequent erosion.

greater in the case of a gently dipping stratum than in the case of one that is steeply inclined. The direction of offset clearly depends upon the direction of dip of the stratum and upon the direction of relative movement on the fault.

On the dislocated ends of ridge-making strata, when the surface is in that stage of erosion at which these stand out in relief, short fault-line scarps, both resequent and obsequent, are developed (fig. 194, *A,* block *d*).

The effects of "heave," which are brought out as landscape features only where differential erosion exposes hard outcrops, somewhat resemble actual dislocations of the landscape which are known to have been produced by repeated horizontal movements along faults of the San Andreas (California) type (p. 166).

Strike faults, while not causing offsets in outcrops, produce either repetition or, on the other hand, complete suppression of certain outcrops (fig. 194, *B* and *C*). Where the outcrop of a ridge-making stratum is repeated many times by a number of strike faults a conspicuous topographic effect is produced as parallel ridges are etched out by erosion (block *d* of diagram *B*).

CHAPTER XV

LANDFORMS BUILT OF WASTE IN THE COURSE OF THE NORMAL CYCLE

Terrestrial deposits. Talus slopes. The waste on graded slopes. Alluvial deposits. Aggraded valley floors. Braided channels of aggrading rivers. River-made lakes. Alluvial fans. Piedmont alluvial plains. Deltas. Delta plains. Instability of river courses on deltas and aggraded plains.

Terrestrial Deposits.—The ultimate resting-place of the bulk of the waste derived from the land is in the sea. Deposits formed along the courses of streams, perhaps in hollows of the initial surface, are, as a rule, less permanent than marine deposits, for if far above base-level they will be cut away in the later stages of the cycle. They represent only pauses in the discontinuous seaward movement of the waste. Such deposits may however be preserved for an indefinite period if they are lowered by earth movements below sea-level. In that case they are buried by marine deposits, and their lowly position preserves them from erosion until they chance to be again uplifted.

Even the shorter-lived terrestrial deposits above base-level may survive for a considerable fraction of a cycle of erosion, and while they last their surfaces form important topographic features. Among forms resulting from accumulation may be placed the more or less continuous mantle of surface waste, creeping and slipping downhill and thus smoothing out irregularities of the surface, accumulating so as to fill up re-entrants, and flowing around the more prominent rock outcrops until eventually these disappear and the waste mantle becomes continuous, the slope being then graded.

Talus Slopes.—*Talus slopes,* or *screes,* are a phase of the waste mantle at the early, discontinuous stage. A talus slope is formed by the actual flow of a stream of newly broken rock fragments which, being unworn, are necessarily angular unless derived from a pre-existing accumulation of gravel. The surface slopes at the angle of repose, and the talus has accumulated as layers parallel with the present surface. A distinct stratification is not present, however, as the material is generally coarse and fragments of different sizes are mixed throughout.

Talus slopes are common features on mountain sides, where the fragments broken by weathering from the bare rocks of the peaks and higher slopes stream down through funnel-like gullies. The talus slopes, confined for some distance in these *chimneys,* or *couloirs,* spread out lower down in conical shape, and generally deliver their surplus waste eventually into streams of water in the larger valleys of gentler declivity. Talus slopes of this kind are particularly abundant in mountains the slopes of which have been

Fig. 195.—Talus slopes (the smooth grey areas) on a mountain-side. View across the Hooker Valley from the Hermitage, New Zealand.
C. A. Cotton, photo.

"oversteepened" by the action of glaciers (Chapter XXIII). There is an extraordinary development of them in the Southern Alps (New Zealand) on the eastern (Canterbury) side (figs. 195, 196), where they receive the local name "shingle slips," the term "shingle" being in this case used for the angular talus material, though it is generally used for water-worn gravel, more especially that found on beaches.

Besides being common features of mountain sides, talus slopes occur fringing cliffs, whatever the origin of the cliffs, provided that the rate of removal of material from the base of the cliffs does not exceed the rate of supply from weathering of the bare rocks above.

Efficient removal of debris maintains a sharp re-entering angle, or "nick," at the base of a cliff; accumulation of talus, on the other hand, causes rapid fading of the sharpness of cliffs. In many places around the southern end of the North Island of New Zealand, for example, the sea-cliffs are not at present being undercut by the sea, for a small movement of uplift of the land has taken place less than a century ago, which has caused the shoreline to retreat

Fig. 196.—Talus slopes ("shingle slips"), a characteristic feature of the mountain-sides of Canterbury, New Zealand, on greywacke terrain (Ben Ohau Range, across Dobson Valley). *Rose, photo.*

from the cliff base. Since this event talus slopes have been formed which are now prominent features. They are accumulations of material which would, but for the uplift, have been washed away by the sea as fast as it slid down.

The angular fragments of more or less fresh rock forming the surface of a talus slope are not, as a rule, exposed long enough to weathering to allow of the formation of a covering of soil, for rock fragments are streaming or glissading down from above, and so the surface layers are either quickly covered over as the talus grows thicker, or else the surface material continues to stream down as it is swept away by running water from the toe of the slope. Vegetation is therefore almost entirely absent from active talus slopes.

The Waste on Graded Slopes.—Where slopes are gentler and the soil is anchored by vegetation, streaming is prevented and downhill transfer of waste takes place by soil creep, occasional spasmodic mass movement, and some surface wash, as described in Chapter IX. The surface of the waste mantle of soil and subsoil remains smoothly graded unless erosion is accelerated.

Fig. 197.—Natural section showing the veneer of gravel on a valley floor cut by stream corrasion, Clarence Valley, New Zealand. (The stream that cut the rock surface and spread the gravel afterwards deepened a trench across it, exposing this section.) *C. A. Cotton, photo.*

Alluvial Deposits.—A flood plain or valley plain is the nearly flat surface of an accumulation of alluvium. This is nowhere of great thickness on the floors of valleys widened by lateral planation unless special circumstances have afterwards caused aggradation. In general the depth of alluvium will be not less, however, than that of the river channel on the valley floor. Fig. 197 shows such a layer of gravelly alluvium spread by a small stream over the bedrock floor cut by stream corrasion.

Above such a gravel foundation fine silt spread during floods attains a very considerable thickness—even scores of feet on the flood plains of large rivers. The alluvium may be of such variable thickness as to give the flood plain a considerable broad relief, greatest in the case of the largest rivers. This results from the abandonment of channels during shifting of courses and cutting

Fig. 198.—Re-dissection of a slope by gully erosion, which exposes a great thickness of gravel deposited in the Esk River valley (Canterbury, New Zealand) in an episode of aggradation. *R. Speight, photo.*

off of meanders and the up-building during floods of strips bordering the river. These latter tend to confine the river to its channel during all but high floods, acting in the same way as the artificially built confining ridges termed "stop banks" or "levees." They are, therefore, termed *natural levees*. These valley-floor relief features on the alluvium are superposed on a broad side-to-side convexity developed on their valley floors by grading rivers as though the floors were radial strips of low-angle cones. In the case of broad valleys developed by exceptionally steep-grade rivers the convexity is sufficiently strong to be visible.

Aggraded Valley Floors.—Where a river has aggraded its valley, the deposit of alluvium forming the valley floor is thicker than the depth of the stream channel, the thickness being perhaps hundreds or even thousands of feet (fig. 198). The causes that may lead to aggradation in a stream already graded need not be enumerated at this point; but as examples of aggraded valleys those may be chosen in which aggradation has taken place because

Fig. 199.—Aggraded valley of the Upper Rangitata River (New Zealand), with a tributary (in flood) flowing in braided channels in the foreground.

R. Speight, photo.

required to steepen slopes initially too gentle to give the streams velocities sufficient to transport their loads. The upper valleys of some large New Zealand rivers—for example, the Waimakariri, Rakaia, and Rangitata—are of this kind, for there, as in many other mountainous regions, the initial forms of the valleys of the present cycle of normal erosion were the troughs excavated by glaciers during the Ice Age. The floors of such aggraded valleys are now broad, and in a general way flat. They may be described as *aggraded valley plains* (fig. 199). Little, if any, of their width is due to lateral river corrasion. As the thickness of the alluvial deposit increases the valley floor necessarily grows wider.

Braided Channels of Aggrading Rivers.—Aggrading streams are not confined to well-defined channels, for deposition goes on in the channels, filling them up. Where a channel is thus filled the stream in it flows at a higher level than neighbouring parts of its valley plain on the strip of alluvium it has just deposited. Such a course is obviously unstable, and the stream will sooner or later overflow at some point, scour out a passage through its low bank, and either take an entirely new course over the valley plain or

Fig. 200.—Braided channels of the Waimakariri River, New Zealand.
C. A. Cotton, photo.

divide into two *distributaries,* to unite again farther down the valley. Aggrading streams repeatedly divide and subdivide in this manner, flowing in anastomosing (or *braided*) courses. A network of ever-changing channels without well-defined banks occupies the gently convex valley floor (figs. 199, 200).

Very broad braided courses are found in the aggraded valleys of the large New Zealand rivers referred to above. Many rivers are aggraded and flow in braided channels near their mouths owing to the rapid increase in the length of the rivers due to the seaward growth of deltas (p. 202). Braided courses occur and indicate that aggradation is in progress in the majority of New Zealand rivers;

but in many parts of the country the change from degradation to aggradation seems to have taken place very recently (fig. 201) as a result of accelerated erosion in the catchment areas of the rivers (p. 119).

Aggraded valley floors are often stony and infertile, as any fine silt deposits become covered over by gravel (fig. 202). Though the

Fig. 201.—A common type of braiding which results from a recent change to aggradation, Ohau River, New Zealand.

G. L. Adkin, photo.

spaces between stream channels may support a scanty vegetation, they are very liable to flooding.

River-made Lakes.—It may happen that a tributary stream is unaffected by a change of conditions which overloads a main stream and causes it to aggrade. Aggradation raises the level of the main river at the junction—i.e., raises the local base-level—and the tributary in its turn is thereby compelled to aggrade its course. Aggradation in the valley of the main river may go on so rapidly, however, that tributaries with a smaller load of waste cannot keep pace with it. They are then ponded by the alluvium of the main valley and spread out to form lakes. In New Zealand the Wairarapa

Fig. 202.—Barren gravel plain of an aggrading river, Canterbury, New Zealand.
L. Cockayne, photo.

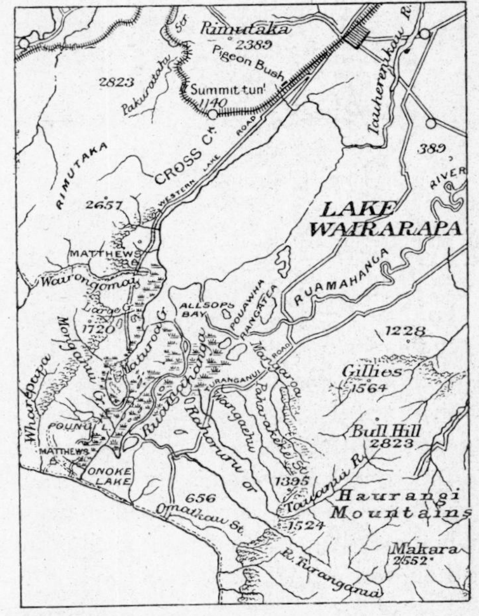

Fig. 203.—Impounding of Wairarapa Lake (New Zealand) by alluvial deposits of the Ruamahanga River.

Lake is thus impounded by alluvial deposits spread by the Ruamahanga River across the course of the Tauherenikau (fig. 203); and along the lower course of the Waikato River numerous lakes, some of them of considerable size (fig. 204), have been formed

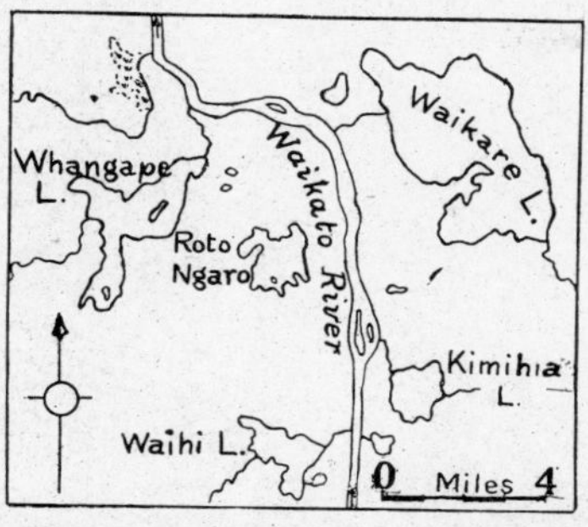

Fig. 204.—Lakes formed in the lower Waikato valley, New Zealand, where tributaries have been ponded as a result of deposit of alluvium by the main (Waikato) river.

in the valleys of its tributaries, which have spread widely over a surface of small relief as the main river has deposited across their mouths its abundant load of waste brought from the volcanic-ash-covered central volcanic district of the North Island.

Alluvial Fans.—As rivers emerge fully loaded from eroded valleys, in which they may have been degrading, into wide depressions where the slope is so gentle that the streams are compelled to aggrade in order to prolong their graded slopes—or, in other words, to build up channels sufficiently steep to give them their needed velocity—they deposit part of their load in such a manner as to build *alluvial fans* (figs. 205-208). The surface of a fan resembles a portion of a low cone with its apex in the mouth of the valley from which the fan-building stream emerges, the slopes being the same from this point down every radius of the fan. The surface of a fan is not strictly conical, for towards the head of the fan the slope is steepest. The front or toe of the fan is roughly semicircular, but necessarily varies in outline according to any irregularities of the surface on which it is built, and also owing to interference of adjacent fans with one another at their confluent margins.

Over a growing fan a stream flows in braided channels characteristic of an aggrading stream, and, taking new courses from time to time, flows by turns down every radius of the fan. In this manner the alluvium is distributed evenly, and the fan grows symmetrically. Any cross profile of an alluvial fan, like a section of a cone, is convex, and this gives an explanation of the convex cross profiles of valley floors previously referred to, for the floor of a river-made valley is really a long narrow fan.

Fig. 205.—Alluvial fan at the base of Mount Hutt, at the rear margin of the Canterbury Plain, New Zealand. View looking across the Rakaia River.
C. A. Cotton, photo.

Very steep fans are called *alluvial cones* (fig. 207A), and there is a transition through these from alluvial fans to talus slopes.

Fans are generally abundant in mountainous regions where a normal cycle following ice erosion is still in its young stage; in broad, aggraded valleys which result there is a fan at the mouth of every tributary stream (figs. 206, 208).

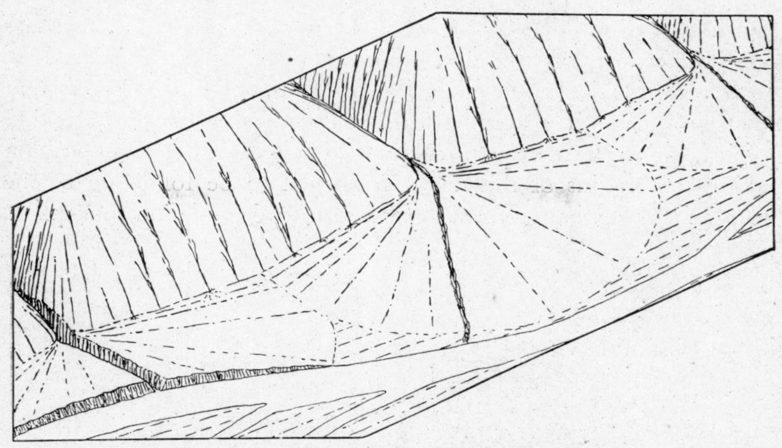

Fig. 206.—Diagram of alluvial fans built by tributaries where they enter the valley of a large river.

Fig. 207.—Fan with a steep slope built by a small stream, near Cass, New Zealand. This fan coalesces with another on the left.

C. A. Cotton, photo.

A fan built by a vigorous tributary may extend completely across the main valley so as to dam the main stream and form a shallow lake, which overflows across the toe of the fan as a series of rapids. Without such actual ponding taking place the fan of a tributary may force the main stream against the valley side, in which it may cut an embayment. Where the growth of fans is less vigorous, or the main stream more energetic, a swing of the main stream to the far side of its valley may allow of the development of a large fan, and a later swing in the other direction may cut a great part of it away. Cliffs will be cut along the front of the fan and the stream that built it will be forced to degrade again owing to the shortening of its course. It will entrench itself and become fixed in position along that radius of the fan it happened to be following at the time when the change from aggradation to degradation took place,

Fig. 207A.—Steep alluvial cones in the gorge of the Arrow River, New Zealand.
C. A. Cotton, photo.

as shown in figs. 206 and 208. Another swing of the main stream away from the mouth of the tributary will lead to the growth of a new fan in front of the remnant of the former one (fig. 208).

Much water sinks into the loose gravel of a fan, and in dry weather streams on the surfaces of fans may dwindle appreciably or even disappear altogether before reaching the margin. The underflow of ground water may come to the surface as springs at the margin of the fan. In Persia the water is obtained for irrigation of the lower slopes by driving tunnels horizontally into the alluvium.

On the stony surfaces of growing fans vegetation is scanty, for, as in the case of aggraded valley floors, all parts are liable to flooding, and there is no certainty as to where the stream will next flow and deposit gravel. Where, however, the growth of the fan has ceased and the stream has become entrenched and fixed in position, the surface is no longer subject to flooding, and soil is formed by weathering of the superficial material, on which fresh gravel is no longer being spread, and some wind-borne sand and dust is captured by vegetation.

Fig. 208.—Truncated and partly reconstructed (two-storied) fan built by a tributary of the Rakaia River, New Zealand.

In arid and semi-arid regions much fine waste as well as gravel is brought down by the intermittent torrents that build fans, and the whole of this may be deposited on the fans as the streams dwindle and disappear. The material of such fans, when irrigated, makes very fertile soils.

Piedmont Alluvial Plains.—Where a number of streams emerge from a mountainous area undergoing dissection on to a lowland, and build fans at their mouths, the fans if large are confluent, and thus form a continuous apron of waste along the mountain foot. The nearly flat surface of such a waste-apron is termed a *piedmont alluvial plain* or *bahada.* It has an appreciable slope away from the mountains, and is made up of a number of convex areas each of which is one of the component fans.

The Canterbury Plain (fig. 209) may be described as a piedmont alluvial plain. (Strictly, it is made up of confluent deltas rather than fans, but the superficial parts of deltas and fans are alike.) The large rivers, Waimakariri (W), Rakaia (R), and Rangitata, by which the plain has been built follow radial courses on broadly convex areas (see fig. 209). Some smaller rivers, such as the Selwyn (S), which have not themselves brought gravel from the mountains follow consequent (or *intersequent*) courses in the depressions between neighbouring convexities. The seaward slope of the Canterbury Plain varies from 25 to 40 feet per mile.

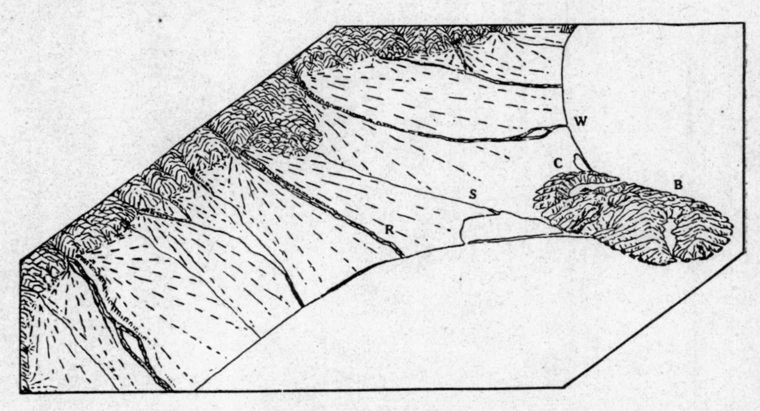

Fig. 209.—The Canterbury Plain, a piedmont alluvial plain in New Zealand.

The slopes of some aggraded plains in the North Island are very gentle as compared with those that might be expected were the alluvial material ordinary gravel in equal abundance. Though somewhat coarse the pebbles are extremely light, being mainly vesicular pumice. This alluvium can be carried by very sluggish streams, and may be transported long distances and ultimately deposited on very gentle slopes, as though it were fine silt.

Deltas.—Where waste is deposited at the mouth of a river in a body of standing water, either the ocean or a lake, the shoreline is generally built forward, some new land being formed. Where such natural "reclamation" takes place the deposit at the river mouth is termed a *delta* (figs. 210, 211). A delta will be built only when more waste is supplied than can be disposed of by wave action and tidal and other currents. Thus deltas are commoner in

Fig. 210.—A bay of Lake Tarawera, New Zealand, completely filled by a delta that has been rapidly built of waste washed from the volcanic debris deposited during the eruption of 1886 (see Chapter XXIV).

C. A. Cotton, photo.

lakes than in the ocean, for in lakes there are no appreciable tides, and currents and wave action are in general weaker than in the ocean. Deltas are frequently found, however, at the heads of sheltered bays (fig. 211).

The small deltas built by steep-grade streams carrying coarse waste into lakes serve as a type of all deltas. Not only are the upper surfaces of such deltas accessible for study, but also, very frequently, the parts laid down under water have been exposed owing to lowering of the level of the lake as the outlet has been cut down, and so the whole deltas have become landforms. The

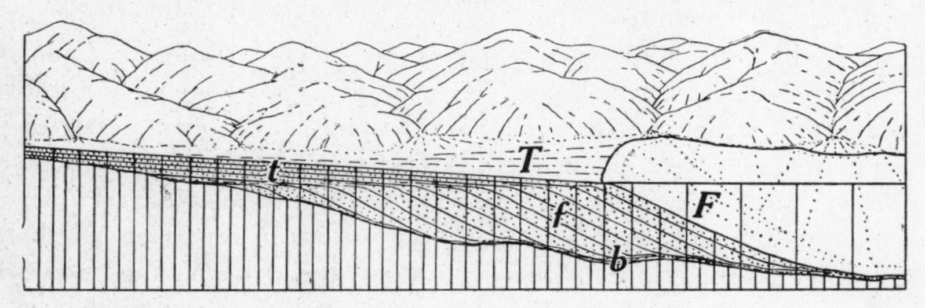

Fig. 211.—Diagram of the structure of a delta of coarse material at the head of a lake or bay.

internal structure may often be seen also, where a delta-building stream has been compelled to degrade again and cut a trench across its delta owing to the lowering of the level of the lake, which is its local base-level (fig. 212).

The upper surface of one of these small deltas exactly resembles the surface of an alluvial fan, having been formed in the same way by an aggrading stream flowing in shifting channels, which was forced to add layer after layer of alluvium to the surface in order to maintain a sufficient slope as the width of the delta increased. This upper slope is termed the *top-set slope* (*T*, fig. 211),

Fig. 212.—Top-set and fore-set beds of a delta, head of Lake Wakatipu, New Zealand. (Compare with fig. 211.)

C. A. Cotton, photo.

and the alluvium of which it is built forms the *top-set beds* of the delta (*t*). The top-set slope extends a little below the water level, and is there replaced by a much steeper slope forming the front of the delta and termed the *fore-set slope* (*F*). The bulk of the gravel forming the delta and underlying the top-set beds is regularly stratified in inclined layers, termed *fore-set beds* (*f*) parallel with the fore-set slope. These entirely subaqueous beds dip at an angle of perhaps 30°, and the surface of each layer marks a former fore-set slope of the delta front, the delta having grown forward as gravel and coarse sand were continuously poured over the edge and came to rest in the still, deep water at the angle of repose. The front of a delta built of gravel in still water is extended forward as convex lobes which correspond in position to the mouths of distributing streams—thus making the delta *lobate*.

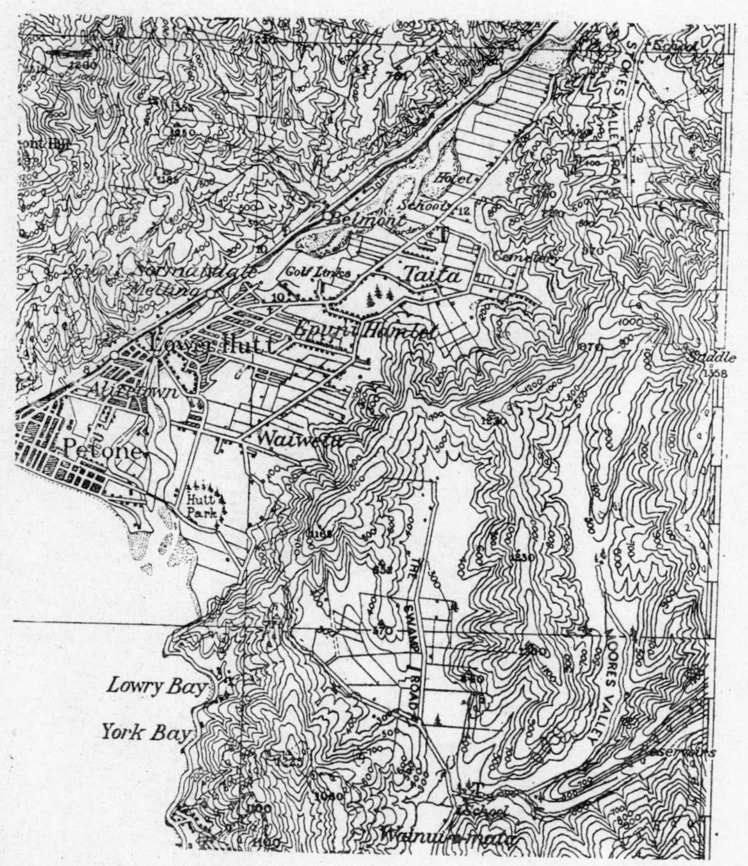

Fig. 213.—Bay-head delta of the Hutt River, New Zealand. Headward-tilted branches of the Wainui-o-mata valley system are included in the south-eastern part of the area, and a fault scarp bounds the Hutt Valley (north-west corner).

The mud that is brought into the lake does not accumulate with the gravel in the fore-set beds, but remains sufficiently long in suspension to be carried some distance. It finally sinks and forms thin layers of silt all over the bottom of the lake, smoothing over its irregularities and lying more or less horizontally. When a lake is drained away by lowering of the outlet the silt deposit forms fertile plains, of which a notable example is the vast plain of the Red River Valley, in Canada. In a delta some of the silt layers are covered over by advancing fore-set beds, and then become the *bottom-set beds* of the delta (*b*, fig. 211).

Deltas essentially similar to those in lakes may be built in the ocean by rivers that descend steeply from mountain sources and carry heavy loads of coarse waste. These are generally *bay-head*

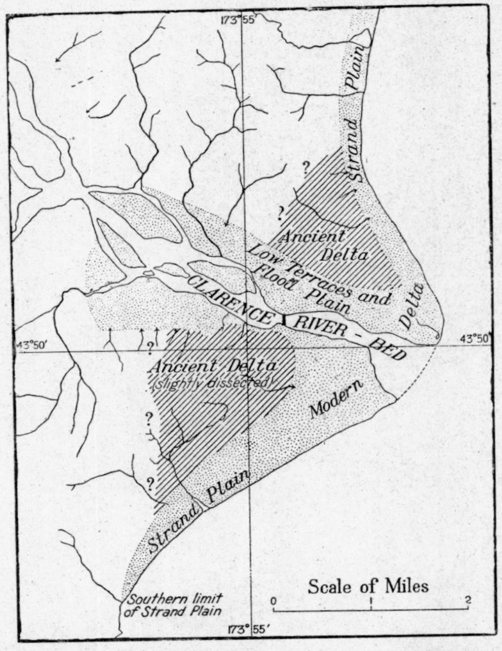

Fig. 214.—The salient delta of the Clarence River, New Zealand—a gravel-laden river from the Kaikoura Mountains. The lined areas labelled "ancient delta" are a coastal salient surviving because protected from marine erosion by the river mouth and its delta. They were levelled as a flood plain and covered with a thick gravel deposit by the river when sea-level was nearly 600 feet higher than now (compare fig. 215).

deltas (fig. 213); but an example of a gravel delta of salient form is that of the Clarence River in New Zealand (fig. 214).

Delta Plains.—Extensive plains of gravel, more or less silt-covered and of less steep gradient than the Clarence delta, fill embayments and, where confluent, form fringes of piedmont alluvial plain around parts of the coast of New Zealand and of other mountainous regions, from which waste supply is abundant.

The deltas built by very large rivers of low gradient, carrying fine waste, are similar in a general way to those described above, but both the top-set and fore-set slopes are much less steep. The former may be almost strictly horizontal and very liable to flooding. Near the margin accumulation of sediment may take place in lagoons enclosed by sand bars thrown up by the waves along the sea margin. Swamps are thus formed, but, as the delta continues to grow, these areas may have their level raised by the accumulation of ordinary alluvium. Outgrowth of the mouths of distributary streams (which form branches from the braided net of channels

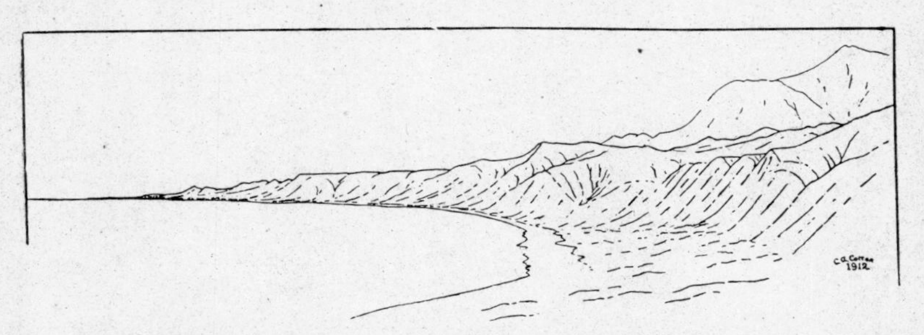

Fig. 215.—A 600-feet-high coastal salient protected from marine erosion by modern delta-growth at the mouth of the Clarence River, New Zealand, viewed from the north. (Compare fig. 214.)

of the delta-building river) may extend over the very shallow-water fringe bordering the shoreline—the sub-aqueous extension of the top-set surface. Bordered still by natural levees they make long finger-like extensions of the delta plain, making it a *digitate* (or "bird-foot") delta (that of the Mississippi, for example).

Seaward of the margin of the top-set surface a fore-set slope descends more steeply—at an inclination of perhaps 2°. Such is the general form of the deltas at the mouths of the Nile, Ganges, Niger, and other great rivers. Seaward delta-growth has caused up-valley aggradation and the resulting extensive aggraded plains (of silt) grade insensibly into the delta plains.

The analogy of great deltas with small is not strictly as close as may appear from the correspondence of surface form. Their enormous weight has caused gradual subsidence of the crustal foundations on which they rest, and, as such subsidence has made room for top-set deposition, great deltas have been built upward as well as outward. So fore-set bedding is less characteristic of their internal structure than is the case in small deltas.

Instability of River Courses on Deltas and Aggraded Plains.—The great plains bordering the Huangho in China, which support a population of many millions, have been built by aggradation. They form a delta with an area of about 100,000 square miles. The river frequently changes its course, and there have been many disastrous floods. The river has discharged sometimes on the northern and sometimes on the southern side of the peninsula of Shan-tung, formerly an island, which has been joined to the mainland by the growth of the delta. The material of which the plains are built is a fine yellow silt.

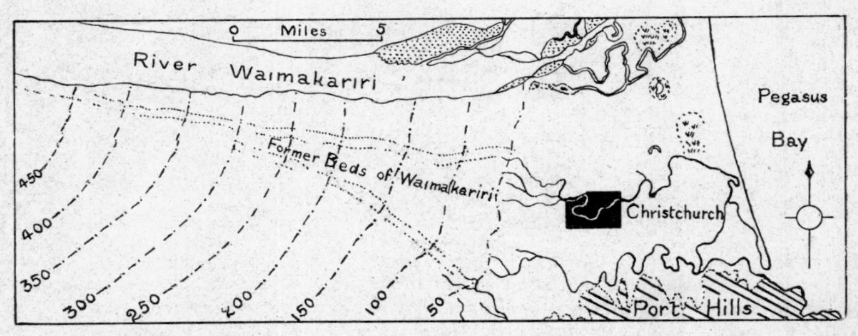

Fig. 216.—Abandoned channels of the Waimakariri River. After Doyne (with interpolated contour-lines, at 50 ft. intervals, on the plain).

Another illustration of the instability of river courses on deltas is afforded by the delta of the Colorado River, in western North America. This delta extends completely across the Gulf of California, with the result that the deep head of the gulf is potentially a lake, but is almost completely dry, the climate being arid. Spilling of the Colorado River into this basin, to form a lake, was accelerated by man's actions. The river enlarged an irrigation canal, and, abandoning its former course for this new one, poured its whole volume into the basin. Eventually the river was again turned into its former channel, but not until a great part of the basin (Imperial Valley), the floor of which is considerably below sea-level, had been converted into a lake.

It is clear that the rivers building all deltas must have had constantly changing courses in order to spread their waste evenly over the surfaces. Some of the more recently abandoned courses can easily be traced. The delta of the Waimakariri, in New Zealand, for example, is still growing, and several former channels of the river—wastes of bare gravel, with occasional sand dunes—are traceable in the vicinity of Christchurch (figs. 209, 216). Apparently the Waimakariri discharged south of Banks Peninsula (fig. 209, B) quite recently.

Great changes in river courses take place inland also where aggradation is in progress. Striking peculiarities in the courses of some of the southern rivers of New Zealand may be thus explained. Alluvial filling of a valley or depression through which a river flows may result in spilling over of the stream of water and waste at some gap in the rim of hills surrounding the depression. The new course of the stream will, in general, be too steep, and when

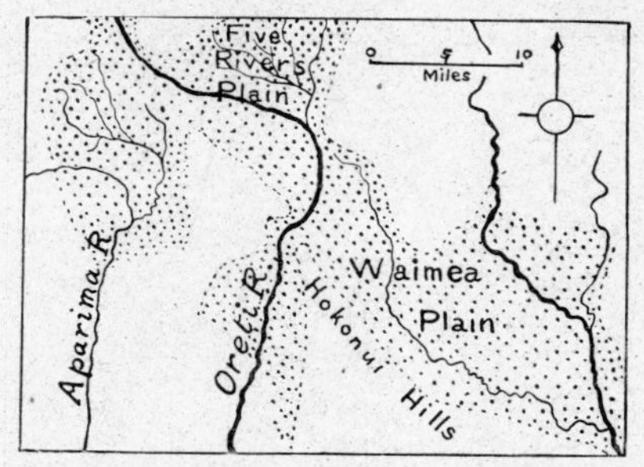

Fig. 217.—The course of the Oreti River, New Zealand.

this is the case degradation will take place in it and will work upstream from the point where spilling over took place. The river will thus become fixed, at least for a time, in the spill-over course. Such a river is sometimes described as "diverted by alluviation."

The diversion, on the other hand, may not be permanent. The new valley and the trench excavated in the aggraded valley upstream may before long become filled up, if the supply of waste keeps up; and when the new course is built higher by aggradation than the original course the stream will spill back again, and it will continue after that to occupy and aggrade the two courses alternately. The Oreti River, in New Zealand, flows south-eastward across a broad alluvium-filled depression known as the Five Rivers Plain, but, instead of following the even slope of the aggraded surface thence across the Waimea Plain farther to the south-east (fig. 217), turns southward through a relatively narrow gap around the north-western end of the Hokonui Hills. The river valley through this gap is aggraded, and the gradient of the course now followed by the river, as given by railway data, is the same as that of what was obviously a former course across the Waimea Plain. It would seem that the great depression of the Five Rivers and Waimea Plains was filled with alluvium by the stream which occupied it until the alluvium spilled over a low col in the already maturely dissected Hokonui Hills, and that the river, wandering freely on the aggraded plains, has since followed sometimes the one outlet and sometimes the other, keeping both courses built up to the same gradient. The aggrading Oreti River has another alternative course available for it down the valley of the Aparima.

CHAPTER XVI

INTERRUPTION OF THE GEOMORPHIC CYCLE

Accidents and interruptions. Various kinds of interruptions. Movements of the land and of sea-level. Effects of uniform rise or fall of sea-level. Initiation of a new cycle. Interruption by submergence. Aggradation not a proof of submergence. Interruption by emergence. Rejuvenation and composite landscapes.

Accidents and Interruptions.—The course of the normal cycle may be cut short at any stage by one of several kinds of *accidents* and *interruptions,* as they have been termed by Davis. Accidents are of two kinds, *climatic* and *volcanic.* The climatic accidents which produce the most important effects are *refrigeration,* which introduces glacial erosion, and a *change to aridity,* which also interferes with the course of normal erosion. By the phrase "volcanic accident" is meant the outbreak of volcanic activity, which, occurring at any stage of a cycle, will very rapidly alter the aspect of the landscape, building up, perhaps, an entirely new surface upon which erosion must begin its work afresh. The work of glacial erosion, desert weathering and wind work, and volcanic activity will be taken up in later chapters.

Various Kinds of Interruptions.—Interruptions of the cycle, which may be now discussed, result as a rule from earth movements, though sometimes also from fluctuations of sea-level. Small changes in the relative levels of land and sea, whether due to movements of the land or fluctuations of sea-level, are negligible in the long run if they are oscillations about a mean position. When, on the other hand, they are cumulative in one direction, the result is that the former base-level is replaced by a new one either higher or lower in the land mass. It may be assumed that the land, after such movement has taken place, again stands still. The former cycle of erosion is cut short as a result of the change in the position of base-level, and a new cycle is inaugurated.

In addition to simple regional movements of uplift and subsidence of the land relatively to sea-level (*emergence* and *submergence*), movements involving deformation, dislocation, and tilting of the former land surface in the area studied are also of great importance.

Movements of the Land and of Sea-level.—The interrupting effects of regional movements—of movements, that is to say, sensibly uniform throughout the area studied—are indistinguishable by their results from those of rise or fall of sea-level due to fluctuation in the volume of the ocean waters or to some change in the capacity of the ocean basins produced by deformation in some remote part of the world. It is sometimes convenient, therefore, to describe such events as "submergence," or "positive movement of the strand," and "emergence," or "negative movement of the strand." Actual rise and fall of the ocean surface must be regarded as a probable cause of some movements of the strand line (and such probable movements are sometimes distinguished as "eustatic"); but it cannot be assumed that all submergences and emergences are due to that cause.

In such cases the former plane of base-level remains horizontal, but after the movement it stands higher or lower than sea-level, which determines a new base-level. Base-level may be said to have moved "parallel to itself"—that is, remaining a horizontal plane—to a new position lower or higher in the land mass. Though such a change of base-level is generally of eustatic origin, it is theoretically possible, but probably of very infrequent occurrence, for a crustal movement to produce a similar result over a large area. Where a whole region is affected by movement, however, the former base-level surface will almost invariably be no longer plane and horizontal, but will be somewhat arched or tilted (together with the terrain containing it). It may be strongly warped or broken by faults; and parts of it may be above while others are below the new base-level. The juxtaposition of emergent and partly submerged blocks, such as occurs in the South Island of New Zealand on either side of the mouth of the Wairau River, may make it evident that observed changes of level are due rather to earth movements than to eustatic effects. Eustatic sea-level changes have occurred, however, in addition to earth movements; so that observed base-level movements may be attributable to a combination of the two causes. Inclination of features aligned along former shorelines or other indications of a varying measure of emergence or submergence from place to place may clearly indicate that earth movements have had something to do with changes of level.

Effects of Uniform Rise or Fall of Sea-level.—Though parallel movement of base-level is a very special case in earth movements, it has been approximately produced in small areas; and obviously it is the normal result of eustatic change of level uncomplicated by the simultaneous occurrence of earth movements. It offers for introductory investigation the simple cases of uniform submergence and emergence of land, with which the general case of more complex movement and its effects in interrupting the geomorphic cycle can afterwards be compared.

Initiation of a New Cycle.—It has been ruled that any change in the position of base-level relatively to the land mass or terrain introduces a new cycle. It must be noted, however, that the effects which follow a simple positive or negative movement are not perceptible as producing landscape changes inland until long after they occur. The cycle of changes which was current with base-level in its former position continues its leisurely progress (so as still to appear to be the "current" cycle) until landforms developed in a newer cycle gradually gnaw their way inland and encroach upon the landscape.

In all cases after an interrupting movement the grading processes, degradation and aggradation, come into operation, grading both streams and surfaces with respect to the new base-level. After the movement has taken place, parts of the beds of formerly graded streams are, for example, too steep under the new conditions. The velocity of such streams is accelerated, and they have energy to spare beyond that required to transport their loads of waste. The streams degrade their channels, therefore, reducing their steepness until the graded condition is again established. If, on the other hand, part of the course of a river has become too nearly level, the stream becomes too sluggish to carry its whole load, and therefore deposits part of it in its channel, thus building up and steepening it until again graded.

In the case of warped and tilted landscapes these processes come into operation at once on all parts of the surface that have been inclined so as to affect stream gradients; but in the case at present under consideration, where there is no tilting, such effects are confined to strips and migrate progressively inland in a manner to be described.

In a general way the stages of a cycle following interruption and initiated by the establishment of a new base-level are similar to the stages of any earlier cycle. Mature and senile landscapes are much alike in any cycle, but even at these stages the landscapes and stream patterns will differ somewhat in successive cycles. Adjustment to structure, for example, will not generally be completed in a single cycle, but will continue in those stages of succeeding cycles in which the streams are vigorously eroding.

The younger stages of the new cycle initiated by interrupting movements demand special attention, for the landforms developed in them are seen side by side with those of the interrupted cycle, and are closely related to them. This phase—replacement of the landforms developed in one cycle of erosion by those developed in the cycle which follows—is characterised by special forms governed by the nature of the interrupting movements.

Interruption by Submergence.—When a cycle of erosion is interrupted by an even, general subsidence of the land, or by a rise of sea-level, the lower part of each river valley is at first invaded by the sea. It becomes a *drowned valley,* and forms an estuary or harbour, like those of the Auckland district of New Zealand (fig. 218), which are the results of drowning due to even submergence, probably eustatic. As the new cycle thus inaugurated progresses, the streams, both large and small, build out deltas in the still water at the heads of the bays or estuaries into which they now flow (fig. 219); and all the streams thus grow in length again seaward. As delta-building streams, if previously graded, must aggrade (as shown in fig. 211) in order to continue flowing and maintain grade, it follows that valleys in a region where submergence has taken place become more or less deeply aggraded.

Aggradation not a Proof of Subsidence.—Aggradation in previously graded valleys may be brought about in more ways than one, and does not in itself afford definite proof of a change in the position of the general base-level. Aggradation is caused by any increase in the load of waste or decrease in the amount of water in a graded stream, the load in the latter case remaining constant; for either of those changes results in overloading, and the result of

Fig. 218.—Rise of sea-level (base-level) has caused partial submergence of a landscape, Whangaroa Harbour, New Zealand.
T. W. Collins, photo.

overloading is deposition of the excess load until grade is re-established. A disturbance of the balance between volume and load may have occurred as a result of stream capture, or it may be a result of a small climatic change. Desiccation of climate (change to drier conditions) both decreases river volumes and, by reducing the protection afforded to the soil by vegetation, increases the supply of waste. Thus aggradation may follow a minor climatic accident of this kind, while degradation may follow a change

Fig. 219.—A bay-head delta, Pelorus Sound, New Zealand.
F. G. Radcliffe, photo.

towards moister conditions. Increased rainfall generally increases the ratio of volume to load, as it augments stream volumes, and may also reduce the supply of waste by encouraging the growth of vegetation, a condition which leads to downward corrasion until grade is re-established.

Interruption by Emergence.—After regional emergence the relief at the close of the cycle thus interrupted (young, mature, or old, as it happens to be) is the initial landscape of a new cycle. There are no immediate changes in the form of the surface as a result of emergence; but the base-level has been lowered, and changes follow in due course. There is a new shoreline, and between this and the former shoreline, bounding the former land area (fig. 220, *A*), a strip of sea-floor has been uplifted to become land, a coastal plain (p. 64), of which only the part nearest the hinterland is shown in the diagram (*B*). The rivers of the hinterland, with redissection of which we are now concerned, are extended across the coastal plain, and in their extended courses their initial gradients are in general steeper than is necessary for the transportation of their loads.

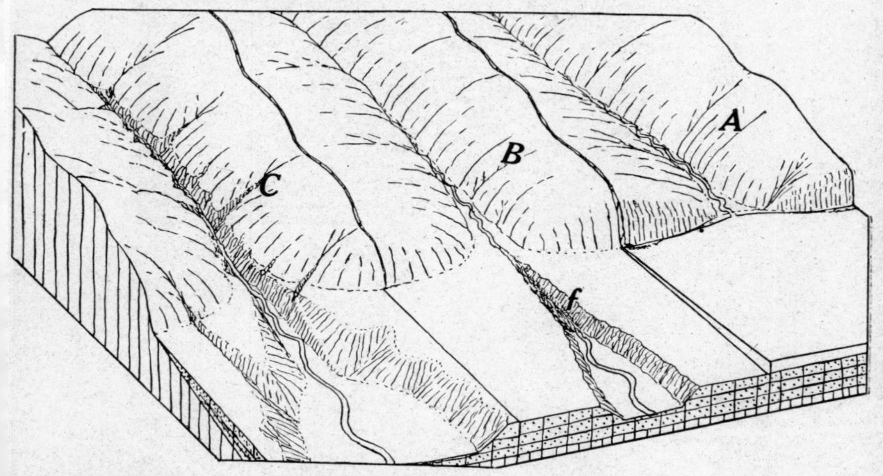

Fig. 220.—A cycle has been interrupted by regional uplift or emergence. *A,* before emergence; *B,* nick at the fall zone; *C,* valley-in-valley form developed as the nick migrates inland.

Trenches across the coastal plain are soon cut, therefore, with their heads near the former shoreline, where the streams have cut down to the hard rocks of the undermass and rapids or falls are developed (fig. 220, *B, f*). For this reason the former shoreline—or, rather, the line or zone at which streams cut down to the floor of older rocks underlying the weak sediments of the coastal plain—is sometimes termed the *fall line* or *zone*. The streams are not now graded throughout their length, their profiles being too steep at the fall line, just above which there is a convex angle (or *nick*) in the river profile between an upper graded segment surviving from the interrupted cycle and the lower segment graded in the new cycle. Each stream in the oversteep part of its course has sufficient velocity and energy to degrade, and so the rapids and nick work upstream,

Fig. 221.—Valley-in-valley form in the valley of the Awatere, New Zealand, a revived river

J. A. Thomson, photo.

Fig. 222.—Valley-in-valley form in the valley of the Shotover River, New Zealand.

C. A. Cotton, photo.

the river downstream from them soon becoming graded with respect to the new (lowered) base-level. This headward erosion with the development of a new valley within the former valley (fig. 220, *C*) goes on rapidly because of the abundance of water, for the streams drain valley systems developed in the preceding cycle. As the head of the newly cut inner valley advances upstream, the cross profile of the valley becomes that of a steep-sided young valley below and of a more widely opened valley of the preceding cycle above. This condition is sometimes termed *valley in valley,* and the river is said to be *revived.* Between the slope of the valley side or valley floor of the former cycle and that of the valley side of the new cycle there is a sharp angle, or *shoulder* (figs. 221, 222).

There is no tendency under these conditions to deepen the valley of the earlier cycle except by headward erosion of the inner valley, and above the rapids or nick marking the head of this the older valley retains its form, undergoing only such slow modification as would have been in progress had an interrupting movement not taken place. It is as though the earlier cycle were still current until the features developed in it are encroached upon by those developed in the succeeding cycle.

It should be noted that this gradual replacement of an older landscape by a new one developing in linear fashion by headward erosion along streams is not the only way in which valley in valley forms can be produced. In the case of differential earth movement streams are revived, degrade, and cut inner valleys in such parts of their courses as are steepened by tilting of the land surface (Chapter XVII).

Rejuvenation and Composite Landscapes.—After a regional uplift the earlier topography is destroyed only a little at a time by the encroachment of the features developed in the new cycle, and when the surface as a whole is considered it is clear that the former cycle is as it were prolonged until the surface developed in it is encroached upon by the young trenches of tributary streams compelled to degrade by the deepening of their mains, and also by the young slopes of the new cycle similarly degraded (figs. 223, 224).

The presence of landscape features developed in several cycles may demonstrate a succession of uplifts. In other cases a succession of uplifts may have taken place but the cycle introduced by the latest of them may be so far advanced that all traces of the forms developed in earlier cycles have disappeared. Large parts of the land surface have been above the sea and subject to subaerial erosion for enormous periods and have been uplifted from time to time so that in the aggregate a vast thickness of rock has been removed by erosion. They are now in their *n*th cycle.

The gradual replacement of forms of one cycle by forms of the next is called *rejuvenation*; and while the relief comprises forms developed in two (or more) cycles the landscape is said to be *composite*. The "surface has been developed partly in relation to one base-level and partly in relation to another" (Davis).

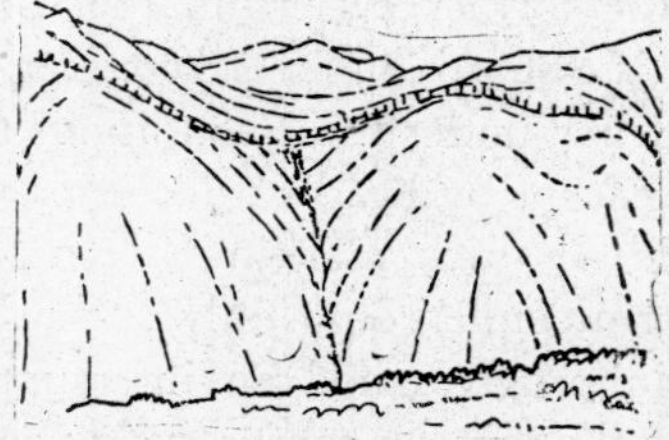

Fig. 223.—Young, steep slopes of a new cycle encroaching on a mature surface (above), in a truncated valley overhanging the Ngahauranga Gorge, Wellington, New Zealand.

Fig. 224.—Forms developed in two successive cycles, separated by a shoulder, Haywards, Wellington, New Zealand.

C. A. Cotton, photo.

Examples of composite topography are very common in New Zealand, where movements involving uplift have been recently in progress—not continuously, however, but separated by fairly long periods of stillstand, during which young, submature, and in some areas mature landscapes have been developed. Among many districts characterised by rejuvenation forms that adjacent to Wellington may be taken as an example. Here features developed in two very distinct cycles are present side by side, and some relics of a still earlier senile landscape are found also (fig. 137). In the

Fig. 225.—Composite landscape of the Makara Valley, Wellington, New Zealand.
Maxwell Gage, photo.

Makara Valley (fig. 225) the older of the two more modern cycles is particularly well represented by well-preserved relics of a wide valley floor, which now make prominent, submaturely dissected benches 100 to 200 feet above a modern flood plain. An unusually wide development of valley floors in both the interrupted cycle and that now current has taken place because of the presence of very easily eroded crushed rock in a belt which is locally of considerable breadth. The hill slopes on the valley sides are still very generally accordant with the valley floor of the interrupted cycle; but rejuvenation extends some distance up the valleys of tributaries, ending in each case in a distinct nick, below which sharp shoulders in the landscape separate an open upper from a young inner V form in a valley-in-valley arrangement.

In several separate parts of New Zealand, of which eastern Marlborough and northern Hawke's Bay are examples, extremely young valley-in-valley rejuvenation is found even in terrains of the softest rocks, which indicates that a very short time indeed has elapsed since emergence interrupted the former cycle. In the Marlborough district the lower course of the Awatere River is contained in a narrow young trench cut to a depth of 100 feet below a valley floor which was enlarged to a width of several miles in the

Fig. 226.—Two-cycle, composite landscape at the mouth of the Kekerangu River, New Zealand.

interrupted cycle. Similar valley-in-valley form near the mouth of a smaller river in the same district is shown in fig. 226. The inner trench of the Awatere ends up-valley in a nick a few miles beyond the part shown in fig. 221. In this valley and in similarly rejuvenated valleys in soft terrains of the North Island (that of the Rangitikei River, for example) small tributaries have been revived as yet only close to the main rivers, to which they descend as falls and rapids from a nick at the level of the former main-valley floor. It is this rejuvenation of very late date that accounts for the presence of very abundant discordant tributary junctions which have been referred to in Chapter IV. (Compare fig. 42).

CHAPTER XVII

INTERRUPTION BY DIFFERENTIAL MOVEMENTS

Results of tilting of the surface. Warping. Ponding. Antecedent drainage. Superposed gorges. Gorges through formerly buried spurs. New Zealand gorges. Basin plains.

Results of Tilting of the Surface. — The results of irregular (differential) movement are in certain respects quite unlike those of the regional movements described in the preceding chapter. With differential movement there is deformation of the surface by warping or dislocation by faulting, or perhaps both. Parts may be raised and other parts lowered, level areas may be tilted into inclined positions, and sloping areas may become steeper or less steep, or may have their slopes reversed.

Fig. 226A.—Entrenchment by rejuvenation of a small river in a continental interior, probably as a result of local earth movement, Magdalena Valley, Colombia, South America.

D. E. Morgan, photo.

Changes in slope due to warping are not generally of sufficient magnitude to affect hill or valley sides appreciably, but where the down-valley slopes of graded streams are altered ever so slightly an immediate regrading of the streams quickly produces characteristic landscape changes.

Fig. 227.—Whiteman's Valley, near Wellington, New Zealand. Above: The Whiteman's Valley group of headwater tributaries of the Mangaroa River aggraded as a result of strong downtilting of the land surface towards the west. (Contour interval: 100 ft.) Below: View looking north-westward across the swampy aggraded flats of Whiteman's Valley.

C. A. Cotton, photo.

Streams the channels of which are tilted to a steeper slope are accelerated, and begin at once to degrade throughout the length of the steepened parts of their courses, producing valley-in-valley forms such as are shown in fig. 226A. This rejuvenation, unlike that produced by regional emergence, is not delayed while the head of an inner trench works its way upstream: it immediately follows the tilting, beginning as soon as the stream flows with increased velocity. Remnants of valley floors dating from the period before tilting took

Fig. 228.—Another valley head aggraded as a result of strong headward tilting of the valley. Western branch of the Wainui-o-mata Valley (compare fig. 213); view from the divide at the head of the valley looking south-east.

C. A. Cotton, photo.

place slope downstream more steeply than the valley floors developed after the streams are graded again.

Graded valleys in which, on the other hand, the downstream slope has been reduced by tilting or warping begin at once to aggrade in order to restore the graded condition. A considerable amount of aggradation due to this cause has taken place in some valleys between the Rimutaka Range and the recently formed tectonic basin which contains the harbour of Wellington, New Zealand. Here a mature land surface has been very sharply bent down to form the eastern side of the Hutt Valley depression (figs. 176, 213). No large valleys are affected by the tilt, for the hinge-line of the movement is parallel to the grain of the terrain, to which rivers are adjusted. The streams in which headward tilting may be manifested are only headwater tributaries coming into the main streams on the western side; but so steep is the tilt that these are strongly affected. Near the head of the valley of the Mangaroa (a barbed tributary of the Hutt River) a group of minor tributary streams enters from the west, and the valleys of these are deeply aggraded (fig. 227), the alluvium even submerging part of the subdividing spur between two of the streams. Similar aggradation, due to the same tilting, occurs in the western headwater branches of the Wainui-o-mata River (figs. 213, 228).

Warping.—The middle part of a long valley may be gently warped upward, resulting in an increase of slope downstream from the point where the valley is crossed by the axis of warping and a decrease of slope upstream from that point; so that down the valley from the axis rejuvenated topography results, while up the valley there is aggradation.

Ponding.—If warping is more pronounced than in the case just cited and actual reversal of the slope of the valley bottom takes place for some distance upstream from the axis of upwarping, the river may be *ponded*—that is to say, a lake may be formed occupying part of the valley (fig. 229 *A*). Thus, when a surface previously eroded is deformed, lakes, in common with rapids and other features characteristic of extreme youth in the cycle of erosion, may appear.

A lake so formed will overflow at the lowest gap, and where the relief is fairly strong and the deformation not very pronounced the lowest gap will generally be along the former course of the river. When the outlet of the lake is cut down through the up-warped arch, and the lake disappears, the drainage of the region in such a case will be much the same as it was prior to the deformation, though for a time there will be some evidence in the landscape that a lake has existed (Chapter XXXIII).

If, on the other hand, the relief is weak, or there is a low gap somewhere in the hills bounding that part of the valley in which the lake has been formed (as at *O,* fig. 229, *A*), and if the warping has been pronounced, the lake may overflow along a course entirely

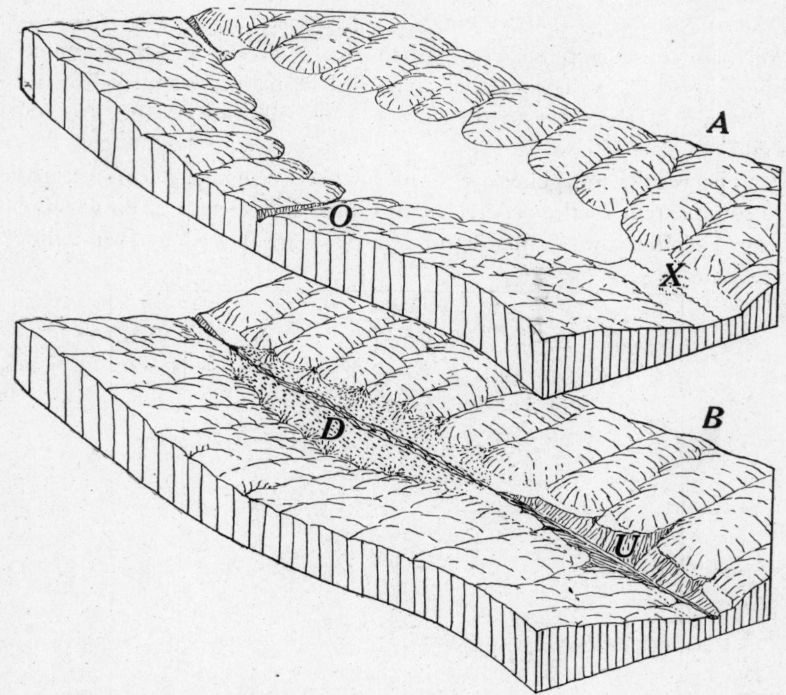

Fig. 229.—Warping transverse to a river valley. *A,* rapid warping results in ponding; the lake so formed overflows at *O*; the drainage is thus diverted to a new course; and the river formerly occupying the valley is beheaded at the axis of up-warping, *X*. *B,* warping (which may be still in progress) has taken place so slowly that the river has been able to maintain its course by aggrading the down-warped part of the valley, *D,* and cutting a gorge across the up-warped part, *U*.

different from that followed by the now diverted river prior to the deformation. This new course of the river is consequent on the warping. The stream in the warped valley downstream from the axis of uplift has been beheaded by warping, and a divide has leaped to a new position (*X*). The new course taken by the overflow from the lake will not, in general, fit the river, and the latter will at once proceed to grade it. This grading usually involves downward cutting, which will lower the level of the lake and, unless its floor has been warped down below local base-level, eventually drain it.

Such lakes are not common; but a magnificent example is found in the many-branched Lake Kyoga, through which the

Nile passes (fig. 230). An axis of upwarping between Lakes Victoria and Albert has reversed the Kafu River so as to impound the lake in the valleys of that river and its tributaries and to cause diversion of the river to the course now followed by the Victoria Nile.

The results are generally similar where warping is complicated to some extent by the occurrence of faults, and, clearly, even without any warping, the formation of a fault scarp across a river valley

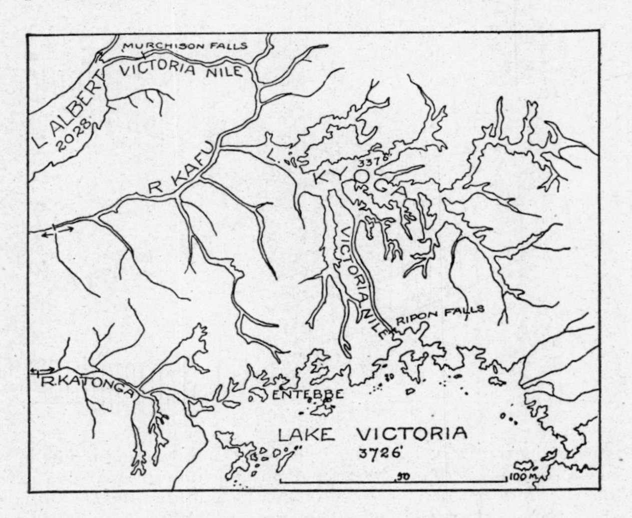

Fig. 230.—The widely-branching Lake Kyoga, formed by drowning of a valley system as a result of up-warping across the course of the Kafu River, Uganda. (After Davis.)

will result in an interruption, and may cause ponding of the river if the scarp faces up the valley.

Antecedent Drainage.—In the foregoing section it was assumed that deformation took place rapidly in order to effect ponding. Such deformation, either warping or faulting, however, commonly proceeds so slowly that ponding does not take place in the valleys of rivers of considerable size that cross the axes of deformation, even though the slopes of their floors are reversed or fault scarps rise across them. A vigorous river is able to maintain its channel by downward cutting across a very slowly rising arch or block, remaining always nearly graded (fig. 229, *B*). Similarly it will maintain a course across a slowly sinking area by aggradation, building, as it were, a bridge for itself across the depression by depositing alluvium (*D*). In drawing fig. 229, *B,* which illustrates this point, it has been necessary to compress the warping into a short section of the valley in order to show the effects of both up-warping and down-warping in the same diagram. In nature, however, the axes of depression and uplift are generally much more widely separated. Aggradation will extend much farther also into the valleys of tributaries.

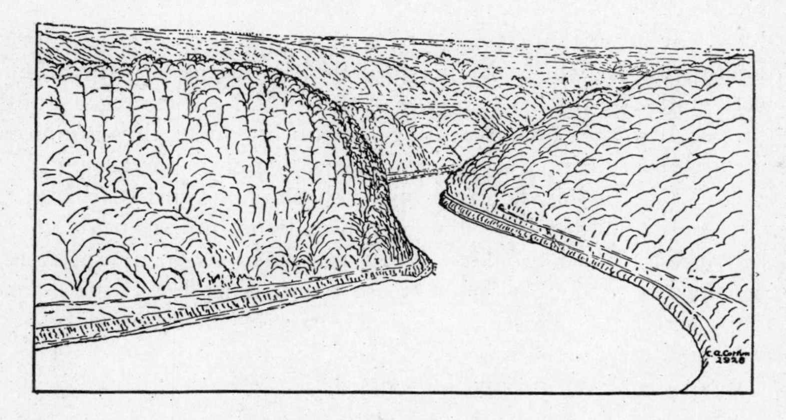

Fig. 231.—The antecedent gorge of the Rhine through the up-warped German highlands.

Such warping may uplift an arch, or faulting may raise a horst or a tilted block, across the line of a river valley to a height of thousands of feet, and parts of a former valley floor may be depressed to a similar extent. The uplifted areas become mountain ranges, through which vigorous rivers that have maintained their courses across them as they rose flow in deep, young gorges, a well-known example of which is the gorge of the Rhine below Bingen (fig. 231). Such rivers are termed *antecedent.* Smaller or less vigorous rivers which are unable to degrade as fast as the land rises are ponded and turned aside (as in fig. 229, *A*) into new, consequent courses, and are said to be *defeated.* Many such streams become tributary to their more vigorous neighbours, which thus, as master rivers, carry away the drainage of considerable areas. Reinforced in this way they are better able to maintain their antecedent courses in spite of further uplift.

A number of New Zealand rivers have the appearance of antecedent streams in that they make their way in gorges across uplifted blocks around the ends of which there are comparatively low tectonic gaps that would guide the consequent drainage if the blocks had risen very rapidly or there had been no rivers in existence in the district prior to the deformation. It is thus reasonably certain that these rivers are antecedent to at least the greater part of the uplift of the ranges they cross, but it is uncertain whether they took their present courses in a cycle of erosion introduced by gentle uplift and preceding the great (Kaikoura) deformation to which the present relief is due, or whether they were guided by the first wrinkles of the surface as it emerged from the sea. If so they maintained the consequent courses thus assumed during a continuation of the movements, though in the later, more intense stage of this deformation the shape of the surface changed very considerably and the low gaps in it do not now coincide with the earliest formed wrinkles. The landforms may be alternatively explained by making either of these assumptions, but if the latter is the correct one the river gorges are strictly one-cycle instead of two-cycle features, as is the case with true antecedent gorges. They cannot, therefore, strictly be classed as antecedent, but, being consequent on the earlier and antecedent to the later stages of a single series of deforming movements, are sometimes termed *anteconsequent*. Some may prefer to regard them, however, as a one-cycle variety of antecedent courses.

Superposed Gorges.—The possibility of mistaking some superposed gorges for antecedent or anteconsequent river courses must not be overlooked. A very remarkable group of small parallel streams pass in separate notches through a hard-rock barrier standing a little in front of the Haldon Hills, in which they rise (fig. 232). These gaps seem best explained as of superposed consequent origin like those of streams descending from the Kaikoura Mountains, as shown in fig. 142, p. 142.

Where streams have taken consequent courses over a widespread cover and have later been stencilled through it on to an undermass, it may be that there are buried mountains or ridges beneath the cover, and the superposed rivers will traverse these in gorges. Gorges in the Rocky Mountains which were formerly thought to be antecedent are now explained in this way (fig. 233).

Fig. 232.—The gorge of the Starborough Creek, Marlborough, New Zealand, one of several streams apparently superposed across the range of front hills fringing the Haldon Hills (at rear), on which the streams rise.

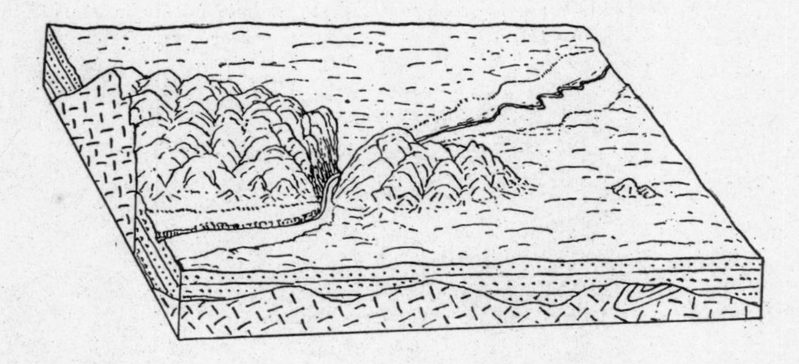

Fig. 233.—Devil's Gate, Sweetwater River, Rocky Mountains. Development of a gorge where a superposed river crosses an exhumed mountain. (After Atwood and Atwood, redrawn.)

Among them is that in which the Green River crosses the Uinta Mountains; it was once considered the type of antecedent gorges.

Gorges through Formerly Buried Spurs.—Alternate aggradation and degradation in river valleys results in the burial of spurs and possibly in their later resurrection. But the degrading rivers commonly become superposed in places on the valley sides and cross exhumed spurs in gorges. For a considerable distance the Manuherikia River, in New Zealand, has experienced valley-side superposition and thus flows in a narrow trench (fig. 234). The

Fig. 234.—Valley-side superposition, which has taken place after aggradation has been succeeded by a degradational episode, has resulted in confining the Manuherikia River, New Zealand, between rocky walls. If it had not been thus caught it would flow on the lowland seen in the distance at the extreme left.

J. Park, photo.

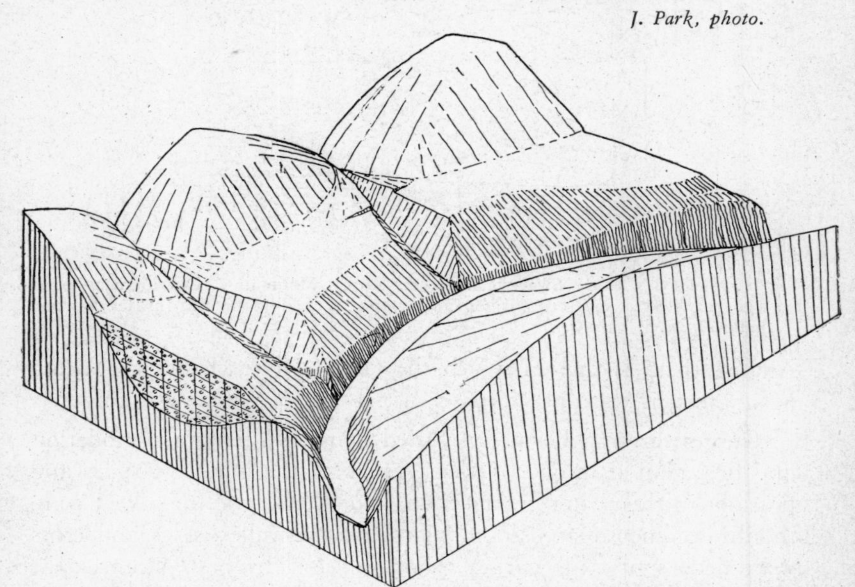

Fig. 235.—The Shotover River, New Zealand, is superposed in this way on valley-side spurs of a former valley which has been filled with alluvium so as to bury the spurs (compare figs. 222, 250).

Shotover River, also, after deeply aggrading its valley, has cut down again but has failed to follow closely the ancient filled valley, cutting instead across spurs in superposed gorges. Thus a peculiar variant of the valley-in-valley form is developed (figs. 222, 235, 250).

New Zealand Gorges.—Perhaps the most striking of the antecedent (or anteconsequent) gorges in New Zealand are those by way of which the Waiau and Hurunui Rivers leave the broad aggraded depression in which Culverden stands (figs. 236, 241) and cross

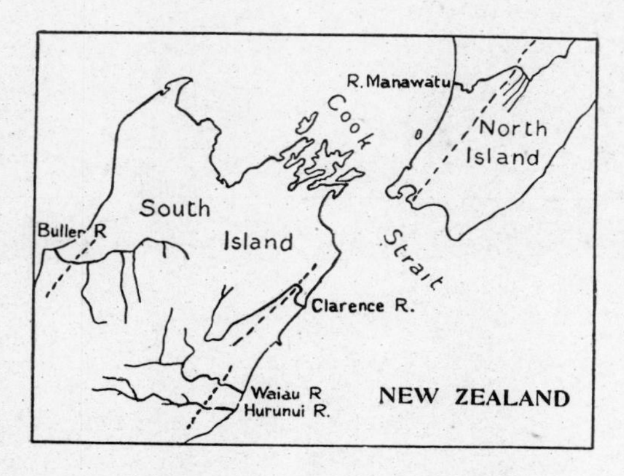

Fig. 236.—Locality map of New Zealand gorges.

an uplifted block which presents towards the plain a dissected fault-scarp front rising 2000 feet. The crest of this mountain block slopes down slightly from both sides towards the Hurunui outlet gorge, which seems to indicate the presence of a sag of the initial surface sufficiently deep to have guided a consequent river during an early stage of the deformation that raised the range and enclosed the basin.

Farther north, in Marlborough, the Clarence River (fig. 236), where it breaks across the northern end of the Seaward Kaikoura Range, appears to be of similar origin. If the lower Clarence is a true antecedent river a number of other streams south of it were, in all probability, defeated by the rise of the massive Seaward Kaikoura arch, thus increasing the volume of the consequent river in the Clarence Valley depression behind it; but if the anteconsequent explanation is the correct one, there is no necessity to assume the existence of such streams.

On the western coast of the South Island of New Zealand some of the larger rivers, such as the Buller (figs. 236, 237), which take direct courses to the sea by way of gorges cut through recently uplifted mountain blocks, are antecedent or possibly anteconsequent.

Fig. 237.—The Buller Gorge, cut through the uplifted block forming the Paparoa-Papahaua Range, New Zealand. View looking upstream.

F. G. Radcliffe, photo.

The lower gorge of the Taieri River is of the same nature, though cut when the land stood higher above sea-level than it does now, slight submergence having since allowed the sea to penetrate through the gorge and drown the floor of the intermont depression which now contains Waihola Lake (fig. 238).

In the North Island the gorge (figs. 236, 239) by way of which the Manawatu River breaks across from the eastern to the western

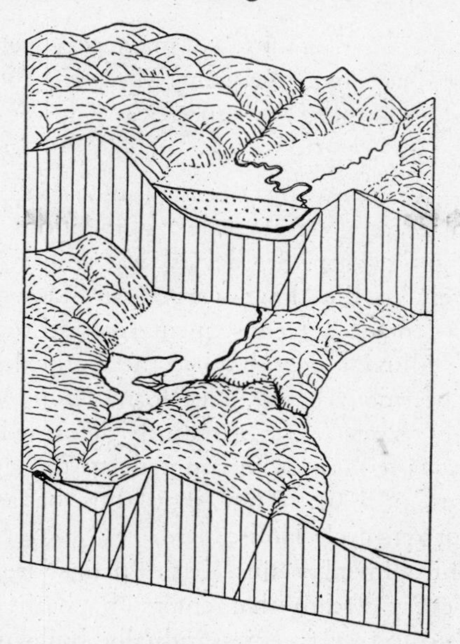

Fig. 238.—The Taieri Gorge across a coastal uplifted block in eastern Otago, New Zealand, and the Waihola Lake—Taieri Plain basin. Section shows structure across the middle of the basin. (After Benson.)

Fig. 239.—The Manawatu Gorge, New Zealand. View from the eastern side, where the river enters the gorge. *F. G. Radcliffe, photo.*

side of the Ruahine-Tararua uplifted mass may perhaps be satisfactorily explained as anteconsequent, though other suggestions have been offered. The gorge is situated at a low sag in the crest of the range.

Basin Plains.—Where warping or faulting, or a combination of the two, takes place on a large scale, aggradation, the beginning of which in a slightly warped valley is shown in fig. 229, *B,* goes on very extensively in the down-warped and down-faulted areas drained by antecedent or anteconsequent rivers through the rising mountain rims. Alluvial deposits become both deep and widespread in these intermont basins, and form *basin plains*—features which are not only characteristic of recently deformed land surfaces, but must also occur as an accompaniment to the grading of any deformed surface (p. 160). They may thus be associated with either two-cycle or one-cycle landscapes.

Like piedmont alluvial plains, basin plains are made up of coalescing fans, every stream that enters the basin depositing its quota of waste as the surface is gradually built up. They are, therefore, made up of a large number of contiguous convex areas, the steepness of which depends on the volumes of the depositing streams and on the coarseness of the alluvium. The complex slopes lead down from either side to the master river, the course of which forms the axis of the basin. The axis is not necessarily central, but may be pushed towards one side of the basin by vigorous growth of the fans on the other side, due to great height or perhaps to rapid rise of the mountains from which their waste is derived or to the capacity of the rocks exposed in them to supply coarse waste.

A basin plain formed by deep aggradation over a surface with relief inherited from an earlier cycle will have an irregular outline, extending in the form of embayments into the valleys of tributary streams, and even if the surface is plane before deformation begins valleys eroded on the rising slopes in the early stages of deformation will later become embayments of the plain as the depth of aggradation increases. Where fault scarps bound the basin, however, their straightness is but little impaired by aggradation, and that little only when movement on the faults has ceased. Fault scarps that become buried beneath a gravel basin-filling are afterwards resurrected if some of this alluvium is removed in the course of later erosion.

Subsidiary blocks or small up-warped areas or ridges of a pre-existing relief may become surrounded by, and even buried beneath, the alluvium of a basin plain, but, whatever their origin, they are subject to erosion during the deposition of alluvium around them, and so they always underlie it "unconformably."

Fig. 240.—View across the basin plain at Trentham, near Wellington, New Zealand, from the fault scarp forming its north-western boundary.

D. J. Aldersley, photo.

When earth movements have ceased, grading of the rivers draining intermont basins results generally in lowering of the outlets, accompanied by dissection and terracing of the basin-plain deposits, and followed later by extensive planation and perhaps by complete removal of the alluvium if the floor upon which it was laid down is far above base-level.

The small Trentham basin plain near Wellington, New Zealand, forms part of the valley of the Hutt River, which traverses it longitudinally (fig. 240). The aggraded depression is of very recent origin, and was formed in the same way, and probably at the same time, as that containing the harbour of Wellington, with which it is almost continuous. It is bounded on one side by a fault scarp. On the south-eastern side, however, the alluvium of the plain embays the valleys of a surface of considerable relief warped down to form the boundary of the basin just as it is in the lower valley of the Hutt River (figs. 176, 191).

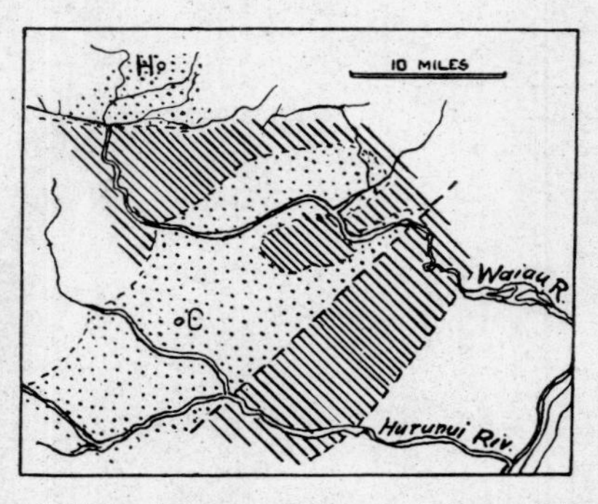

Fig. 241.—Hanmer and Waiau-Hurunui (Culverden) basin plains, New Zealand (*H,* Hanmer; *C,* Culverden). Basin plains stippled; lined areas are bedrock.

Examples of basin plains in the South Island of New Zealand are the Hanmer Plain and Waiau-Hurunui Plain (fig. 241). The latter is traversed by two rivers which break through the mountain rim to the south-east by way of independent gorges (p. 233). The landscape of this range-and-basin district (as noted on p. 230), may perhaps be correctly explained as the result of two cycles of erosion; but if, on the other hand, the outlet gorges from the basin plains are of anteconsequent instead of antecedent origin these basin plains should be classed with the one-cycle forms described in Chapter XIII, instead of with those resulting from interruption of the cycle of erosion.

Both plains are bounded by continuous fault scarps on the sides in which the outlet gorges are situated, while their other boundaries are less regular (figs. 241, 241A). Both have been subject to planation by their main rivers since the deposition of their alluvium. Though some aggradation is now again in progress, evidence of considerable degradation is found in the presence of high terraces bordering

Fig. 241A.—Outlet gorge by way of which the Waiau River leaves the Hanmer basin plain, New Zealand. (Compare fig. 241.)

C. A. Cotton, photo.

the basins and their outlet gorges (figs. 241A, 242A); and so the fault scarps in part bounding these basins must be "resurrected fault scarps."

In the southern part of the South Island of New Zealand there are some large tectonic depressions now occupied by basin plains, of which the Five Rivers and Waimea Plains (shown in fig. 217) are examples.

Other New Zealand tectonic depressions, including those of Central Otago (fig. 159), may be regarded as basin plains that have passed far beyond the stage of aggradation. Alluvial accumulations in them have long ago been dissected and removed by river planation as the outlet gorges have been cut down.

CHAPTER XVIII

RIVER TERRACES AND INCISED MEANDERS

Cyclic or valley-plain terraces. Incised meanders. Slip-off slope terraces. Cut and built terraces. Structural terraces and splinter terraces. Alternate or meander-scar terraces. The slopes of river terraces.

Cyclic or Valley-Plain Terraces.—In some districts in which relics of more than one geomorphic cycle survive in composite landscapes

Fig. 242.—Valley-plain terrace of the Clutha River, at Clyde, New Zealand. The river has very recently entrenched itself below a valley plain cut to a great width on basin-filling gravelly alluvium.

C. A. Cotton, photo.

valley plains of interrupted cycles, or remnants of them, form well-marked terraces. They record the occurrence of at least one episode of base-level standstill of sufficient duration to rank as a brief cycle—or, at least, an "epicycle," as it has been termed—and it is possible to correlate one remnant with others in the same or perhaps in adjacent valleys and so to reconstruct in imagination the landscape of which it once formed a part. Fig 226 shows a broad valley-plain terrace bordering the Kekerangu River at its mouth, and the coastal salient shown in fig. 215 consists of terraces bordering the mouth of the Clarence River, in the same—Marlborough—district of New Zealand, in this case at an elevation of 600 feet (compare fig. 214). Such terraces are of extremely common occurrence in the valleys of New Zealand—a land of terraces. In addition to broad low terrace plains which border the lower Awatere River (p. 222) with a combined width of several miles distinct remnants of similar valley floors at several higher levels are present as terraces that bear witness to the interruptions of

Fig. 242A.—Cyclic terrace on hard rock (with also a flight of higher discontinuous terraces) Waiau Gorge, near Hanmer, New Zealand.

N.Z. Tourist Department, photo.

successive cycles or epicycles. Other examples are shown in figs. 242-243. They are found for the most part on soft-rock terrains, the surfaces of which were widely planed by rivers during brief pauses punctuating the progress of discontinuous valley-excavation by vertical corrasion. In adjoining hard-rock areas the same halts in vertical corrasion may be traceable only by the occurrence of valley-side shoulders in composite V-shaped valleys, though during the longer pauses some vigorous rivers have developed valley floors wide enough even on hard rocks to survive as terraces (fig. 242A).

The term "berm" has been introduced for any remnant of a surface developed to full maturity in a cycle that has since been interrupted. Though it has been said to be a kind of "terrace," a berm may include more than the valley floor which becomes a true river terrace, and the term cannot be considered to be synonymous with "valley-plain terrace."

Incised Meanders.—When valleys with flood-plains on the floors of which rivers follow meandering courses are present in a land-

Fig. 243.—Valley-plain (cyclic or epicyclic) terrace and incised (ingrown) meander of the Rangitikei River, New Zealand. *F. G. Radcliffe, photo.*

scape affected by rejuvenation so that valley-in-valley forms are developed, the incised inner valleys are guided by the river-channel meanders on the flood plains (figs. 243, 244). This will be the case whether the inner valley is developed by headward erosion or continuously as a result of tilting. The inner-valley windings are termed *incised meanders;* but the meaning of this term is sometimes extended to include all free-swinging curves developed by a combination of vertical and lateral corrasion, even in a one-cycle landscape.

Free swinging of meanders on the flood plain must, obviously, be checked at once when the stream begins to cut downward;

but there is still the same tendency as before to undercut the concave bank, against which the strongest current impinges. Thus as the meandering channel is deepened, if the stream is a vigorous one, the curves are generally enlarged by lateral corrasion, and each is pushed also down the valley, just as in the first development of stream curvature. As a result the slopes descending from the ends of spurs of the abandoned flood plain and from their downstream sides to the stream below are slip-off slopes and are less steep than those descending to the stream along the undercut concave banks (fig. 244, *B*). Such incised meanders (with slip-off and undercut

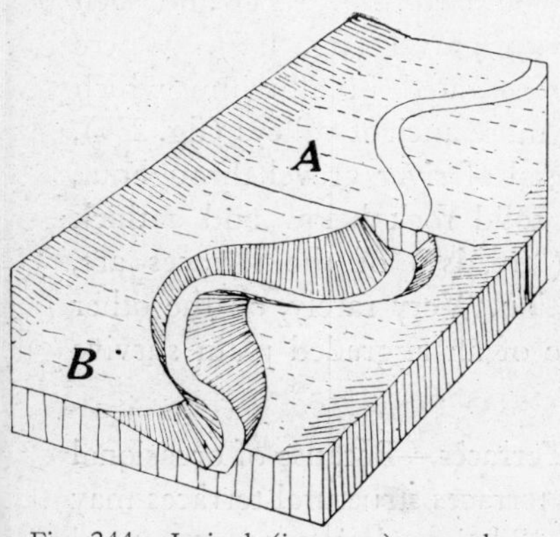

Fig. 244.—Incised (ingrown) meanders flanked by matched (cyclic) terraces.

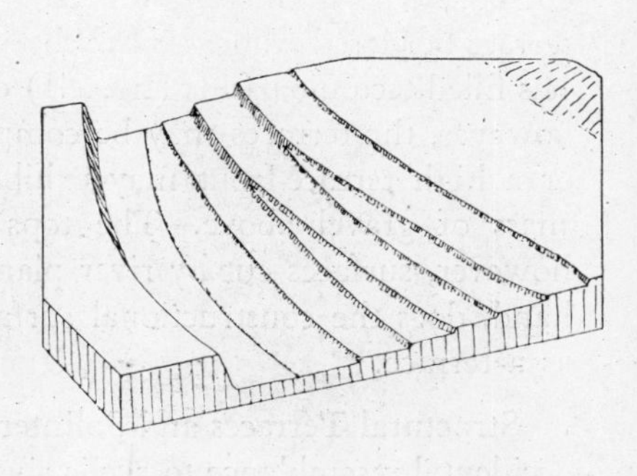

Fig. 245.—Generalised diagram of slip-off slope terraces in the Awatere River valley, New Zealand.

slopes) are termed *ingrown*. Where, as sometimes occurs, but much more rarely, the meanders are incised without enlargement to make a winding trench of symmetrical profile, they are distinguished as *intrenched* (or "entrenched").

Slip-off Slope Terraces.—In some cases slip-off slopes, especially those in ingrown meanders, descend as flights of step-like terraces instead of as smoothly convex spurs. These may mark either a series of pauses during discontinuous uplift or tilting or some other checks in the process of continuous excavation. During each pause or check the river is able to corrade laterally and on a soft-rock terrain may cut a narrow flood plain, only to go on deepening its valley later, and perhaps to repeat the performance. The resulting valley form is shown in fig. 245. Like the general convex valley-side-spur form of the slip-off slope on which they are present the lines traced by these terrace fronts are convex. Occasionally two terrace fronts merge into one, where a part of one terrace has been cut away during the development of the next lower temporary floor. Some of the temporary floors may thus have been entirely destroyed.

Cut and Built Terraces.—"River terraces as a rule are carved out, and not built up. They are always the vestiges of flood plains, and flood plains are usually produced by lateral corrasion" (Gilbert). The material in which these vestiges of former flood plains have been cut may be the solid rock (soft or hard—fig. 242A) and such cut surfaces are merely veneered with gravel (fig. 197). Where terrace-bordered valleys have been excavated in alluvium which has filled tectonic basins (fig. 241) or more ancient valleys (fig. 235), however, the terraces may be composed of river gravel throughout, or a high terrace-front may exhibit solid rock below and a thick mass of gravel above. The tops ("treads") of the terraces are, however, surfaces cut by river planation. Very rarely, on the other hand, does the constructional surface of an aggraded plain survive as a terrace.

Structural Terraces and Splinter Terraces.—Because of occasional accidental resemblance to cyclic river terraces structural terraces may be mentioned again (see p. 95). Their relation to structural outcrops of stratified rock is generally obvious. Clearly they are not river terraces. Neither are the pseudo-terraces bordering some New Zealand grabens which are in reality fault splinters exposing on their surfaces strips of a resurrected fossil plain (fig. 246).

Alternate or Meander-scar Terraces.—Cyclic (valley-plain) terraces, such as have already been described, may be correlated on opposite sides of a valley. They are "matching," or "matched," terraces; but "unmatched" terraces (fig. 247) occurring at alternate levels on opposite sides of a valley must be differently explained. These commonly occur as *flights* of many steps, and must have been formed during the progress of continuous excavation of the valley at a slow rate (figs. 248, 249).

A degrading river may be constrained to deepen its channel very slowly, perhaps owing to very slow uplift, but more frequently owing to the fact that it crosses a barrier of hard rock. Upstream from the barrier the river may flow over weak material across which

Fig. 246.—A terrace-like resurrected remnant of a fossil plain exposed on a fault splinter, Waitaki Valley graben, New Zealand, which might be mistaken for a river terrace.

C. A. Cotton, photo.

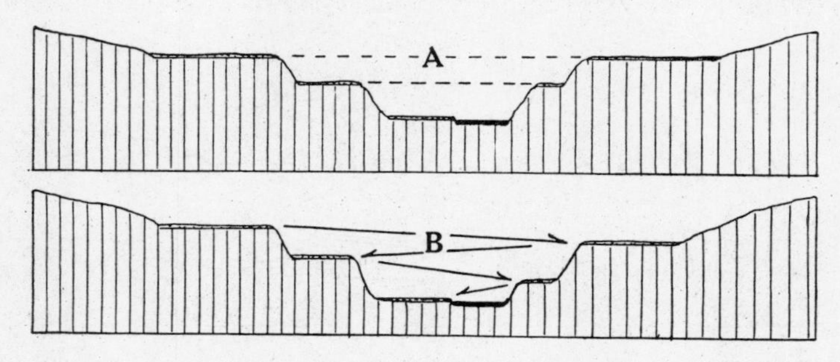

Fig. 247.—Matched (*A*) and unmatched or alternate terraces (*B*). During the development of the latter a meander belt must have swung to and fro as indicated by arrows.

it maintains with ease a graded condition while the hard-rock outcrop —a local base-level—is gradually lowered. Such conditions exist where transverse rivers cross alternating weak and resistant strata or have been superposed on hard-rock bars from a cover of soft material (figs. 250, 251). They occur also in somewhat winding valleys that have been filled with alluvium. A river re-excavating a valley of this kind and becoming superposed across a buried spur has its down-cutting so retarded thereby that it develops a graded,

Fig. 248.—Terrace flights in the Esk River valley, Canterbury, New Zealand, excavated in alluvial gravel. *V. C. Browne, photo.*

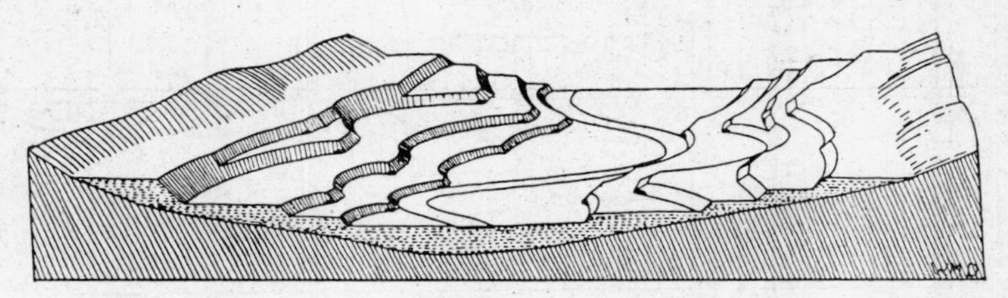

Fig. 249.—Valley-side flights of unmatched terraces excavated in weak valley-filling material and protected by rock outcrops where buried spurs are re-exposed by erosion. (After Davis.)

fully mature, and broadly opened valley farther upstream. The river continues in its graded reaches to follow a course over a flood plain; meanders may migrate downstream, and the meander belt or wide valley floor may swing from side to side as the valley is deepened. Each time it approaches the valley side the floor is at a lower level than that of the previous swing. If it quite reaches the valley side it completely cuts away the former flood plain, but if not it leaves a strip or a remnant as a terrace. Fig. 249 illustrates this method of terrace development; see also fig. 250.

Such terraces as these are not commonly found in the valleys of rivers that are degrading in homogeneous material, even though the material be soft, for in this case there is nothing to check the lateral swinging of the meander belt at the lower levels, and so the higher floors are liable to be entirely cut away. When, however, there are bars of solid rock such as are provided by bedrock spurs buried in the weak alluvium of a filled valley, these when

Fig. 250.—Terraces of the Shotover River, New Zealand, cut in the gravel filling of a former valley while the river has been excavating new gorges through buried spurs on which it is superposed. (Compare fig. 235.)

they are exposed by erosion prevent further swinging, and so protect flights of terraces both upstream and downstream from the hard-rock outcrops. Such outcrops are indicated in fig. 249 at points over which concave terrace-front "scars" meet in cusps.

More continuous rock barriers, through which rivers cut gorges, also protect terraces. As the streams are constricted in gorges at the barriers, these form fixed nodes at which swinging of the stream is prevented, but both upstream and downstream from the barriers, the influence of which extends but a short distance, the streams swing freely from side to side as they cut downward through the relatively soft material. Close to the gorges, therefore, terraces survive (fig. 251) which are remnants of flood plains that may be completely cut away in other parts of the valleys, for these open

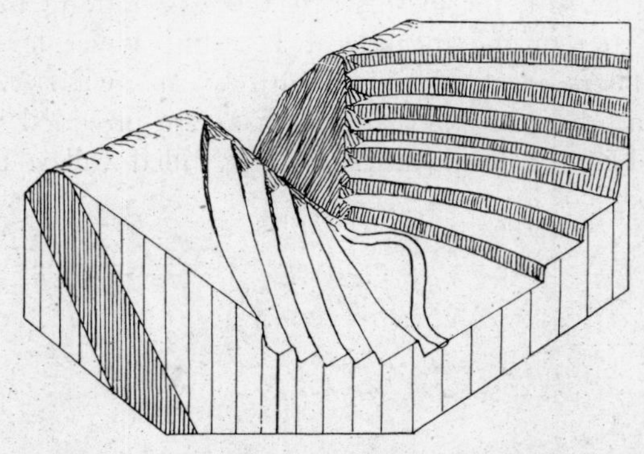

Fig. 251.—Development of terraces in soft material progressively with the cutting of a gorge through a hard-rock bar.

out as basins above or below the rock bars (figs. 252, 253). At the Rakaia Gorge (New Zealand), shown in fig. 252, long flights of terraces on the 600-feet walls of the valley (cut in the alluvium of the Canterbury Plain, fig. 205) deploy both upstream and downstream from the narrows, which are fixed in position by superposition of the river on a buried mass of volcanic rock.

Fig. 252.—Terraces at Rakaia Gorge, New Zealand.

The Slopes of River Terraces.—Apart from complications resulting from burial of terraces under accumulations of valley-side talus or fans built by side streams (fig. 248), which may occur before flood plains are abandoned as terraces, all river-cut terraces have smooth down-valley slopes determined by the stream gradients at the time the terraces were parts of valley floors, unless the slope has been altered subsequently by tilting or warping. In the direction across the valley they may be observed to be practically horizontal but for the presence of the small relief characteristic of flood plains

Fig. 253.—Terraces bordering the Waimakariri River, New Zealand, where it emerges from its mountain gorge.

C. A. Cotton, photo.

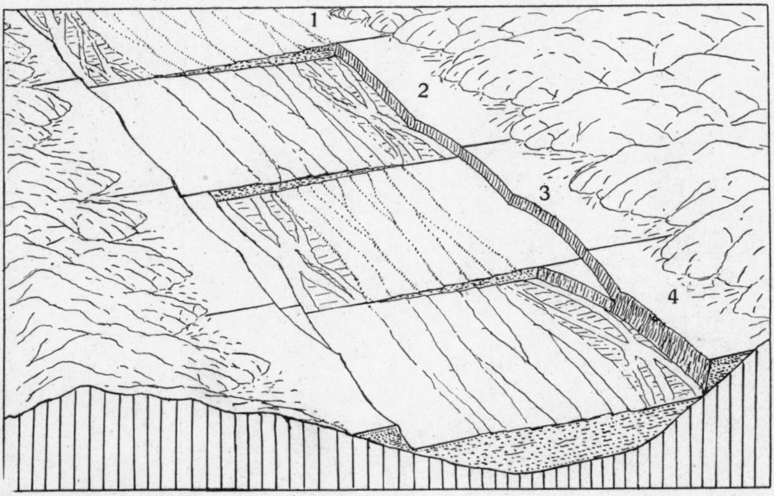

Fig. 254.—Development of slip-off cross-valley slopes and their progressive destruction during early stages (1, 2, 3, 4) of river-terrace cutting. (Compare fig. 247).

(p. 192). A low strip along the back, now generally swampy, marks the last position of the river channel during a sideward swing, from which the river has been withdrawn by a cut-off. It is generally of ox-bow form in a concave valley-side scar.

The side-to-side swinging of a meander belt or broadly braided river-bed which takes place while alternate, or meander-scar, terraces are in course of development implies movement across the valley down slip-off slopes, either smooth or minutely terraced, as shown in fig. 254. Sloping terraces which might be remnants of these slopes, if they occur at all, are rare. Most known terraces are remnants of the approximately horizontal floors of meander belts or wide river-beds such as are also shown in fig. 254. The slip-off slopes on the valley floor are ephemeral, each usually being destroyed during the next sideward swing.

PART II

CHAPTER XIX

SEMI-ARID AND ARID LANDSCAPES

The cycle of semi-arid erosion. Aridity, a climatic accident. Mountainous deserts. Back-wearing or slope retreat in deserts. Pediments. Maturity in desert mountains. Basin filling. Broad pediments. Plains of lateral planation. Wind work: deflation. Desert hollows and breakaways. African inselbergs.

The Cycle of Semi-Arid Erosion.—Those regions may be described as semi-arid which have scanty rainfall, just sufficient to maintain systems of rivers capable of carrying away the rock debris produced locally by the processes of weathering and erosion, but insufficient to support forest growth or indeed any continuous cover of soil-protecting vegetation.

Because the surface is ineffectively protected and bound by vegetation the conditions of equilibrium on slopes differ from those in humid regions. Slopes to become graded and stable must be much less steep, for the superficial waste is liable to be washed off, and talus slopes of partly weathered rock debris may be formed even on hillsides that have been reduced to a very moderate declivity. Thus well graded slopes are rare or absent, outcrops of bare rock persist, and rugged hill profiles survive into late stages of the geomorphic cycle (fig. 255).

Retrogression of formerly graded slopes to a rugged, ungraded condition may be produced by climatic change towards aridity; and the detail features that appear are in general similar to those that result from accelerated erosion due to human agency or interference with the balance of nature (p. 113). Structural terraces instead of fading as a cycle proceeds and as slopes become graded, as they do under humid conditions, remain sharp-edged (fig. 256). Badland erosion also actively attacks outcrops of certain rocks, especially unconsolidated sandy clays, for the bare ground is exposed to the effects of raindrop impact, and most of the rain that falls runs off immediately owing to absence of an absorbent soil (fig. 257).

During the early stages of the cycle under semi-arid conditions there is a great development of accumulation forms. The supply of waste from the poorly protected surface is considerable. The streams, however, being of small size, are capable of transporting this material only down steep declivities. Thus abundant fans of rather steep slope are built in all depressions of the initial surface, and these may coalesce to form broad piedmont and basin plains. As the thickness of alluvium increases aggradation extends up the valleys into the mountains. The alluvium may overtop divides and

Fig. 255.—Slopes of moderate declivity, but ungraded, in a semi-arid climate, Raggedy Range, Otago, New Zealand.
C. A. Cotton, photo.

isolate portions of the mountain masses, and a system of basin plains may be united by the spilling-over of alluvium from one to another, so that perhaps half the region may become a plain of aggradation. Fans and aggraded plains will cease to grow, however, when the supply of waste falls off as a result of lowering of relief and reduction of the area subject to degradation. As the supply of waste continues to diminish and the cycle proceeds farther the aggraded surfaces will be gradually cut down by stream planation. At this stage, which may be seen in New Zealand in the basin plain of the upper Waitaki (Mackenzie Plain) remnants of the maximum fans separate valleys containing plains and terraces of gentler slope cut in the alluvium.

Continued erosion will result in removal of all the alluvium that lies well above the local base-levels determined by lines of main drainage, leading to a stage illustrated in New Zealand in the tectonic basins forming the Maniototo Plain and the Ida Valley

Fig. 256.—Structural terraces bordering the Grand Canyon of the Colorado River, in a semi-arid climate. (After Davis.)

(figs. 111, 159), where the slopes of the valley plains, all cut on soft bedrock, are so steep on account of the high ratio of waste to water in the streams from the northern highland that they resemble fans. They are indeed "rock fans," and where they are laterally confluent they make a piedmont plain of lateral planation, or river-cut "pediment," cut on the soft-rock terrain that fringes harder-rock mountains to the north (p. 106).

When the mountains of a semi-arid region are ultimately destroyed by erosion they will be replaced by a peneplain of which such plains of lateral planation form a large part. A *peneplain of semi-arid erosion,* being developed by headward extension of surfaces with appreciable slopes, will thus have considerable undulating broad relief—amounting in regions initially mountainous to perhaps thousands of feet.

Fig. 257.—Death Valley, California, showing an early-mature desert basin with extensive steep bahada slopes leading down to a playa (white salt-covered strip). Badland sculpture of the Funeral Range in foreground.

Frasher's, photo.

Aridity, a Climatic Accident.—Semi-arid conditions may supervene and modify the course of a normal cycle; but a change to extreme aridity ranks as one of the "climatic accidents" which may bring a normal cycle to an untimely close, substituting different conditions of erosion. A landscape—young, mature, or old—developed under pre-existing humid (normal) conditions may furnish initial forms as a starting point for arid erosion. In regions that have been continuously or predominantly arid for a long period, on the other hand, the initial forms of the current arid cycle have been produced by upheaval, perhaps with deformation or dislocation, of a former land which may have been a peneplain or any other kind of surface.

As an introduction to the *arid cycle* some points of divergence of arid from normal erosion may be indicated.

Even in the most arid deserts rain does not fail altogether. There are no permanently flowing rivers[1]; but intermittent streams and ephemeral floods that result from "cloudbursts" at long intervals move great quantities of waste. The work of running water may not, therefore, be left out of account; in most deserts it is still the dominant agent.

The general base-level has not the importance, however, that it has in the normal cycle as a controlling level towards which humid landscapes are lowered. The ephemeral, or at least intermittent, streams and floods do not join up to form systems of rivers feeding a main trunk which flows to the sea. Instead they dwindle, deposit their loads of detritus, and either sink into alluvium-covered ground or, at times of high flood, flow somewhat farther and discharge into lakes which occupy the lowest parts of basins. Most of the flow towards these lakes takes place underground, however, through sandy and gravelly alluvium. Evaporation, which removes a volume of water proportional to the free surface, prevents the lakes from growing large enough to spill over and form integrated systems of drainage. Their waters become concentrated solutions of salts, and, generally, in dry seasons they dry up altogether, leaving plains of saline silt (fig. 257). These shallow, inconstant salt lakes are termed *playas*. A lake of this kind forms a temporary base-level for the area that drains into it, but this is a base-level that rises as waste accumulates in the basin; and the base-levels of separate basins are entirely independent of one another.

Mountainous Deserts.—In "mountainous deserts"—i.e., in regions undergoing reduction by desert erosion from strong initial relief of tectonic origin towards the desert equivalent of a peneplain—there is a wide development of alluvial fans in the intermont basins in early stages of the cycle. There is thus in the young stage of this arid cycle a very strong similarity in the course of erosional and constructional events to those in landscapes developing under normal conditions as modified by semi-aridity. The dissection of the ranges, where these are initially tectonic blocks, arches, or domes, goes on on similar lines.

[1] Rivers like the Nile which rise in humid regions and flow through deserts are exceptions to this rule.

The boundaries between semi-arid and arid regions must be drawn, it should be noted, not at any arbitrarily chosen rainfall lines but at the lines separating "external" and "internal" drainage. Where drainage is internal there is insufficient excess of precipitation over evaporation to maintain systems of outflowing rivers, however meagre and intermittent. In arid regions, therefore, all the coarse and much of the fine debris that results from gullying and dissection of the mountains accumulates in the intermont basins. (Only a certain proportion of dust is exported by wind.) Alluvial fans become laterally confluent, forming continuously sloping bahadas along mountain fronts (fig. 257). These now take up a great part of the area of each basin, and their basin-plain slopes lead down to the playas, dry-lake floors, or saline mud flats, at which the ground-water level outcrops.

It is thus true that the level of the low-lying centre or axial strip of every basin acts as a local base-level for the mountains surrounding it. This is a rising base-level for as long as basin-filling proceeds rapidly. Each such base-level is independent of that in other basins; but high-perched basins may become filled to such an extent that gravel—carried by the occasional floods that follow infrequent desert storms—spills over the basin rims. Thus one centre-seeking system of intermittent streams or gravel rivers becomes added in tributary fashion to another. In some cases of such integration—or, it may be, of capture of a higher basin by a vigorous ravine gnawing headward through a mountain rim—erosion in a higher basin becomes subject to control by the local base-level of a lower basin. Then some dissection of the gravel plains in the higher basin takes place, just as would be the case under more humid conditions of climate.

Back-wearing or Slope Retreat in Deserts.—The most important difference between arid and humid (normal) erosion among mountains is the way in which mountains are "worn back" rather than worn down. Under the influence of continual weathering of bare-rock surfaces (unprotected by vegetational cover and soil mantle) all slopes remain steep. A characteristic declivity for granite slopes is 35°; but some rock materials that crumble readily into fine debris when attacked by physical weathering develop gentler slopes. In granite terrains this uniformly steep gradient persists to the base of every rock slope, making there a very distinct re-entering angle, or concave nick, in the landscape profile.

The slope once determined remains constant, and *back-wearing* or back-weathering causes slope retreat. Passing through a stage at which it forms a superficial layer of crumbling boulders, the rock breaks down into waste which is eventually of coarse sandy grade. This disintegrated debris does not accumulate as talus, but is washed away at intervals by floods. Thus the mountain slopes retreat not only from lines parallel to the initial outlines of tectonic blocks but also from the sides of eroded valleys which have been cut by ravines in the early youth of the landscape, and which develop in this way flat floors. The line along which back-wearing causes the base of a slope to retreat is not horizontal but slopes up, so as to leave a rock surface with a sufficiently steep gradient to allow the debris of further back-wearing to be carried away across it by floods. It is, or becomes, a smooth surface, on which the floods are sheetfloods. Infrequent and local but very heavy downpours of rain (desert cloudbursts) carry the rock debris intermittently down this sloping piedmont (mountain-foot) slope in the direction of the playas as though it were sluiced forward at intervals by pouring gigantic buckets of water upon it.

The general results of back-wearing are twofold. First, it pares back the mountains to smaller and smaller area and dimensions, isolates parts of spurs and ridges as island-like residuals, eventually reduces even the crest-lines to similar isolated knobs (*nubbins*), and ultimately destroys these also. Secondly, back-wearing results in the replacement of the mountains by plains left progressively at the bases of the back-worn slopes. These plains, which are floored by bedrock, are by no means level, though notably smooth; they slope up strongly towards the remnants of the mountains.

Pediments.—The sloping plains of cut rock are at first a narrow strip continuous in slope with, and perhaps indistinguishable from, the bahadas which continue their forward inclination (figs. 257, 258). They are termed *pediments,* and together with the fringing bahadas make up the *piedmont slopes.* When mountains have been destroyed by back-wearing and extensive pediments have taken their place, so as to form a peneplain of desert erosion or surface of *coalescing pediments,* these join up in broadly tent-shaped (or arched) and bluntly conical (or domed) forms. The landscape is now *senescent,* or entering on the stage of old age.

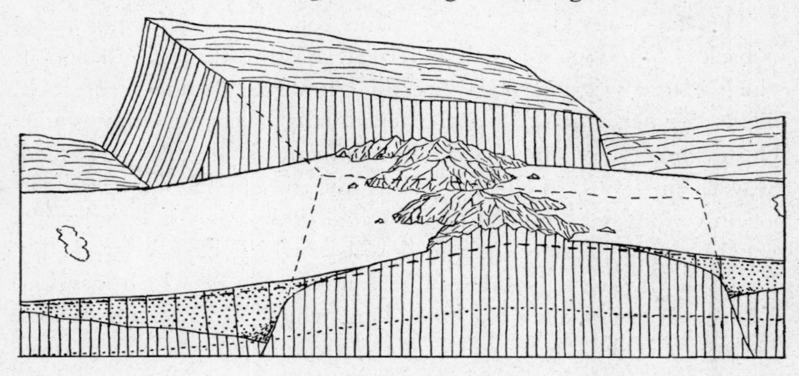

Fig. 258.—A much-reduced eroded remnant of a tectonic mountain range fringed by piedmont (mountain-foot) slopes consisting of pediments and bahadas which lead down to playas in tectonic basins. The initial tectonic form is suggested at the rear. Broken and dotted lines on the front section suggest possible surface profiles of the future and of a very distant future.

Maturity in Desert Mountains.—Long before the senescent stage is reached—i.e., during mature stages of desert erosion—pediments, though as yet incomplete, have become quantitatively important features of the landscape (fig. 258). While massive residuals of the mountains still survive the pediments slope up rather steeply to their bases at gradients increasing to perhaps 200 feet per mile, though farther out on the piedmont slopes the gradients may diminish to 50 feet per mile. The steeper rear fringes (and to a less extent pediments as a whole, and bahadas also) are worn down progressively as back-wearing of the mountain front proceeds. An important wearing-down process is *rock-floor robbing,* which has been termed also "sheetflood erosion." It operates as weathering causes disintegration of bare-rock surfaces, where these emerge from the discontinuous sheet of detritus intermittently in transit, and their crumbling debris is removed by sheetfloods.

Basin Filling.—While mountains are undergoing destruction and replacement by pediments, accumulation continues in the tectonic basins. Debris layers are added by aggradation to the surfaces of bahadas as playa-floor levels (local base-levels) also rise. This causes a feather edge of alluvium to encroach on the pediment, thinly burying the worn rock surface strip by strip and converting it into a *concealed* pediment or rock floor. A lowering of base-level may lead to a later removal of this gravel veneer by sheetflood or other erosion, however; and if for some reason the base-level does not rise, the encroachment of bahada on pediment does not take place.

Broad Pediments.—The most extensive exposed (bare) pediments are developed in regions that are strictly only semi-arid in that they are drained by intermittent rivers to the ocean. By these rivers, however inefficient they may seem, the waste is removed instead of accumulating indefinitely in desert basins, and, after some considerable aggradation in the stage of youth, which results in grading slopes towards outlets, local base-levels do not further rise. This is a condition prevailing in semi-arid Southern Arizona and the adjoining Sonora district of Mexico, where bare-rock pediments of vast extent are known. Even in a basin of interior drainage the rise of base-level characteristic of youth may fall away almost to zero in maturity as the waste supplied by erosion from the mountains becomes less abundant and is more widely spread. Later the movement of base-level may be reversed; for in old age waste-supply will be very slow, and may be more than counterbalanced by an "exportation" of dust from the desert by wind. Dust is one of the products of desert weathering, and still more dust is produced by abrasion when gritty debris is drifted about by wind. Dust storms are observed to be of common occurrence, and great columns of dust are frequently whirled high in the air during storms. A proportion of such dust is carried by wind beyond the limits of the desert basin.

Plains of Lateral Planation.—It is not possible to distinguish with certainty in all cases between pediments formed in the main by back-wearing, sheetflood transportation, and rock-floor robbing and plains of lateral planation. The latter, which are river-cut (pp. 106, 253), may grade into fringes of confluent, steep, stream-cut rock fans along mountain bases. Though a phase of normal river work, rock fans are most conspicuous in low-rainfall regions, where graded stream gradients are relatively steep. Here confluent plains of lateral planation with a pronounced slope fringing a mountain front assume the landscape form of pediments and are commonly so called. It is generally agreed that stream erosion takes some part in shaping the forms of desert pediments also; and its share, though difficult to evaluate, may vary in different cases from zero to a hundred per cent.

Wind Work: Deflation.—The foregoing explanation of the landscapes of mountainous deserts, which applies especially to those of the western American type, known also in Africa and Asia, by no means accounts for all desert landscape forms. It does not take into account the development of extensive steep-walled hollows that have been excavated in some desert regions, especially those which have initially been elevated plains or surfaces of moderate relief. Both in the Libyan Desert and in parts of Mongolia, for example, considerable relief has been developed—probably under conditions of climate either continuously or intermittently and predominantly arid—from smooth initial surfaces. In the excavation of large hollows wind has acted, not in the main as a direct corrading (abrading) agent, but as an efficient remover of debris—in some cases in the form of sand, in other cases dust—and has thus co-operated with the ubiquitous "normal" agents of erosion. This work of wind has been termed *deflation*.

Desert Hollows and Breakaways.—Steep-walled excavated hollows have resulted from the enlargement possibly of minor hollows actually scooped out by wind, eroded by water on locally warped areas, or due to minor local subsidence. The walls of such an expanding hollow are generally gullied by normal erosion and retreat in terrains of horizontal structure as escarpments. In some cases the back-wearing process may cause their retreat. Waste is carried by water from the scarp bases across bare-rock pediment fringes of small inclination towards central playas, and during its many halts is dried, pulverised, and exported by wind. Large oasis hollows in the Libyan Desert have been opened out in some such way, and hollows of similar large extent and many hundreds of feet deep have been excavated in Mongolia. In each case they are surrounded by extensive higher-level plains.

Such excavation is controlled very strictly as to depth by the level of the surface of ground water. Down to this surface excavation proceeds; but it is only above the level of saturation, where the debris is almost always thoroughly dry, that wind can do its work. Thus the floors of the hollows as a whole are approximately plane and horizontal, and extensive plains can be developed in this way. In Western Australia vast areas have been planed to form "dry lake" floors. Scarps (termed "breakaways") are still retreating from them. The Australian breakaways are only from 30 to 100 feet high, however (fig. 259). Very probably the extensive plain which is a step higher and is now undergoing dissection was similarly formed. Clearly, where ground-water level thus controls

Fig. 259.—A "breakaway" scarp in Western Australia.

a developing plain of arid erosion, further lowering of the water level would make possible the initiation and excavation of new hollows within those now existing, and two-storied breakaways separating stepped plains might result. These, though uncommon, are not unknown.

African Inselbergs.—Steep-sided, isolated residual mountains and hills (or monadnocks) termed "inselbergs," which are surrounded by extensive and very nearly level plains in parts of Africa have been thought to be of desert origin, though the climate of most districts in which they occur is not now arid. Probably they are of more "normal" origin and must be regarded as a special variety of monadnocks kept steep-sided by the processes of weathering and waste-removal in a climate alternately dry and wet with long dry seasons. Similar landscapes occur extensively in southern

India. The plains must be mainly plains of lateral planation. They do not slope up to the bases of the mountain residuals as conspicuously as do typical pediments. Where confluent pediments slope less steeply than usual, as in parts of the Libyan Desert, how-

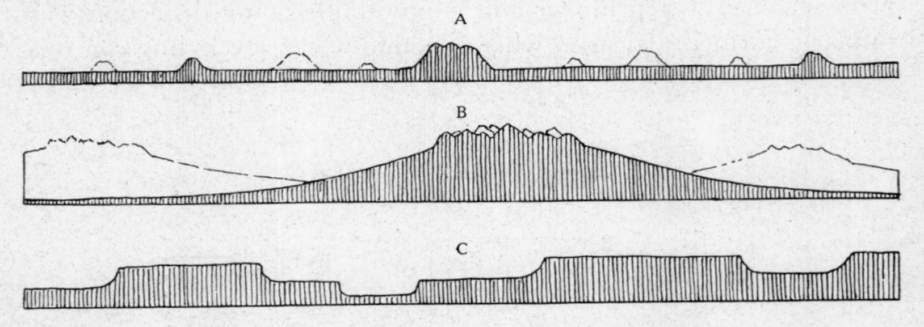

Fig. 260.—*A,* inselbergs and plains; *B,* a mature mountainous desert, with conspicuous pediment profiles; *C,* profiles of wind-excavated desert hollows.

ever, and small unconsumed mountain residuals stand above them, the landscape profiles come to resemble rather closely those of typical inselbergs and plains. So close is the resemblance that such landscape profiles can perhaps not be regarded as characteristic of any definitely climatic type. In fig. 260 the inselberg-and-plains landscape profile is compared with those of a "pedimented" mountainous desert and of a desert containing breakaway-bounded hollows excavated below an elevated plain.

CHAPTER XX

BLOWN SAND AND DUST ACCUMULATION

Sand and dust. Deposition of sand. Drifting sand. Dunes and ergs. Forms of dunes. Fixation of dunes. Partial fixation leads to irregularity of dunes. The dune complex. Ancient blown-sand deposits. Loess. Lunettes.

Sand and Dust.—Sand transported by wind is swept along close to the ground; dust, on the other hand, is whirled high in the air. Sand grains move forward in short leaps, whereas dust particles travel many miles without falling to the ground. It is thus obvious that when a mixture of sand and dust becomes dry and is subject to transportation by wind the dust is rapidly blown far away leaving a residue of clean sand. Dust produced by the wear of grains of blown sand on one another is likewise removed by this winnowing action of the wind. Sand also may be winnowed from the products of desert weathering, as larger residual fragments too heavy to be moved remain behind. On level surfaces, from which there is no means of removal of debris other than this "deflation" by wind, a "lag gravel" or "desert armour" remains, which tends to protect the landform. The residual fragments are termed "gibbers" in Australia. They lie on *gibber plains,* termed also *hamadas* in North Africa. On such plains a natural sand-blast effect may wear rock surfaces somewhat. Some pebbles have flat facets thus cut on them, converting them into "ventifacts"—known also as faceted pebbles, aeolian stones, and by various other names. Effects of sand scour are occasionally seen also along the bases of cliffs in the sandiest and windiest places; but the total result of actual wind abrasion in producing or strongly modifying landscape forms is small. Transportation of sand and dust by wind is not negligible, however, and in some cases it may remove all talus from the bases of slopes.

Apart from desert erosion other sources of sand are the silts spread by flooded rivers and the outcrops of unconsolidated sands in escarpments and river terraces. The former source yields also much dust where the rivers carry the debris of glacial erosion. Sand of rather even grain size is thrown up on beaches by the sea, and may be dried and blown inland in quantity. Such sand has already been separated from fine particles as well as from gravel by the sorting action of water. It is composed of the most resistant minerals of decayed and disintegrated rocks. A very important source of sand for making new accumulations is the development of *blowouts* in sand hills formerly held in place by vegetation. Blown sand is very liable to suffer such reversion to a mobile condition, and to be rebuilt into new forms.

Deposition of Sand.—Since sand and dust are so effectually separated by the action of wind, it is not surprising that they should be deposited in different situations under widely different conditions. Much of the dust, indeed, is scattered far and wide. Some falls into the sea and some is washed out of the atmosphere by rain or, having fallen to the ground, is washed away into streams. Some of it, however, after travelling far from the source forms accumulations on the land. Sand, on the other hand, may accumulate not far from the source of supply, though some is blown and washed into rivers and into the sea. Moreover, dry sand accumulations on the land, like deposits of alluvium, are liable to be short-lived unless lowered by earth movements below base-level and thus placed beyond the reach of erosion.

Drifting Sand.—A constant supply of sand carried forward by the wind—from a beach or blowout, for example—may result in its spreading as a thin sheet over a considerable area of country. If a mere sheet of sand results it is not a conspicuous topographic form, as the layer of sand conforms fairly closely to the pre-existing form of the surface. Such *sand drifts,* however, ruin much good agricultural land. Owing to destruction of the vegetation on the ground over which the sand passes (where sand drifting temporarily occurs), sand hitherto held in place by vegetation is left at the mercy of the wind. It is thus that blowouts develop. The wind hollows out and variously modifies the surface, and carries away the sand to redeposit it somewhere else.

Dunes and Ergs.—In deserts, to leeward of playas and wind-scoured hollows which supply sand, very extensive areas are covered by bare drifts and thicker masses. The sand accumulated in these *ergs,* as they are termed, is generally much thicker than mere drifts, and the surface has the billowy form of clustered sand hills or *dunes* (fig. 261). Though extensive in area in great deserts like the Algerian Sahara, ergs are small as compared with the extent of bare stony-surfaced desert. Evidently sand derived from large areas has become, and has remained, segregated in the ergs, in some cases as numerous narrow parallel belts of dunes.

Forms of Dunes.—Bare surfaces of drifting sand, when the sand accumulates to greater thickness than a "drift," develop undulations of the surface transverse to the direction of the wind. When the

Fig. 261.—A small desert erg in Death Valley, California.
Frasher's photo.

wind blows constantly from one quarter these grow in height. After reaching a certain height they develop sharp crests and obstruct the wind so as to cause an eddy in the lee of the crest. Sand is now dropped at the crest-line and slides down the lee side adding layers to it as the sand billow grows into a dune or ridge form transverse to the wind and from 20 to 100 feet, and even more, in height.

The sand on the slope facing the wind does not remain undisturbed, but whenever the supply from farther back falls off, so that the wind sweeping over the dune is not fully loaded, it picks up sand and carries it over the crest, only to drop it again as a new layer on the leeward side. Thus a dune moves slowly forward, and where the supply of sand is intermittent a small dune or group of dunes may travel forward, leaving the ground bare behind them.

The leeward side, or *sandfall* (fig. 262), of a dune, on which the sand comes to rest when dropped by wind as it comes over the crest and loses velocity or forms an eddy, has a steep slope, generally about 33°, that being the inclination at which the streaming sand comes to rest. The slope of the windward side, up which the sand

Fig. 262.—Crestline and sandfall of a wandering dune, coastal lowland of western Wellington, New Zealand. *L. Cockayne, photo.*

is driven by the wind, is much less steep. This side is generally "ripple-marked"—that is to say, there is on it a pattern of small ridges a few inches apart, which form and re-form.

Other conditions being the same, low dunes or the low parts of dunes move forward more rapidly than high parts, as they use up less sand in advancing a given distance. Thus short dunes become crescentic in outline, as wings at the sides move forward in advance of the centre, and the crest lines of elongated dunes become sinuous (fig. 261). Such forms are often obscured, however, by the effects of strong winds blowing successively from different directions.

Coastal dunes are found chiefly on low-lying land recently abandoned or built up by the sea; but the sand may ascend cliffs, travel inland, and spread over the country so as to bury a former relief, as has occurred extensively on the west coast of the Auckland district of New Zealand. On advancing, or "prograding," coasts, where the waves are throwing up sand abundantly on the beach, much of the sand, when it dries, is blown inland. In a humid climate, however, it is arrested by vegetation before it has travelled

Fig. 263.—A recently built foredune, near Plimmerton, New Zealand.

far, and forms a ridge, or *foredune,* parallel with the shoreline (fig. 263). This may grow landward to a considerable width by sending out tongues of sand in that direction as the sand spills over the crest of the ridge (fig. 263A). The plants which arrest sand thus and cause it to accumulate in ridges or dunes (sand-binding plants) are those which can remain alive and grow upward vigorously though their original roots are deeply buried. As the sea retreats, a succession of *dune ridges* may be thus built, each in its turn being the foredune. While these are growing they are fairly even-crested and have smooth slopes towards the sea, while landward the sandfall slopes may be somewhat irregular, salients projecting where sand has come over the crest in the largest quantities. The older dune ridges, however, unless rapidly and permanently fixed by a cover of vegetation, are "most irregular in form, and much cut into and denuded by the wind. . . . . These chains of hills resemble miniature mountain ranges with their prominent or rugged peaks, rounded tops, saddles, deep or shallow gullies, and at times quite precipitous faces. Frequently the parallel chains have lateral connections. Near the coast they are generally but semi-stable, the plant covering usually only occupying half their surface, and in many places they are so bare as to be a transition

Fig. 263A.—A fixed dune ridge, originally a foredune, showing tongues of sand jutting out landward. *L. Cockayne, photo.*

to the wandering dunes" (Cockayne). Other (longitudinal) ridges extend in the direction sand is carried by steady winds from unfailing sources.

Wandering dunes (fig. 262) "are broad, high masses of sand extending over many acres, so gently sloping on the windward side as to be apparently flat in places, where they are quite firm to the tread. On the leeward side they are very abrupt—so much so, where absolutely sheltered from the wind, as to merit the title of 'sandfall,' the extremely loose sand moving with the slightest touch. . . . At the angle formed by the ascending slope and descending sandfall is often a sharp ridge, the result of the eddy.

In other cases the angle may be rounded, a sign of contrary winds" (Cockayne). In New Zealand "the wandering dunes as now met with inland . . . . are a *reversion* from perfectly fixed sandhills held in position not only by shrubs or grass but by loam, to the original wandering state" (Cockayne).

Barchans are isolated mounds of sand travelling forward as dunes of crescentic form. The sandfall is on the concave side and the horns of the crescent trail forward in advance of the main body.

Fixation of Dunes.—Where dunes accumulate in a humid climate they are always more or less fixed (or "anchored") by the growth of vegetation on them, and such fixation may become complete, the vegetation becoming quite continuous and resulting in the formation of a layer of soil rich in humus. Large areas of coastal dunes in New Zealand, especially in western Wellington, are thus fixed, and in some cases the original forms of the coastal dune ridges are preserved (fig. 263A). It is certain that the area of fixed dunes was much greater before the disturbance of the vegetation and surface caused by man and introduced animals started sand drifts which have resulted at many places in the formation of wandering dunes.

Thoroughly fixed sand dunes in a humid climate form the initial surface for a cycle of normal erosion. Dunes built of calcareous sand derived from comminuted shells of marine organisms on the beaches of warm seas are quickly cemented into limestone. The loose sand of non-calcareous dunes long remains incoherent, on the other hand, thus offering little resistance to normal erosion; but this weakness is offset by the porosity of the material, which reduces run-off to a minimum. Weathering of grains of silicate minerals produces clay, however, and below the level of water-saturation the sand becomes somewhat cemented. These changes make it less porous. Some grading of slopes soon takes place, producing smooth convexo-concave profiles. In all cases, indeed, the chaotic dune topography, with its irregular hollows, must be replaced sooner or later by systems of continuous valleys, with graded streams and graded slopes, and this eventually must become a peneplain. In New Zealand large areas of partly indurated sandstone on the west coast of the Auckland province, which accumulated at least in part as dunes, now display surface forms due to normal erosion only.

Partial Fixation leads to Irregularity of Dunes.—Without complete fixation taking place sand-binding plants may grow in irregular patches on accumulating and migrating dunes, with the result that the dunes lose all regularity of form. Sand accumulates around clumps of vegetation, forming irregular hillocks, and, when the supply diminishes, some sand is scoured away from spots that remain bare. Saddles and gullies are thus hollowed out of the dune ridges, cutting these into rows of irregular shaped mounds

Fig. 264.—Wind channels among sand dunes, western Wellington, New Zealand.
W. K. Field, photo.

(fig. 264). Eddies of the wind on such an irregular surface build also irregular accumulation forms.

When the supply of sand from windward fails the dunes may be completely blown away over considerable areas, *sand plains* being formed, where the lower limit of erosion is governed by an approach to the level of ground water. These persist, perhaps clothed by vegetation, until buried by a fresh invasion of sand and replaced by dunes.

The Dune Complex.—The various types of dunes—accumulating, fixed, and in course of destruction—with sand plains and ponds, lakes, and swamps caused by the blocking of streams, make up the *dune complex*.

Fig. 265.—Lake impounded by a wandering dune, near Auckland, New Zealand.
T. L. Lancaster, photo.

Fig. 266.—Advancing dune stopped by the Turakina River, New Zealand.
L. Cockayne, photo.

Small streams are frequently blocked by sand drift or dune migration, forming shallow lakes, such as the lakes of the coastal district of western Wellington, and many small lakes in various parts of New Zealand (fig. 265); but where a river of considerable size crosses the dune complex it may be capable of transporting all the sand spilled into it. Such a river effectively checks the migration of dunes (fig. 266).

Ancient Blown-sand Deposits.—Blown sand sometimes forms permanent accumulations, which are analogous to alluvial deposits laid down where aggradation is in progress. The supply of sand may be so great that the level of the land must be to some extent built up by it. Individual dunes march forward, but all the sand at the base does not move on. Thus the stump of the dune remains, and where accumulation is in progress the resulting deposit consists of the stumps or bases of innumerable dunes, each roughly lenticular in shape, and each built of inclined layers, which are sometimes very distinct in cuttings through blown-sand deposits.

This inclined stratification, to which the name *cross bedding*[1] is given, is the result of the manner of growth of sand dunes previously described. It is analogous to the fore-set bedding of deltas. The layers are successive additions to the sandfall slope, and they are distinguished by slight variations in the coarseness of the sand in successive layers, due to variation in the velocity of the wind during their accumulation. Very thick accumulations of ancient dune sands are found among the strata of the lithosphere.

Loess.—The fine dust which is carried high in the air, and if dropped is readily picked up again, does not come finally to rest in arid regions, but is exported from them. Some of the dust from deserts, however, and also some of that derived from river-beds is caught by grass in more humid regions. The grass continues to grow up through the slowly accumulating dust. This is the source of great accumulations of superficial yellow clay known as *loess*. Loess covers large areas in various parts of the world, notably in northern China, where it is in places said to be 300 feet thick. It occurs also in Europe, in North and South America, and in the South Island of New Zealand, particularly on the Port Hills and

[1] Cross bedding, though generally on a smaller scale, is found also in current-carried sands and gravels deposited in river-beds and shallow seas.

plains of Canterbury, on subdued hills about Oamaru and Timaru, and in Southland. Though much loess has resulted from accumulation of dust blown from deserts, and such is the origin of the great loess layer in China, loess-forming dust has been derived in great quantities from the silt of flooded rivers draining from glaciers. This is the source of the material in the loess of North America, Europe, and New Zealand, most of which accumulated in the Ice Age. Where foehn winds blow down mountain valleys con-

Fig. 267.—Cutting revealing a thick deposit of loess, Oamaru, New Zealand. The subdued hill forms of the loess surface are seen above.

A. C. Gifford, photo.

taining glacier-fed rivers, they emerge laden with dust, a phenomenon frequently observed in New Zealand, Alaska, and Patagonia, and in such regions accumulation of loess is still in progress.

There is no distinct stratification in loess, but there is an indistinct vertical structure of a kind of tubes strengthened by a deposit of carbonate of lime. The loess is thus made permeable, so that it stands with vertical walls in cliffs or cuttings (figs. 267, 268). It is not, however, really a hard stony substance, but may be easily powdered with the fingers. It is remarkable for the extreme

Fig. 268.—Dissected loess in China. (After Bailey Willis.)

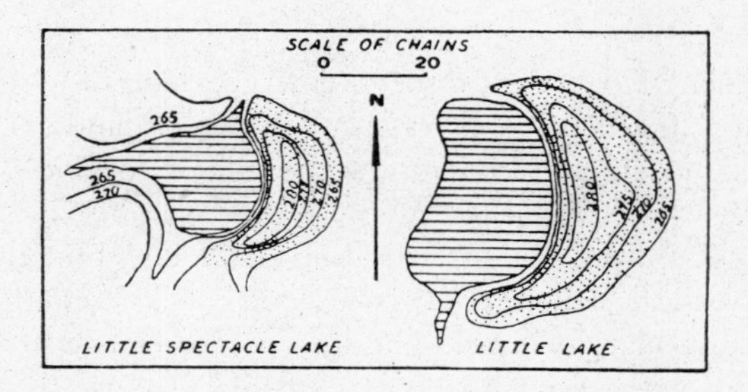

Fig. 269.—Lunettes to leeward of lakes in Victoria, Australia. (After E. S. Hills.)

fineness of all the mineral grains in it. These are fragments of ordinary rock minerals and their weathering products. Substances necessary for plant growth are in an available form, and loess furnishes, therefore an extremely fertile soil.

Accumulation of loess does not affect topography to any great extent, as it is distributed impartially by the wind over hills and valleys. Loess deposits are, however, very easily dissected, and in China the mature stage of dissection is characterised by the presence of remarkably steep-sided ridges and spurs, which are pierced in places by arches over which are natural bridges (fig. 268). Much loess is carried down from hillsides by streams and deposited in low-lying areas, mixed in some cases with coarser waste derived from underlying rocks, as river and lake deposits.

Lunettes.—Dust captured from the air during gales that produce dust storms is brought down by spray whipped up from lakes, so that crescentic mounds of loamy material of this origin grow up immediately to leeward of the lakes. Being rarely more than 20 or 30 feet high these broad mounds are not conspicuous unless they rise from very level plains, as is the case in south-eastern Australia, where there are many examples of such landscape forms, there termed *lunettes* (fig. 269).

CHAPTER XXI

GLACIERS

Snowfields and glaciers. Mountain-and-valley glaciers. Glacier ice. The flow of glaciers. Crevasses. Moraines. Lower limits of glaciers. Ice sheets. Piedmont glaciers.

Snowfields and Glaciers.—Apart from the effects of frost action as a component of ordinary weathering in shattering rocks by alternate freeze and thaw in crevices, it is in the form of glaciers that ice exerts, and has exerted, its most important geological action. *Glaciers* are streams of ice flowing, as rivers do, from higher to lower levels, though infinitely more slowly than rivers, taking their rise in snowfields, and thus carrying off the snow that falls on high mountains, and also at lower levels in polar regions, where the annual precipitation as snow is in excess of the amount disposed of by summer melting. Above the "snow-line," the height of which above sea-level varies from zero in the polar regions to about 17,000 feet near the Equator, snow lies from year to year, forming permanent snowfields (fig. 270). Such snow-fields, or *névés,* themselves, whether they give rise to definite, elongated ice-streams (*glacier tongues*) or not, are to be regarded as glaciers, or as parts of glaciers, and part of the erosion ascribed to glacial action is due to them—some of it, apparently to the freeze-and-thaw process working in close association with them, as will be explained.

At the present day glaciers are acting as corrading and transporting agents, but (outside the polar regions) only over small areas. In spite of the restricted occurrence of glaciers, however, the ways in which they modify topographic forms, and also the form and structure of the materials deposited by them, are worthy of detailed study, for at various times in the past glacial action, or *glaciation,*[1] has been in operation over very much wider areas than at the present day, large regions having been at these times overswept by ice. The latest of these glacial periods, which may be referred to as the "Ice Age," came to an end so recently that the

[1] The mere overspreading of a region with glacier ice has been termed "glacierisation." The use of this word is a relic, however, of the excessive caution engendered by the promulgation of the "glacial-protection" theory (p. 305).

landscape features resulting from the erosive action of the glaciers and the deposits of superficial material left by them have been very little modified since by normal erosion.

There is great difference between the topographic setting and landscape-carving activities of the generally discontinuous glaciers of mountainous regions and the continuous *ice sheets* (and smaller *ice caps*) which cover (and have covered) regions of small relief. Though now confined to polar regions, the latter partially covered

Fig. 270.—Glacier-clad mountains rising above the snow-line, the Minarets, viewed across the Tasman Glacier, New Zealand.
F. G. Radcliffe, photo.

the northern continents in the Ice Age. The former continue to exist among high mountains even in the temperate belts at the present day, though of small dimensions as compared with the giant glaciers of the Ice Age. The largest outside polar regions are in the South Island of New Zealand, and in this region, which affords excellent examples of glaciated (i.e., glacier-modified) landforms, glaciers formerly existed very extensively and have very thoroughly altered the aspect of the landscape in some districts.

Mountain-and-valley Glaciers.—Glaciers found now on and among mountains may be classed as *valley glaciers* and *hanging* *glaciers*. In the former the ice originating in a névé (figs. 271, 272) flows as a glacier tongue (figs. 271-273) far down a valley, and, especially if its volume is augmented by the confluence of *secondary glaciers* (smaller glaciers of the same kind joining it as tributaries) and by falls of snow and névé ice (*avalanches*) from the valley sides, may push its way down far below the snow-line, until eventually, unless in a high latitude, it dwindles and disappears owing to melting. Hanging glaciers are smaller, and consist practically of the

Fig. 271.—Head of the Tasman Glacier, New Zealand.

F. G. Radcliffe, photo.

névé portion only. The névé accumulates in a shelf-like hollow on the mountain side, from the edge of which there is a steep descent to a valley. A hanging glacier may completely fill its niche (fig. 274), and in this case the ice as it moves forward breaks away at the edge, falling as avalanches down the steep slope beyond to melt in the valley below or to make a "reconstructed" glacier there (fig. 275).

The distinction here made between valley glaciers and hanging glaciers is not a sharp one, for instead of discontinuous avalanches a steeply-sloping, rugged tongue of broken ice—an *ice fall* (p. 285) —may be formed where the ice from the high névé pushes its way over the edge of its niche (fig. 276). Also it is clear that some hanging glaciers of the present day are the shrunken remnants of former valley glaciers.

Fig. 272.—Névé (in distance) and glacier tongue of the Fox Glacier, New Zealand.
M. C. Lysons, photo.

Fig. 273.—Surface of a glacier tongue, Tasman Glacier, New Zealand. At the left the Rudolf Glacier (a secondary) joins the Tasman, bringing with it much surface moraine, which joins forces with the lateral moraine of the Tasman to form a median moraine.

F. G. Radcliffe, photo.

Fig. 274.—Hanging glaciers on Mount Sefton, New Zealand.

F. G. Radcliffe, photo.

Fig. 275.—Two avalanches (at left) streaming down from the edge of a hanging glacier on Mount Sefton, New Zealand. At a lower level a reconstructed glacier is formed.

F. G. Radcliffe, photo.

Fig. 276.—The Hochstetter Glacier descends as an ice fall to join the Tasman Glacier, New Zealand.

F. G. Radcliffe, photo.

A hanging glacier as a whole is homologous with the head of a valley glacier. Below this névé portion the glacier tongue, or ice stream, of a valley glacier is often narrower, has an appreciable slope (steeper than that of the névé), and may be confined between the rocky walls of an enormous trench (fig. 272 and frontispiece).

Though flowing in a channel like a river, a valley glacier has an enormously greater cross-section, being hundreds, or even thousands, of feet in depth, and also of great width. This large cross-section as compared with that of an equivalent river is a necessary accompaniment of a slower rate of flow.

The cross profile of the surface of the névé, and of the glacier generally where it is still being fed by avalanches from the sides, is concave, that of a glacier tongue in the zone of wastage convex. The convexity of a large glacier tongue is generally quite inconspicuous, however.

Glacier Ice.—The superficial layer of the névé is loose snow, but beneath the surface the material is more granular, and the amount of air entangled between the grains decreases downward. This granular *firn* grades into compact ice where it enters the glacier stream. In glacier ice the large crystal grains are closely fitted together in optical contact, so that the lines of division between them are not apparent on a freshly broken surface as yet unaffected by melting. Such ice is clear and blue by transmitted light. On the surface of a glacier, where the ice is melting under the rays of the sun, there is a layer of loose grains which appear white and crunch underfoot.

Farther down the valley in the glacier tongue, though the ice is compact, layers of white ice (containing a little entangled air) generally alternate with clear ice, so that the ice appears stratified. Some stratification originates in the névé, marking snows of successive storms or winters, and such layers become much distorted by the flow of the glacier. A pseudo-stratification—a kind of "schistosity," to borrow a term from metamorphic rocks—is produced also by shearing movements which facilitate flow, and this structure also becomes distorted. Near the terminus of the glacier, where the ice is thinned by melting and does not flow freely, slabs of ice slip over one another as the deeper layers are retarded by friction, and horizontal thrust planes are developed (figs. 284, 285).

The Flow of Glaciers.—Ice streams flow at rates varying from an inch or two to many feet per day. The velocity depends on a number of factors, among which is the general slope of the land surface; but the most important factor must be the volume of ice that has to be carried away, which will depend on the area of the gathering ground and on the precipitation. The most rapidly flowing glaciers are those of Greenland, which act as outlets from the great inland ice sheet through gaps in the mountain rim. In New Zealand the glaciers of the western slopes of the Southern Alps flow much more rapidly than those of the eastern side, the average western slope being steeper, while the snowfall on the western side of the divide is much heavier than on the eastern side. The Franz Josef and Fox Glaciers—the two largest glaciers of the western slope—because of their rapid flow combined with large volume extend to within 700 feet of sea-level, whereas on the eastern side the Tasman Glacier, which is the largest and reaches to the lowest level, ends at a height of over two thousand feet. The rate of flow of the Tasman Glacier opposite the Malte Brun hut is two feet per day in the centre, diminishing to a few inches per day at the sides. In the dwindling snout of the glacier, however, the rate of flow is only a few inches per day.

The fact that the rate of flow of a glacier is not the same throughout its width but is more rapid in the middle than at the sides shows that an ice stream does not simply slide forward as a rigid body, but, though crystalline, really flows somewhat after the manner of a fluid, being retarded by friction close to the sides and bottom of its channel. Such flow of crystalline material, in which the molecules must maintain definite geometrical relations to neighbouring molecules in the same crystal, is essentially different from the flow of a non-crystalline substance like pitch, which is really only an extremely viscous liquid, but more nearly resembles that of a solid metal when it is hammered or pressed.

Rotation of ice grains would allow the material to flow forward like a mass of shot, and it has been calculated that only a very small rotation of each grain would be required to produce the observed differential movement. The problem is not so simple as this statement would imply, however, for the grains cannot roll freely, being interlocked.

Fig. 277.—Crevasses in the névé of the Franz Josef Glacier, New Zealand.
V. C. Browne, photo.

Fig. 278.—The Melchior ice fall at the head of the glacier tongue of the Franz Josef Glacier, New Zealand.
M. C. Lysons, photo.

Glacier ice resembles crystalline rocks in texture, and flow of deep-seated crystalline rock is known to occur. It takes place only under great pressure, and is a matter of slow readjustment of the crystals of minerals composing the rock partly by transfer of material from one part of a crystal to another and from one crystal to another by solution and redeposition. The flow of the granular ice of glaciers is probably analogous to this, though the pressures involved and the very important time factor are much smaller. Melting takes place where the greatest stresses occur, followed by refreezing in crystal continuity with pre-existing grains as the stresses are relieved, and this possibly permits some rotation of the grains. At any rate constant recrystallisation is in progress under shearing stresses, closely imitating the recrystallisation that takes place in the metamorphism of rocks.

Crevasses.—It is gravity that causes a glacier to flow, and so the surface of the ice must have a general slope in the direction of flow. A continuously forward slope of the floor over which the ice moves is not essential, but where the slope is forward this promotes and facilitates movement. The surface slope of the ice is generally very variable in present-day glaciers and changes of slope correspond to inequalities, breaks of slope, and even actual hollows in the rock floor.

Stresses set up by the distortion of the ice where it passes over steep parts of the floor result in the formation of fissures, which are termed *crevasses* (fig. 277), and where the slope is very steep the multiplication of crevasses transforms the glacier into an "ice fall" (figs. 276, 278). Crevasses are formed also by various irregularities in the channel such as sharp bends, and others are due to the more rapid flow in the middle of the stream. The deeper ice, being under pressure, and so acting more like a plastic substance, adjusts itself to the differential movement by flow, but that near the surface may be torn apart, leaving crevasses that extend to a depth of perhaps 200 feet. Tension due to the more rapid movement of the middle portion of the glacier results in the formation of two sets of crevasses, one on each side of the middle line, pointing down-valley in a chevron pattern at angles of 45° with the sides (figs. 279, 280). Crevasses when once formed may remain open for a long time, and they are twisted away from their original directions by the differential movement of the ice. Thus the crevasses due to

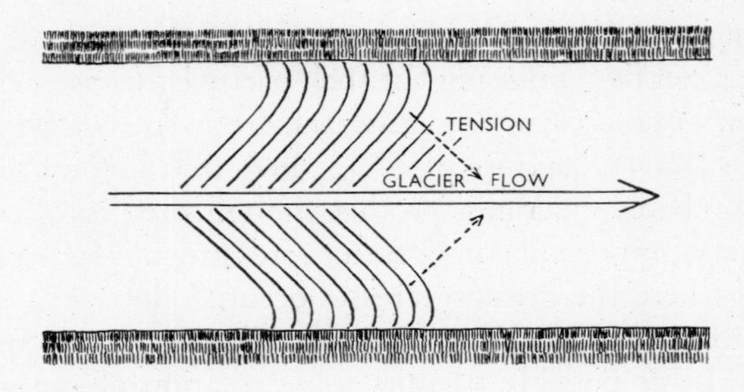

Fig. 279.—Chevron pattern of crevasses on a glacier developed by differential flow.

Fig. 280.—Chevron pattern of crevasses on the Tasman Glacier, New Zealand. Owing to foreshortening only the nearer half of the crevasse pattern is seen. (Compare fig. 279.)

C. A. Cotton, photo.

tension, which point diagonally down-valley near the middle of the glacier, become more and more nearly transverse as the sides are approached, and close to the sides may even curve around still farther and point up-valley (fig. 279). A glacier that spreads laterally may be torn apart, developing longitudinal crevasses (fig. 277).

When a glacier is broken into slices by numerous close-set crevasses its surface naturally becomes very uneven. The irregularities of the surface when modified into sharp ridges and pinnacles by melting are termed *seracs* (fig. 281).

Fig. 281.—Seracs on the Franz Josef Glacier, New Zealand.
L. Cockayne, photo.

Moraines.—Rock fragments, large and small, broken by weathering from mountain peaks and slopes, fall or stream as talus on to the surface of a glacier, and others are carried down by avalanches of snow, firn, or ice from hanging glaciers and snowfields. This rock material, which accumulates in heaps on the glacier, is termed *moraine,* and the same name is given to all the rock debris carried and eventually deposited by glacier ice. Various kinds of moraines are distinguished. *Surface moraines* are carried on the surface, but some waste originally on the surface falls, or is washed by streams of water, into crevasses, and some waste also is plucked or scraped from the bottom and sides of the channel. When dragged along under the ice it is *subglacial moraine,* and when carried in the body of the glacier, *englacial moraine.* The enormous quantity of morainic material that may be seen on the surface and embedded in the ice of glaciers testifies to their efficiency as transporting agents. That they are corrading agents also is shown by the large amount of finely powdered rock ("rock flour") carried away by the rivers that flow from glaciers, which are given by it a characteristically "milky" appearance. This rock flour must be produced

Fig. 282.—Median moraine, Ramsay Glacier, Southern Alps, New Zealand. *R. Speight, photo.*

by the abrading action of rock fragments dragged along in the bottom layer of ice. So finely powdered is this material in the water of the rivers from the Tasman and Godley Glaciers of New Zealand that sufficient remains in suspension to make the water milky after it has passed through the settling basins provided by the large lakes Pukaki and Tekapo.

Surface moraines at first form ridges, made up of coalescing heaps of fragments, along the sides, and are then termed *lateral moraines;* and where two glaciers join, their adjacent lateral moraines join also to form a ridge in the middle of the combined glacier, which is termed a *median moraine* (figs. 273, 282). There may be several median moraines, resulting from the junction of a number of secondary glaciers with a trunk glacier, so that the surface of the ice becomes covered practically from side to side. Towards the head of a glacier—in the *zone of alimentation,* where snowfall and avalanches are adding to the volume of ice—surface moraines are being constantly buried, and very little moraine may be visible at the surface; but down the valley at lower levels—in the *zone*

Fig. 283.—Moraine-covered surfaces of the Mueller (foreground) and Hooker Glaciers, Mount Cook, New Zealand.

of ablation, where the surface ice is wasting away by melting and evaporation—the moraine is again exposed. The larger glaciers of the eastern side of the Southern Alps are so full of rock debris that for the last few miles of their courses they are completely covered by sheets or coalescing heaps of such *ablation moraine* (fig. 283).

Steep and rapidly flowing glaciers, such as the Fox and Franz Josef Glaciers, on the western side of the Southern Alps, are relatively free from surface moraines, partly because their rapid flow allows the rock debris to be carried in a thinner stream, and

Fig. 284.—Terminal face of the Franz Josef Glacier, New Zealand.
R. Speight, photo.

Fig. 285.—Another part of the terminal face of the Franz Josef Glacier.
N.Z. Geological Survey, photo.

partly because it is swallowed up by the very numerous crevasses on the broken surface of the ice of such glaciers.[1]

Lower Limits of Glaciers.—As glaciers descend towards low levels they dwindle in thickness as a result of ablation (loss by melting and evaporation). Streams of water are formed on the surface. These make their way eventually down crevasses and circular pits, termed *moulins,* originating in a manner somewhat analogous to the formation of sinkholes in limestone, and may

Fig. 286.—A melt-water river emerges from a cave in the snout of a Norwegian (Brigsdal) glacier.

unite to form a single trunk stream beneath the glacier. At the lower extremity, or *terminal face,* of the glacier there is generally a cliff of ice (figs. 284, 285), and from a cave in this the subglacial stream emerges (fig. 286).

In Greenland, Alaska, Spitsbergen (fig. 287), and Antarctica glaciers descend to the sea, and blocks "calving" from the cliffed margins of some such glaciers become icebergs. In the temperate

[1] In the case of the glaciers mentioned it is explained also that the rocks forming their valley sides shed less waste than do the shattered, crumbling rocks of the eastern side of the Southern Alps; but this alone does not account for the almost complete absence of surface moraines.

zones, on the other hand, the terminal faces of glaciers, the positions of which are determined by balance between rates of ice supply and ablation, are commonly several thousand feet above sea-level.

Fig. 287.—A "tide-water" glacier in Spitsbergen.
Morris Wilson, photo.

Ice Sheets.—Ice sheets, or, as they are sometimes termed, "continental glaciers," covered large areas of the northern continents in rather low latitudes in the Ice Age, but are now confined to polar regions, the largest being that which almost completely covers Antarctica, while another occupies a great part of the surface of Greenland. Central parts of such glaciers are thousands of feet thick. They have smooth surfaces, highest at the centres of accumulation and sloping very gently outwards to the margins. The ice moves slowly outward so as to dispose of the snow that falls on the surface and feeds the glacier. Crevasses which indicate some such movement have been observed even in those parts of Antarctica where precipitation is so exiguous that little snow is added to the surface and the ice is almost stagnant.

In Victoria Land ("Ross Sea Dependency"), which lies south of New Zealand, the inland high-level ice sheet of Antarctica is cut off from the the sea by a range of mountains, and the ice flows through gaps in the mountain rim as enormous glacier tongues. In some parts of the Antarctic continent, however, the front of the continental glacier advances into the sea.

Piedmont Glaciers.—In high latitudes—and in glacial periods in low latitudes also—the ice of a valley glacier debouching on a plain may spread out as a flat "expanded foot," or that of several glaciers may become laterally confluent and join up to form a sluggish *piedmont glacier,* which, considered apart from the ice streams that feed it, behaves somewhat like an ice sheet. An example of a large piedmont glacier at the present day is the Malaspina Glacier, Alaska. In the Ice Age low-level confluent glaciers were common. In New Zealand, for example, such a piedmont glacier occupied the southern part of the basin of Lake Te Anau, being fed by glacier tongues from the Clinton Valley at the head of the lake and from the three large arms forming the "fiords" of the western side of the lake.

CHAPTER XXII

GLACIAL EROSION

Ice stream erosion. Glaciated or mammillated surfaces. Glacial terraces. Scour and pluck. The sculpture of mountains by glaciers. Sculpture above the general ice level. Cirques. Glacial sapping. Corries. Initial forms of cirques and corries. Fretted-upland forms: arêtes and horns. A cycle of glacial erosion.

Ice Stream Erosion.—Moving ice is an active corrading as well as transporting agent. Both valley glaciers and ice sheets erode, though the resulting landforms are somewhat different in the two cases. The characteristic sculpture of glaciated mountains has resulted from the co-operation of processes among which rock-rending by freeze and thaw plays an important part. Such parts of the land surface as are permanently covered by snow and ice are to a great extent protected, however, from ordinary weathering. Where such a covering is stagnant it may be entirely protective, but where in motion it erodes, being responsible for the "ice-plough" action manifest in the deep groove or trough forms assumed by "over-deepened" valleys, and also for the occasionally polished and more generally hummocky ("mammillated") rock surfaces characteristic of landscapes that have been covered by widely spreading glacier ice.

Glaciated or Mammillated Surfaces.—These latter *glaciated* surfaces are common on the less steep slopes that have been submerged beneath ice, especially where the terrain has offered rather a low resistance to glacial erosion. In New Zealand, for example, such terrains are the joint-broken greywacke of Canterbury and the mica schist of the Queenstown district of Otago. The ice markings left on glaciated surfaces of these terrains take the form generally of irregular benches or terraces parallel in a general way to the direction of movement of the ice. Commonly the benches are short and ripple-like and very irregular in pattern—whale-backed mounds (compare with "roches moutonnées," p. 299) alternating with rock-rimmed hollows in some of which are tarns.[1] This is the mam-

[1] The term *tarn* is applied to the innumerable water bodies too small to be called lakes that are found occupying hollows of various kinds in glaciated districts.

Fig. 288.—Strongly mammillated (and deeply eroded) surface, Lake Wanaka, New Zealand.

C. A. Cotton, photo.

Fig. 289.—Ice-terraced slope, Lake Luna, Queenstown district, New Zealand.

J. Park, photo.

millated variety of glaciated surface, in which hollows appear to have been dug out on the weaker parts of the rock by selective glacial erosion (fig. 288).

Glacial Terraces.—In other cases the benches run continuously for longer distances, separated by distinct grooves. They are rarely horizontal or quite parallel to one another, however; but give the

Fig. 290.—The rock of a valley side smoothed and fluted by glacial scour, valley of the Fox Glacier, New Zealand. *R. Speight, photo.*

impression (from far off) of gigantic sheep tracks. These are *glacial terraces.*

Near Lake Luna, Queenstown district, New Zealand (fig. 289), "these ice-cut terraces . . . . vary from 30 feet to nearly 70 feet in height, and from a few yards to over two chains in width. They are excavated in a fairly hard quartzose mica schist. The broader benches often have an undrained depression at the back, generally close under the slope ascending to the next platform" (Park).

The harder rocks of the Westland and Fiordland districts of New Zealand are grooved and mammillated in lower relief as a rule by the passage of the ice over them. Here very steep (glacially oversteepened) slopes predominate (fig. 290), and, though the mammillated pattern may often still be traced on these, it is less conspicuous than on gentle slopes, and distinct terracing does not occur.

Glacial sculpture such as that just described does not itself indicate deep erosion, but frequently where it occurs, even on gentle slopes, the extent to which preglacial normal landscape forms have been destroyed shows that a very considerable thickness of rock has been removed.

Scour and Pluck.—The erosive work of moving ice is accomplished by *scour* and *pluck*, and both these processes, no doubt, took part in producing the mammillated surfaces described above. *Scouring* (fig. 290) is the work of rock-waste dragged along with the ice. Ice alone, though capable of removing loosened waste, is too soft to abrade compact rock. The ice of glaciers, however, being armed with fragments of rock, acts as a rasp. Its effectiveness as a powerful grinding agent is shown by the terraced and mammillated surfaces it leaves behind it. Where the "glaciated" surfaces of the rock hummocks of such a scoured region are well preserved, as they sometimes are in the case of very hard rocks, or even in the case of softer rocks if protected by a layer of fine waste, they are found to be not only roughly rounded but also smoothed and polished, though grooved and scored as well by the angles of the last rough fragments that were dragged across them (fig. 291). The direction of the striation shows the direction of movement of the ice.

Scouring goes on beneath the glaciers of the present day, shrunken and weak though they are as compared with those of the Glacial Period, as is proved by the rock flour that they yield on melting at the terminal face, and by the rounding of the edges and scoring of the surfaces of pebbles and boulders that have been transported as subglacial moraine.

By *plucking* blocks of rock are removed from the floor and sides of a glacial channel. As a result of long-continued heavy pressure the ice grips the rock, mainly by freezing to it but partly by friction, separation takes place at a joint or some plane of weak-

Fig. 291.—Ice-scoured, mammillated surface of a knob of granite forming a large roche moutonnée, Boulder Lake, Nelson, New Zealand.

N.Z. Geological Survey, photo.

Fig. 292.—A roche moutonnée in the Waimakariri Valley, New Zealand.

R. Speight, photo.

ness, and a block is dragged away. This takes place generally on the downstream side of some projection that is in course of removal —a mass of relatively resistant rock or the basal remnant of a partially truncated spur of the preglacial landscape. Such projections are scoured smooth on the upstream side ("scour side"), but are also generally minutely (fig. 291) mammillated; and are termed *roches moutonnées,* from a fancied resemblance of their forms to

Fig. 293.—A hill at Lake Tekapo, New Zealand, that was overridden by the ice of the Godley Glacier, the direction of glacial flow being from right to left. The side of the hill (above the bridge) shows terraces due to glacial scouring, and the steep face on the left is the result of plucking.

Rose, photo.

fleeces of gigantic sheep (fig. 292). The downstream side ("pluck side"), on the other hand, presents a ragged, quarried appearance (fig. 292). This is seen also on larger landscape forms, such as preglacial hills that have been submerged under ice (fig. 293). Plucking takes place also where ice passes over steep descents in valley floors or overflows divides (fig. 294).

The Sculpture of Mountains by Glaciers.—Though the ice sheets of Antarctica and Greenland and the glaciers now found in Alpine valleys throw important light on the process of glacial erosion, it is in regions where glacial erosion no longer operates, or where the glaciers have now shrunk to insignificant proportions, that ice sculpture has produced its most important topographical effects. Such regions were subject to the action of glacier ice during the Ice Age, the oncoming of frigid conditions—a "climatic accident" (p. 211)—putting an end to one cycle of normal erosion, and the disappearance of the ice leaving a glacially sculptured surface on which normal agents have now begun to work in a new cycle.[1]

Fig. 294.—McKinnon Pass, between the Clinton and Roaring Creek cirques, Fiordland, New Zealand. Direction of ice-movement, right to left. Plucked surface in foreground: scoured surface above this and in centre. *Rose, photo.*

In these regions the surfaces upon which glacial erosion began to work were, in general, normally eroded land surfaces, with well-developed valley systems in various stages of youth, maturity, and old age. In high and mountainous areas the ice flowed away as valley glaciers along the lines of pre-existing valleys, and the peaks and portions of the ridges and spurs stood out above the

[1] Investigation of some details of a landscape may make it necessary to take into account also normal erosion during mild interglacial epochs which separated the glacial epochs or "ice floods" of the Glacial Period.

ice level. Over more nearly level landscapes, on the other hand, given cold conditions and ample snowfall, thick ice sheets came into existence. Such ice sheets carved no very striking topographic forms, except locally where the ice was guided and crowded into certain channels by pre-existing surface features, when some enormous grooves were ploughed out somewhat similar to the troughs described below as produced by valley glaciers. Generally continental glaciers merely smoothed and rounded prominences, removed all the waste mantle from the rocks underlying the thicker parts of

Fig. 295.—Cirque at the head of the Clinton Valley, between Lake Te Anau and Milford Sound, New Zealand. From McKinnon Pass, a gap in the cirque wall.

Rose, photo.

the ice sheet, sometimes excavating in the process innumerable hollows, which are now lakes, and at the same time grooved, polished, and scratched the bare surfaces of the hard rocks by means of the rock fragments they dragged along with them.

The most striking effects that have been produced by glacial erosion are those found in mountainous areas that have been occupied by valley glaciers and snowfields or névés, the erosive action of which has carved features that contrast very strongly with those associated with normal erosion. The chief of these are as follows:

(1) The heads of valleys that have been occupied by glaciers are different in form from those shaped entirely by normal agencies. Glaciated valleys retain their width to their heads or even expand there to form great amphitheatre-like hollows, enclosed by almost vertical walls (fig. 295). Hollows on the sites of former hanging glaciers are also of similar form. These are the armchair-like niches

Fig. 296.—Hanging cirque, or corrie of armchair form, overlooking Lake Ada, Milford Sound, New Zealand.
C. A. Cotton, photo.

so common in glaciated mountains, and belong, with the valley-head amphitheatres, to the class of forms termed *cirques* (fig. 296). Being very striking landscape features, they have received vernacular names in most of the European countries in which they occur. They are, for example, called "cwms" in Wales, and "corries" in Scotland. Though the steep-walled heads of the larger glaciated valleys and the perched "corries" appear to be of similar origin (p. 306), the former may be conveniently referred to as *valley-head cirques*, while the latter may have the Scottish term *corrie* reserved for them, or may sometimes be termed *hanging cirques.*

(2) The valleys both large and small are broad-floored and steep-sided (U-shaped) (figs. 297, 298). Their curves are few in number and of wide radius. In longitudinal profile they are uneven, occasional steep descents (*steps*) being met with (fig. 316), which are separated by nearly level stretches, commonly with reversed slopes that give rise to lakes in the postglacial cycle.

Fig. 297.—Glacier-cut U-shaped valley of the Greenstone River, Wakatipu district, New Zealand. *V. C. Browne, photo.*

(3) Tributary valleys almost invariably join the main valleys with strongly discordant junctions—that is, as *hanging valleys* (figs. 298, 299). The stream of water which now occupies a hanging tributary valley either plunges from its lip into the main valley as a waterfall or cascade, or has cut but a small notch in the lip in the postglacial cycle of normal erosion—that is, since the Ice Age.

(4) In addition to the numerous small lakes occupying more or less adventitious rock basins or dammed by glacial deposits on the upper-valley floors, the down-valley parts of large valleys, where

Fig. 298.—U-shaped, glaciated valley of the Pembroke River, entering Milford Sound, New Zealand. The sound is here very deep, and so the valley here shown is hanging high above the floor of the main valley (the fiord, or "sound").

Muir and Moodie, photo.

Fig. 299.—Hanging valley entering the Tasman Valley, New Zealand. The discordance has been considerably reduced by deep aggradation in the main valley.

they pass through an outer zone of mountains, are generally occupied, or furnish evidence of having been occupied since the melting of the glaciers, by long and deep lakes that have filled the trough-shaped valleys from side to side. Morainic barriers, dropped by the ice, have held up the water in some of these lakes at a level above that of the bedrock rim; but the lakes are of such great depth (with floors below sea-level even in the case of some lakes far inland) that it is quite clear that the presence of the lake does not depend on the deposited dam. Deep rock-rimmed basins, that is to say, have been hollowed by glaciers out of the valley floors.

Fig. 300.—Shoulder above the inner trough of the Hooker Valley, New Zealand, which is still occupied by a shrunken glacier.

C. A. Cotton, photo.

These features, which are constantly found in regions that have been occupied by glaciers, and which are strikingly unlike the forms produced by other sculpturing agencies, are confidently attributed to glacial erosion. Attempts have been made, however, to explain the most striking and characteristic features of glaciated landscapes by an appeal to a supposed protection afforded to parts of the landscape by glaciers while other parts were trenched by rivers; but these attempts have been based on a mistaken interpretation of deeply eroded troughs as river-cut valleys, which they do not resemble in reality.

Sculpture above the General Ice Level.—In most regions of glaciated mountains there is a very striking contrast between the landforms developed below the level of the surface of the main glacier tongues of the Ice Age and those developed above it. Below this level (which is, of course, not everywhere the same, but rises towards the centre of maximum snow-accumulation) wall-sided troughs and featureless glaciated slopes dominate the landscape; above it (except in and near centres of accumulation among high mountains, where these precipitous slopes intersect in sharp peaks and mountain crests), the forms are much more diversified, and the average mountain profiles are much less steep (fig. 300). Though the average slopes are relatively gentle, however, the surface is often extremely rugged and precipices abound. The average upper slopes are a relic of the preglacial topography, but this may be modified very considerably by the development of cirques.

Cirques.—The formation of cirques is clearly the result of a combination of the downward erosive action of forward-moving ice with another phase of glacial erosion whereby the steep enclosing walls are formed and are caused to retreat, thus enlarging the area of the cirque. The former action is evidenced by the scraped and polished, mammillated bedrock floors of the cirques, sometimes hollowed out to such an extent that reversed slopes occur and the disappearing ice leaves hollows that become lakes or tarns. The other phase of cirque-formation is clearly active at the base of the surrounding cliffs, for the rugged walls can be satisfactorily accounted for like most other cliffs if an active gnawing-away of the rock at their base has taken place. The undercutting which has thus caused the cirque walls to retreat is well termed *glacial sapping*.

Glacial Sapping.—The most satisfactory hypothesis to account for the sapping of cirque walls ascribes it to frost action—freezing and thawing of water in crevices of the rock. Some of this has taken place at the bottom of the *bergschrund,* a curving crevasse which is open in summer around the margin of the névé (where cirques are still occupied by glaciers), separating it from the rock walls. It is known from observation that, though at the top both walls of the bergschrund are composed of snow, at the bottom (in one case observed, at a depth of 150 feet) one wall is ice, the other rock. The rock wall, moreover, has been found to be wet, which indicates that thawing takes place during the day, for freezing will certainly occur every night in such a place. Frost action must, therefore, be actively rending the rock. Rock fragments of various sizes, recently quarried, form the floor of the rift, and others have

Fig. 301.—Successive stages in the symmetrical development of cirques in a domed mountain. (After W. M. Davis.)

been found embedded in the opposite (ice) wall, as though in process of removal by the glacier.

Whether freeze and thaw in the bergschrund be the full explanation of the mechanism of the process or not, sapping is a fact of which there is ample evidence in the presence of the precipitous walls, in some cases thousands of feet in height, surrounding the numerous cirques found in glaciated mountains. Some of these cirque walls are so high that it seems impossible that bergschrunds can have penetrated to their bases if the cirques were well filled with névé. So the bergschrund hypothesis is supplemented by another, which supposes that melt-water penetrates deeply between the ice of a glacier and the back wall, freezing and thawing in the crevices of the rock.

Since the disappearance of the ice from the majority of cirques, though sapping has ceased, crumbling of the oversteep walls has

Fig. 302.—A large corrie perched above the Routeburn trough, New Zealand. Note the col, or gap, in its back wall.

Muir and Moodie, photo.

continued under the action of normal weathering and stream erosion, and the cirques are to some extent encumbered by talus slopes and alluvial cones. The form of many cirques remains remarkably fresh, however, the work of grading in the normal cycle following glaciation being scarcely begun. Some seem to have been overswept by thick ice after their formation. This has removed the morainic debris, and has smoothed and rounded off all salient angles, producing the perfect armchair form seen in many of the corries of Scotland.

Corries.—Hanging cirques, or corries, sometimes have floors so concave that they hold lakes or tarns (fig. 303). In less extreme cases, where there is not actually a backward slope on any part of the bedrock floor, it is at least so nearly horizontal as to present

Fig. 303.—Lake Quill, in a huge corrie, overflows as the Sutherland Falls (1,904 ft.) into the Arthur Valley, New Zealand.
V. C. Browne, photo.

a striking contrast to adjacent slopes. The shape of the floor is not governed by the sapping process. The floor begins either as a smooth forward slope or as a nearly horizontal floor at a definite line, sometimes termed the "schrund line," which separates it from the upper, quarried, rugged wall. Cirque floors have been strongly scoured and hollowed out by the forward-moving glaciers. Such "overdeepening" takes place chiefly where the ice is thickest; and so concave floors may be explained, at any rate in the case of cirques excavated by hanging or corrie glaciers, as a consequence of thinning of the ice by ablation towards the front or lip of the corrie.

Some corries hang above non-glaciated slopes, where apparently only hanging glaciers existed even at the peak of Ice Age conditions. Others, hanging above the slopes of glaciated valleys, were perhaps hollowed out to their present form during the period of glacial retreat, when the glaciers occupying them had shrunk to small dimensions, or during an epoch of minor glaciation that has occurred since the main ice flood. The corries shown in figs. 296, 302, 303 are in the very heavily glaciated Fiordland district of south-western New Zealand, where some enormous corries contain lakes which spill over as waterfalls (fig. 303) into greatly overdeepened glacial troughs.

Initial Forms of Cirques and Corries.—An initial gathering place in form of a ravine, niche, or shelf must have existed to collect snow to make the glacier which has enlarged such an initial form so as to convert it into a cirque. Preglacial valley heads may have provided initial basins, especially where headwater branches converged to a confluence in funnel-shaped ravines. Many corries (hanging cirques) on the other hand which pit or dimple convexly rounded summit forms may have their beginnings in shallow dimples of the surface sufficiently large to hold snow patches that survive summer melting. At times of relatively mild climate, when the snow cover is much reduced in summer, the summer melt-water from surviving snow patches alternately freezing and thawing in the ground under the snow and at its margin pries into the rocks and comminutes debris, which the run-off of thaw-water removes. It has been observed that this process of *snow-patch erosion,* or *nivation,* taking place at elevations in the vicinity of the snow-line, enlarges the dimples in which snow lies to the dimensions of incipient cirques deep enough to allow the snow collecting in them to become firn. Snow patches thus give place to small glaciers which carry on the work of corrie excavation.

Fretted-upland Forms: Arêtes and Horns.—Owing to the enlargement of neighbouring cirques by sapping, the residual portions of the mountain-tops between them are frequently much reduced (fig. 301). It is as though the mountains had been splashed with some mysterious rock-devouring acid. The steep walls of adjacent cirques may meet in a ragged *comb ridge* or *arête* (fig. 304). In other cases a high peak of pyramidal form remains, with its steep

Fig. 304.—Arêtes between cirques on Mount Cook, New Zealand.
F. G. Radcliffe, photo.

Fig. 305.—Mount Aspiring, a typical horn, the "Matterhorn of New Zealand."

sides formed by the intersecting walls of three or more cirques, as in the case of the Matterhorn, in Switzerland, or Mount Aspiring, in New Zealand (fig. 305). Thus originates the *horn* type of summit, but somewhat similar forms (*tinds*) may be isolated as high outjutting spurs are sharpened between the walls of glacier troughs or the side walls of greatly enlarged cirques. Mitre Peak, at Milford Sound, New Zealand, is an example of this type (fig. 306). Mount Cook, though not a perfect horn form, has been sharpened to a somewhat similar pyramidal shape by the development of a larger number of small cirques (corries) (fig. 304). It is probably the

Fig. 306.—Mitre Peak, New Zealand, a tind.
F. G. Radcliffe, photo.

remnant of a preglacial peak maturely dissected by glacial erosion (compare with fig. 301).

Cols (gaps in a ridge) also result from the intersection of the walls of opposing cirques, or of the wall of a cirque with that of a glacier trough (fig. 302). Many mountain passes have originated in this way. Perhaps ice overflows through the gap from one cirque to the cirque or valley beyond, and the col is thus enlarged, lowered, and smoothed in outline to a U shape. In New Zealand, McKinnon Pass, between Lake Te Anau and Milford Sound, originated in this way when ice from the cirque at the head of the Clinton Valley (fig. 295) overflowed westward across the main divide (fig. 294). Arthur Pass, one of the very few gaps in the Southern Alps, is of similar origin (fig. 307), and has been deepened to trough form by a "through" glacier.

A Cycle of Glacial Erosion.—As in the case of normal sculpture, complete or almost complete destruction of the initial (in this case preglacial) forms marks the passage from young to mature dissection.

Near the margin of a glaciated area the summits retain their

Fig. 307.—Arthur Pass, Southern Alps, New Zealand.
V. C. Browne, photo.

preglacial forms developed by normal erosion, while towards the centre of glaciation—the heart of the mountain range—these are more and more encroached on by forms due to high-level glaciation, until often, as in the central parts of high mountain ranges, such as the Alps, the latter alone are to be seen. Glacial erosion is then mature, whereas when normal preglacial forms still occupy an appreciable part of the surface glacial erosion is still young (fig. 308).

The contrast between glaciated forms and preglacial summits is most striking in regions of undulating-plateau initial relief (fig. 309)

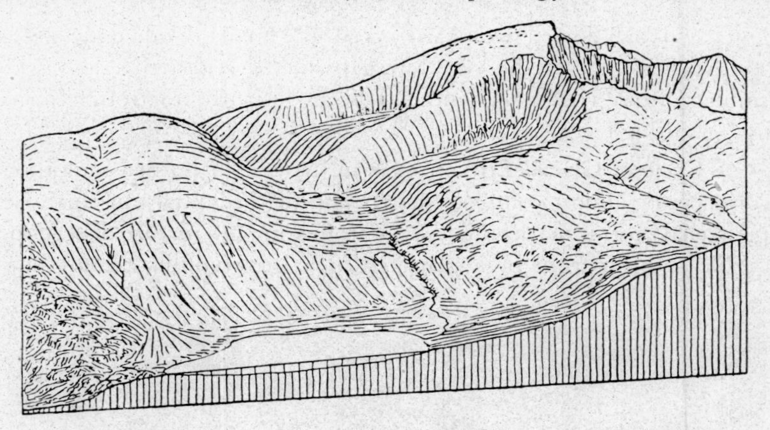

Fig. 308.—Immature glacial dissection of a preglacial mountain of broadly convex form, Snowdon, North Wales. (After Davis.)

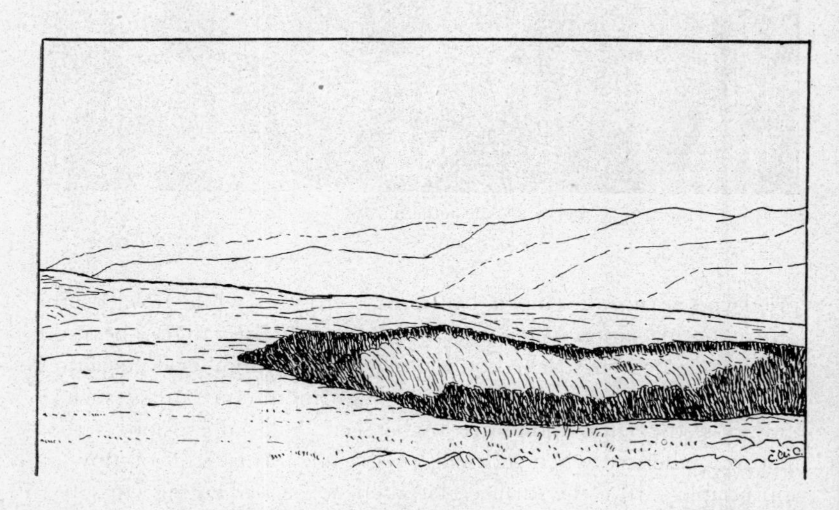

Fig. 309.—The "biscuit-cutting" effect produced by young glacial-cirque dissection of a plateau, Yellowstone National Park, North America.

or of subdued mountain forms of coarse-textured dissection (fig. 308). Where the relief due to preglacial erosion was fine-textured the contrast between the non-glaciated summits and the glaciated summit topography is less striking. Such is the case in the glaciated parts of the Southern Alps in Canterbury, New Zealand. There snowfields accumulating in the numerous preglacial ravines became névés and glaciers; these sapped back to form corries of somewhat irregular form which sharpen the mountain crests (fig. 304).

Glaciated troughs also may be termed mature when "graded" —i.e., when fit to accommodate glaciers with smoothly sloping surfaces, free from ice falls. The floors of graded troughs do not necessarily have smooth, even slopes, however. They may retain steps corresponding to sudden expansions of the ice streams where they receive tributaries (p. 320).

CHAPTER XXIII

GLACIAL EROSION (*Continued*)

The trough form and hanging valleys. Bastions. Glaciated valley profiles. Complex cross profiles. Spur truncation. Glacial lakes. Fiords. Ice-dammed lakes. The postglacial cycle. Changes in drainage due to glaciation.

The Trough Form and Hanging Valleys.—The trough-like and U-shaped transverse profiles of glaciated valleys and the presence of hanging tributary valleys point alike to the principal erosive

Fig. 310.—Glacially oversteepened trough walls of the 4,000-feet-deep Yosemite Valley, California.
Douglas Johnson, photo.

activity of ice streams confined in valleys, which has been termed *overdeepening*. The glacier cuts vigorously downward, especially where it is thickest. This leads also to *oversteepening* of the sides of the valley (fig. 310). Some hanging valleys, however, though not those with very strong discordance, may be attributable to over-

Fig. 311.—Above: Valley glaciers with accordant junctions. Below: The glaciers have melted away leaving troughs and hanging valleys.

steepening of the sides of the main valley as a result of widening accompanied by little or no deepening.

Even where the floors of main valleys have been sunk by the overdeepening process far below the preglacial floors and also far below the depth attained by the floors of tributary valleys, it does not appear that when the glaciers in the valleys reached their full dimensions secondary glaciers in general joined the trunk glaciers as ice falls. It is probable, on the contrary, that the majority of

Fig. 312.—Accordant junction of the Ball Glacier with the main (Tasman Glacier), in the foreground, New Zealand. *C. A. Cotton, photo.*

glacier junctions were then accordant (fig. 311), as a few still are even at the present day (fig. 312).

In an accordant junction, however, whether it be of ice streams or water streams, it is the surfaces of the streams that join at grade. There is a tendency both in glaciers and in rivers to adjust the size of every cross-section of the channel to suit the volume of ice or water that must pass through it. (This is the *law of adjustment of cross-sections*). The cross-section of a glacier is, of course, enormously greater than that of an equivalent river, and the whole trough or glaciated valley, in so far as it is occupied by the glacier, is analogous with the actual water channel in a river valley. The glacier tributary has a smaller cross-section, and is thus shallower, than the main, and so the floor of the tributary valley must be at a higher level than that of the main, so that it forms a hanging valley when no longer occupied by the ice (fig. 311). The same is true of the channel of a tributary river the surface of which joins that of its main accordantly, and if the rivers were diverted so as to leave the channels empty a hanging junction of the floors would be seen,

Fig. 313.—A hanging valley developed from a cirque, Rangitata Valley, New Zealand. *R. Speight, photo.*

though on a much smaller scale than in the case of glacier channels, on account of the much smaller cross-sections of the streams.

Some hanging valleys are simply cirques that have developed on upper valley-side slopes, have grown to considerable dimensions, and have been extended headward by retreat of the head wall (due to sapping) until they have contained glaciers of quite large size, and now carry vigorous streams of water in the postglacial cycle. Such hanging valleys have considerable development on the eastern flanks of the Southern Alps, in New Zealand (fig. 313).

Not all hanging valleys in which the discordance is due to glacial overdeepening are themselves glaciated. Near the margins of glaciated areas, and in districts that have been only slightly glaciated, some of the side valleys tributary to the glacier troughs have themselves escaped glaciation. Such valleys are left hanging owing to enlargement of the main valleys by the ice. They have the transverse profiles of normal stream-eroded valleys (fig. 311, left).

Fig. 313A.—A bastion projects below the lip of the Stirling Falls hanging valley, Milford Sound, New Zealand.

Bastions.—Pronounced salients of rock that project from some trough walls below the lips of hanging valleys of the glaciated variety are termed *bastions* (fig. 313A). Their presence indicates weakening of the erosive power of the trunk glaciers as a result of thrust from the tributaries.

Glaciated Valley Profiles.—The law of adjustment of cross-sections explains also many of the steps which occur in the longitudinal profiles of glaciated valleys.

Where a valley glacier expands at the head into a wide field of névé—i.e., is fed by the snow accumulating in a broad, composite cirque, or group of converging cirques—the ice stream flowing away through the narrower valley below demands a deeper channel (unless its size is much reduced by ablation). When such a channel has been excavated, the glacier trough, as seen after the disappearance of the ice, ends headward in a step—the *trough-end,* a feature found in many of the valleys of the European Alps—below the level of the feeding cirques (fig. 314). The trough-end was not, in such cases,

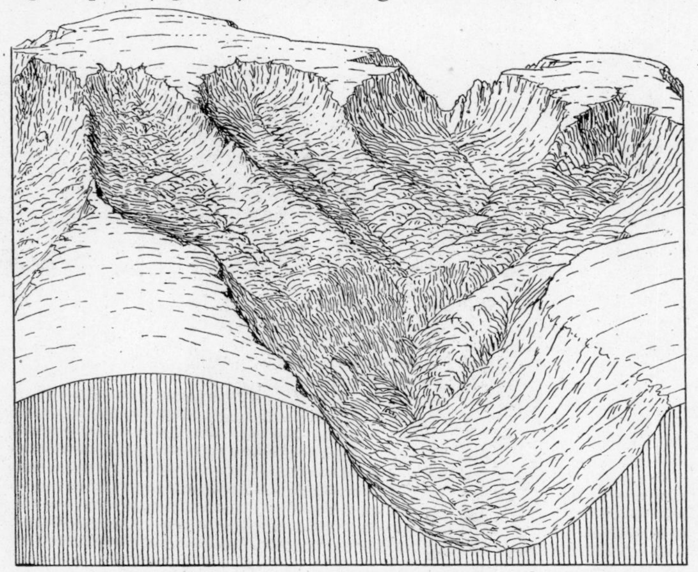

Fig. 314.—A trough-end step at the place where ice from converging cirques has been collected in a trunk valley. (Compare fig. 315.) (After W. M. Davis; redrawn.)

the head of the glacier, but merely a step in the glacial valley profile. In New Zealand the great glaciers west of the main divide (Fox and Franz Josef) have expanded névés, and undoubtedly steps must be present in the rock floors beneath them where the ice is gathered into narrow trunk streams (fig. 315).

Where the volume of a glacier is increased by the incoming of a tributary an expansion of the cross-section of the channel is required, and generally a step results (fig. 316).

Other steps, however, are directly traceable to differences of rock in the valley floors, some rocks—particularly shattered rocks—being much more easily eroded by ice than others. These steps belong to the young stage of glacial-valley erosion. Being related to the structure of the terrain they would either retreat up-valley or would

Fig. 315.—Ice from converging cirques feeds the Franz Josef Glacier, New Zealand. (Compare fig. 314.)

M. C. Lysons, photo.

Fig. 316.—A step in the Arthur Valley, New Zealand, just above the point where the Sutherland Falls enter the valley. At this point a tributary glacier joined the ancient Arthur Glacier.

be worn down by prolonged glacial erosion which would thus eliminate them, producing a mature, or graded, glacial floor profile.

Immediately up-valley from step fronts low transverse ridges of rock, which were overridden by the glaciers, occur commonly in the valleys of the Swiss Alps, and convert the treads of the steps into basins. These barriers are termed *riegels*.

Complex Cross Profiles.—The transverse profile of a glaciated valley is generally not simply U-shaped, but is commonly made up of two distinct elements, giving a U-in-U form—a steep-sided inner U within a flatter, widely opened U or less symmetrical valley form. The steeper inner slope meets the upper slope at a distinct *shoulder*. Apart from effects due to stranding of lateral moraines (p. 340) and to development of structural benches by either glacial or preglacial erosion (which are common in parts of the European Alps) the bench above a shoulder has the appearance of a remnant of a valley existing before the inner trough was cut. In some valleys of the European Alps traces of several shoulders have been recognised one above another, but the upper benches are in most cases somewhat indefinite, having suffered much from erosional wear and tear.

In most glaciated regions, including Norway and New Zealand, one distinct shoulder is commonly present. Multiple benches are relatively rare; but, strangely enough, several shoulders appear in places on the extremely steep massive-rock walls of the fiord valleys in the Fiordland district of New Zealand.

A single satisfactory explanation of benched glacial profiles cannot be given, for it is probable that shoulders result from various causes. The complex cross profile does not seem at all analogous to the "valley-in-valley" form in normally eroded river valleys, for the glacier bed as a whole is not analogous to a river valley, the whole of the former being covered by the ice stream, but only a narrow ribbon of the latter by the water stream. Moreover, the downward limit of glacial erosion is not closely governed by base-level, as is that of river erosion.

To ascribe the excavation of the inner trough to overdeepening due to a thicker, heavier, and more rapidly flowing middle portion of the glacier would leave unexplained the sharpness of the angle at the shoulders between the upper benches and the slopes of the inner trough.

The benches have been regarded as remnants of the preglacial valleys (see figs. 300, 317), and from this point of view the inner trough only was the real channel of the glacier, and such marks of the presence of the ice as are found above the shoulders might then be ascribed to temporary overflow of the "banks," not enduring long enough to destroy the preglacial landforms. Evidence of

Fig. 317.—Trough separated by shoulders from upper, preglacial valley-side slopes, Routeburn Valley, New Zealand.

Rose, photo.

glacial erosion above the shoulders does not necessarily imply that a great thickness of rock has been removed from the benches, or that their form has been much modified.

Another explanation of glaciated shoulders ascribes inner, U-shaped glacier troughs to an epoch of glaciation later, and characterised by smaller glaciers, than that in which wider valleys above the shoulders were cut and glaciers reached their maximum size. Somewhat similar is the hypothesis that shoulders separate remnants of troughs cut in successive cold epochs of the Glacial Period. A variant of this hypothesis ascribes to glacial erosion in successive epochs the shaping of successive valley floors, but allows for very little glacial overdeepening, and assumes that the chief work of the glaciers has been to widen young river valleys cut as a response to uplift of the Alps immediately before the Glacial Period and in interglacial epochs of mild climate.

Fig. 318.—Benches separated by shoulders from the trough walls in the Vallée des Etançons, European Alps.

If, as seems probable, the inner glacial trough is commonly due to glacial overdeepening, the sharpness of the shoulder separating the inner trough from the bench above appears to emphasise the importance of the time factor. The duration of the period, or periods, of wide overflow must have been short as compared with the time during which the somewhat shrunken glacier has been engaged in overdeepening the inner trough. This is made evident by the manner in which the inner trough becomes prominent as existing glaciers—those of the Tasman system in New Zealand, for example—are approached. In the lower Tasman Valley (formerly occupied as far as the foot of Lake Pukaki by a glacier of enormous size) no inner trough is seen, but farther up the valley one appears, separated at first by shoulders from upper, gentler slopes. Still farther up, where the Tasman Glacier still exists, the trough form becomes dominant and in some places the shoulders are entirely cut away.[1]

A further cause of bench-development on the sides of glaciated valleys is a joining-together of the floors of adjacent corries where arêtes which formerly separated them have been eliminated by sapping (fig. 318). It is clear that shoulders of this kind will be found only in those parts of glaciated districts, generally the axes of mountain masses, where glaciation has been most intense and the preglacial forms have been destroyed, while remains of a preglacial landscape may be looked for on the outskirts of a glaciated district, where glaciers occupied only the trunk valleys.

Spur Truncation.—As glaciers deepen the valleys that they occupy they at the same time eliminate the smaller and smooth the larger curves by cutting off the ends of spurs. In some cases, where glaciers had insufficient time to modify their valleys to the form best suited to accommodate them, spurs may be seen partly truncated, the base of a spur surviving as a *knob field* (figs. 319, 320). Individual knobs may be large or small; they always exhibit the effects of scour and pluck, and smaller knobs may be typical roches moutonnées. Spurs in course of elimination may be the interlocking valley-side spurs of preglacially winding valleys that have not been greatly deepened by glaciation; in other cases they have projected between ice streams at a glacier confluence. Remnants of the latter kind may be found on the floors even of very deeply excavated troughs.

Where valley-side spurs have been merely cut off, so as to straighten a valley which is not overdeepened, the truncated ends of the spurs form gable-ends or enormous facets along the valley side (fig. 321). Here side valleys may enter almost accordantly and this type of trough is thus distinct from the overdeepened variety with continuous wall sides below the level of high-perched hanging tributaries (fig. 322).

---

[1] The Tasman Valley has been deeply aggraded during the retreat of the glacier; and the deep filling has much obscured the trough form in the lower valley.

Fig. 319.—Basal remnants of a great spur truncated by glacial erosion, entrance to South Fiord, Lake Te Anau, New Zealand. The tapering spurs to the north (right) have escaped truncation.

Fig. 320.—A knob field on the site of a worn-down spur of large dimensions, west side of Lake Wanaka, New Zealand.

C. A. Cotton, photo.

Glacial Lakes.—Lakes, both large and small, and innumerable tarns, are characteristic features of glaciated landscapes. Tarns occur in the scoured-out hollows of mammillated slopes and surfaces diversified by roches moutonnées, and on the uneven surfaces of morainic deposits, while some are enclosed by avalanche ramparts. These are built of fallen boulders accumulating at the present day around the fringes of aprons of winter avalanche snow which have been formed along the bases of steep side walls in abandoned glacial troughs (fig. 322A). Rock debris slides and rolls down the snow slopes.

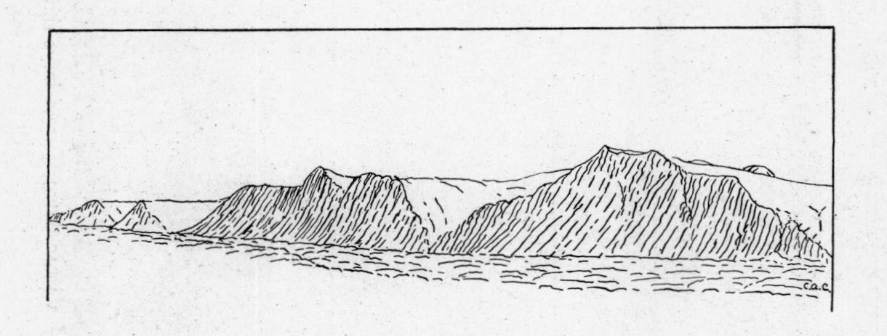

Fig. 321.—Trough-side facets bordering the Mackay Glacier, near Granite Harbour, Antarctica. (Drawn from a photograph.)

Some lakes, as previously mentioned, lie in rock-rimmed hollows (*rock basins*) due to differential erosion by valley glaciers and ice sheets, while others occur in valleys blocked by the deposition of morainic material. Many of the largest lakes—those occupying considerable lengths of greatly overdeepened troughs—owe their origin to a combination of the two causes. Such lakes are generally very deep, and, though the actual barriers that hold them up to their present levels may consist of moraines, the bottoms of the lakes are far below the levels of the bedrock foundations on which the morainic dams rest.

These long and deep lakes are present in the outer fringes of the mountain masses that have nourished great glaciers in the Ice Age, and occupy the distal parts of great mountain valleys overdeepened by the long ice tongues which have thrust their way far down towards the lowlands. They are therefore termed *piedmont lakes*. Classic examples are the North Italian lakes in the southern fringe of the Alps. Lake Wakatipu, in New Zealand, is

Fig. 322.—A wall-sided overdeepened trough, Clinton Valley, Fiordland, New Zealand. *Rose, photo.*

also a good and typical example. The greatest depth of this lake is 1242 feet and the lowest part of its floor is 227 feet below sea-level. It has a flat bottom and the trough-like transverse profile characteristic of the largest glacially eroded valleys. The morainic dam that holds it up rests on bedrock at no great depth, the lowest part of the rim of the rock basin being not less than 1000 feet above the deepest part of the lake bottom. In addition to the large piedmont lakes which still exist as such far more numerous smaller ones have had a short life and have been filled and buried beneath valley gravels or drained by deepening of the outlets, as has been the case, for example, in the Rakaia Valley, New Zealand, where lake silts are revealed by renewed river erosion.

Fig. 322A.—An apron of accumulated avalanche snow at the foot of the steep side wall in the Clinton Valley, New Zealand.

Rose, photo.

The rock basins in valleys that have been occupied by trunk glaciers, like those in corries (p. 309), appear to be due to heavy glacial corrasion where the ice was thickest—that is, between the regions of active alimentation and active ablation. Farther down the valleys, where the glaciers were dwindling, the thickness of the ice would be less, and so also would its weight and its ability to deepen the valleys. Thus reversed, or up-valley, slopes, giving rise to rock basins 1000 feet or more in depth, are the rule rather than the exception towards the outlets of the valleys formerly occupied by the great trunk glaciers of mountain regions. The up-valley slope of the floor does not imply a reversed slope of the ice surface, in which case it would be necessary to suppose that a considerable portion of each glacier near the terminal face was forced uphill as a rigid mass by pressure transmitted through the ice from the valley head. Reversed slopes of the ice surface, though not unknown in existing glaciers, are uncommon and are likely to occur only on a small scale. The great glaciers that excavated lake basins were thousands of feet in thickness where the ice was deepest, and, though the valley bottom sloped upward towards the terminal face, the ice surface had everywhere a down-valley slope sufficient to maintain the glacial flow. Even in a water stream it is only the surface that must slope always down the valley in order to maintain the flow; in the bottom of the channel there may be many holes and pockets.

Though piedmont lakes were among the first of the Alpine features to be confidently attributed to glacial erosion, it was with great reluctance that some European geologists would admit the ability of glaciers to excavate so deeply and locally. Thus alternative hypotheses of tectonic origin of rock-basin lakes were long maintained. So general is the occurrence of piedmont lakes that hypotheses of local down-faulting to account for each case were discredited; but some credence was given to a theory of general downwarping of the land surface along certain zones so as to impound lakes in the valleys. The drowned spurs and intricately branching outlines of lakes thus formed—Lake Kyoga, in Africa (p. 227), for example—are very different from the simple, wall-sided lines of piedmont lakes, however, and the theory is now discarded. If piedmont lakes branch at all it is generally in Y pattern with the arms of the Y directed distally—as in the case in Lake Como—where the glacier formerly in the valley divided in two by spilling over a preglacial divide and sending off a distributary ("glacial diffluence").

Fiords.—There is a very close family resemblance between piedmont lakes and *fiords*, which are sea-marginal glaciated troughs entered by the sea since the Ice Age. They differ only in that in the case of fiords a "threshold" considerably below sea-level takes the place of the rock-basin rim that impounds a lake. The depth of water on the threshold may be measured in hundreds of feet, but within the fiord the depth may be many times as great, indicating a strong probability that the glacially worn rock floor below such morainic deposits as may be present ascends seaward.

Ice-dammed Lakes.—Ice sheets and large glaciers lingering on lowlands towards the end of the last glacial epoch impounded water to form lakes in many valleys, and some enormous sheets of water existed in North America where it was held up between the edge of the continental glacier and a northward regional slope of the land. These were *proglacial* lakes; and a few small examples of the same kind exist to-day—notably in Greenland. Ice-borne debris came to be deposited abundantly in proglacial lakes, making important constructional landforms (Chapter XXIV). Shoreline terraces (Chapter XXXIII), in some cases perfectly preserved, indicate the lake levels; and where there are several of these—as at the Parallel Roads, Glen Roy, Scotland, for example—successively lower stands of the water are indicated, which are related to the levels of outlet gaps made available successively by shrinkage of the ice dams. Many deserted stream courses and eroded notches, now air gaps, in the hills forming the lake rims show also the positions of the temporary spillways of these ephemeral lakes.

The Postglacial Cycle.—A postglacial cycle of normal erosion and river deposition is now in progress in those regions from which glaciers have recently melted away. In the current cycle the general surface has not yet developed beyond the stage of youth, though parts of the courses of large rivers are graded so that such parts may be said to have entered on the stage of early maturity in the river cycle.

Small streams draining from cirques in hard rocks have succeeded as yet in cutting only very insignificant notches in their rims. Larger streams have cut some deep but extremely young trenches in trough-floor steps and the lips of hanging valleys (fig. 323). A well-known deep, but very narrow, "saw-cut" trench, the Aar Gorge, in Switzerland, breaks through a riegel; and many lakes temporarily held up by riegels in the postglacial landscape—as well as moraine-dammed lakes—have thus been drained.

Obviously such degradation has resulted from the presence of very steep descents—breaks of slope—in the initial gradients of postglacial streams. Steep descents of the glaciated profiles commonly alternate with nearly level reaches, or with concave basins, across which the postglacial streams have been compelled to aggrade to maintain their flow. Thus large parts of troughs are now occupied by local plains of aggradation, which not only bury the rock floors but conceal also traces of temporary lakes. A vast number of small lakes still remain unfilled, however, in situations where they have not been invaded by debris-laden rivers.

Fig. 323.—The Eggental, South Tyrol, a young trench cut by postglacial erosion.

The filling of lakes gives rise to some aggradation immediately upstream from them; but much more extensive aggradation is found to be in progress as the larger valleys are followed downstream, for the declivities of the bedrock floors soon become very gentle, approaching the horizontal. A little farther downstream, indeed, in many valleys the glaciated floors slope upstream, a condition which, as already noted, determines the existence of piedmont lakes in the postglacial cycle, while other lakes result from the presence of barriers of moraine. Where lakes due to one or other or both of these causes occur in the lower parts of the valleys they are rapidly reduced in size by the growth of deltas at their heads, and the growth of deltas is accompanied by aggradation farther up the valleys. Even where there are no initial lakes—that is, no reversed slopes of bedrock or morainic barriers—the declivities in large glaciated valleys are, in general, so gentle that the postglacial rivers, heavily laden as they are with waste from the erosion of glaciated slopes, must aggrade them strongly.

The valleys abandoned by large glaciers in New Zealand are thus very deeply aggraded. They have wide, gravel-covered bottoms, on which rivers such as the upper Waimakariri, Rakaia, and Rangitata,

Fig. 324.—The glaciated and more lately aggraded valley of the Dart, at the head of Lake Wakatipu, New Zealand.
F. G. Radcliffe, photo.

in Canterbury, and the Dart, Routeburn, and others at the head of Lake Wakatipu, in Otago, wander in braided courses (figs. 199, 324).

Part of the aggradation of glaciated valleys takes place while diminished glaciers still occupy the valley heads, their moraines supplying much of the waste. In the Tasman Valley, for example, a wide aggraded valley-plain of outwash gravel is actively growing and advancing as a delta into Lake Pukaki (Chapter XXIV).

Sources of the very abundant loads of postglacial rivers are to be found in the rapidly weathering bare-rock surfaces exposed on the oversteepened sides of troughs and in the steep, glacially sapped walls of cirques. At the bases of all such slopes talus is accumulating, and their postglacial grading is still very immature. So broad, however, are cirques and trough floors, on which talus and fans can accumulate, that little of the debris of postglacial disintegration has as yet been removed from hard-rock landscapes. On terrains of soft rock, however, screes meet at the axial lines of valleys and there deliver into rivers the rock rubble glissading down from the crumbling heights (fig. 325); and in the soft-schist mountains of western Otago, New Zealand, the flaring sides of the catenary

Fig. 325.—Talus slopes of rock debris from the sides of a small glacial trough, which are becoming graded in the postglacial cycle, Otira, New Zealand.

R. Speight, photo.

troughs of Ice Age glaciers are already submaturely dissected by postglacial ravines (fig. 326).

Changes in Drainage due to Glaciation.—Though many rivers, large and small, follow approximately the same lines in the postglacial as in the preglacial cycle, considerable changes in the drainage pattern may be brought about in various ways by glaciation.

Blocking of a drainage channel by an ice sheet or glacier tongue thrust across it so as to form an ice-dammed lake causes a stream to take a new course where the lake overflows, either around the snout of the glacier forming the obstruction or through some gap

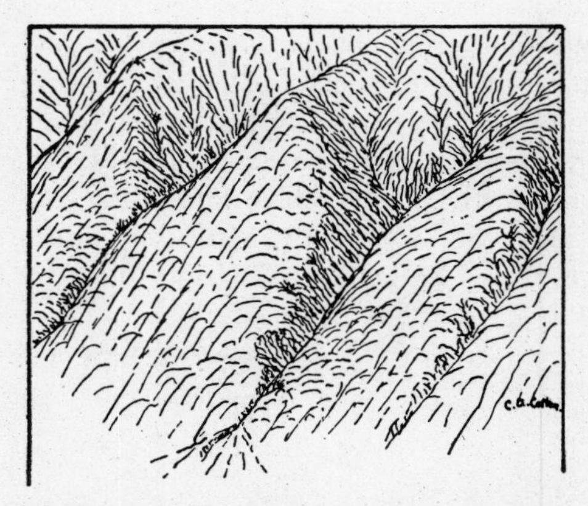

Fig. 326—Y valleys of superglacial with stems of postglacial origin, Lake Wakatipu trough, New Zealand.

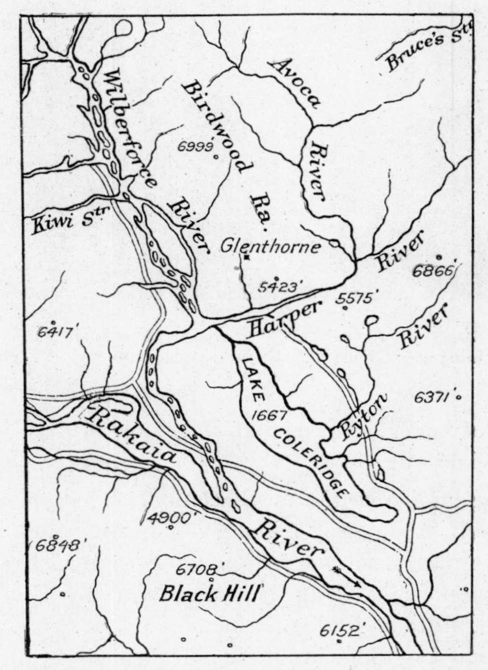

Fig. 327.—Map showing the diverted course of the Wilberforce River and the reversed drainage of Lake Coleridge, New Zealand.

in the surrounding hills, and when this condition persists long enough to allow the outlet gorge to be deeply cut the diversion of the stream may be permanent.

Another cause of changes in drainage is glacial "diffluence," where a glacier has split in two by spilling either over a preglacial divide or through a gap resulting from sapping of a cirque wall. The channel of the distributary thus formed has been in some cases so deepened by the ice as to be followed by a postglacial water stream in preference to its former course, which may also be partially blocked by morainic deposits. The latter cause alone may pond a stream so that it spills over along a new course.

On the southern slopes of the European Alps diffluence frequently took place in the widely extended glaciers of the Glacial Period. In New Zealand also numerous departures from the preglacial drainage pattern due to this cause have taken place. In the neighbourhood of the Rakaia Valley the preglacial course of the Wilberforce River, for example, was through the valley now occupied by Lake Coleridge, the direction of drainage in which has been reversed (fig. 327).

CHAPTER XXIV

CONSTRUCTIONAL FORMS OF GLACIAL DRIFT

Glacial deposits. End moraines. Moraine loops. Lateral moraine terraces. Erratics. Glacial drift. Drumlins. Kames. Eskers. Outwash plains.

Glacial Deposits.—Ice streams like water streams may become overloaded. When the ice of a glacier or ice sheet has moved far outward from the centre of accumulation it has picked up so much waste that it loses its erosive activity, and as the thickness of the ice dwindles owing to melting it begins to deposit its load. *Ground moraine* is then plastered on the landscape overrun by ice. When, finally, owing to climatic change increasing the rate of melting, the ice front rapidly retreats, or a glacier, or part of one, becomes stagnant and melts in place, the remaining load is dropped. Many large boulders, as well as vast quantities of finer material, remain scattered over large areas, and help to indicate the former great extension of the ice. Boulders left standing conspicuously on slopes and hilltops are termed *perched blocks* (fig. 332).

Some of the boulders and pebbles of hard rocks which have been dragged along under the ice show evidence of considerable wear, having the angles rounded, while the sides are worn more or less flat and are polished and striated. The striae (grooves and scratches) sometimes run in various directions, showing that the boulder was twisted about as it was dragged along. Such boulders and pebbles are the tools with the aid of which the ice did its erosive work.

End Moraines.—Some of the morainic material delivered by a glacier at its terminal face is carried away by the streams formed by the melting of the ice, but some of the coarse waste is dropped in heaps, forming *terminal* or *end moraines*. Rapid melting of one of the heavily waste-covered glaciers east of the main divide of the New Zealand Alps would leave stranded a broad belt of its surface moraine (fig. 283) and englacial debris.

Glaciers are subject to short-period fluctuation in length owing to variation in the snowfall at their heads. Thus a glacier may deposit moraine as it retreats for a few years and later advance again over it. End moraines are thus overridden, or may in some cases be rucked up into ridges; but most moraine barriers in which ridges are present consist in the main of heaps of boulders (or, in other cases, of the finer glacial debris carried in quantity by some glaciers) lying just as the material has been dropped or has fallen from the melting snout of a glacier.

At or near the position of the ice front at the stage of maximum advance of the ice morainic barriers of considerable dimensions may

Fig. 328.—End moraine at Kingston, New Zealand, blocking the end of the Lake Wakatipu basin (partially planed and terraced by a river that was temporarily the outlet of the lake).

C. A. Cotton, photo.

be present. Piedmont lakes, as noted in Chapter XXIII, are generally impounded in part by such barriers (fig. 328).

Ridges of end moraine deposited after the maximum of glaciation has been passed—that is, dropped while the glacier front has halted for a time during the final shrinkage—are sometimes distinguished as *recessional moraines*.

Along the lines marking the fronts of former continental glaciers both terminal and recessional moraines assume the dimensions of belts of low hills with the characteristic hummocky ("knob-and-kettle") forms of indiscriminately dumped material.

Moraine Loops.—A glacier debouching from a mountain valley on to a lowland and there spreading to form a paw-like expansion (an *expanded-foot* glacier), deposits around its margin a long arcuate terminal moraine. Such a *loop* is well developed where the Mueller Glacier debouches into the wide Hooker valley, in New Zealand (fig. 329). Moraine loops, which are really end moraines, may pass at the sides into stranded lateral moraines.

Fig. 329.—Moraine loops (older and younger) which enclose the somewhat expanded foot of the Mueller Glacier, New Zealand. The glacier is at the left, and the loops are viewed from the distal end.

C. A. Cotton, photo.

Lateral Moraine Terraces.—Shrinkage of a glacier in a valley that is not too steep-sided results in the stranding of its lateral moraines, which form distinct terraces on the valley sides, sloping down the valley with the inclination of the ice surface at the time of deposit (fig. 330).

End moraines and stranded lateral moraines are built alike of material of all sorts and sizes, from boulders as large as houses to the finest rock flour, but rather coarse material generally predominates.

It is all deposited without sorting and without stratification. Some boulders are smooth and polished by attrition, while others (which have been carried on the surface of the ice) are quite angular. The proportion of rounded to angular boulders, and of coarse to fine material, varies very much in different glaciers, on different terrains, and with the extent to which glaciers have buried the landscape.

Fig. 330.—The broad surface of one of several lateral moraine terraces deposited during rapid shrinkages of the great Tasman Glacier, New Zealand.

F. G. Radcliffe, photo.

The topography of moraines is remarkable chiefly for its irregularity (fig. 330), organised valley systems such as are produced by normal erosion being naturally absent. There are many undrained hollows forming lakes and tarns, or swamps when partially filled in. The moraines deposited in the latest glacial epoch of the Ice Age have generally been little modified since by normal erosion; but where moraines are found which have survived from earlier epochs they are generally somewhat dissected, and the materials composing them may be considerably weathered, contrasting strongly in this respect with fresh morainic material more recently deposited.

Erratics.—Glaciers did not always remain confined to the pre-existing valley systems, but, where the ice accumulation became thick enough, overflowed former divides, which, unless much worn down by glacial erosion, have become divides again after the disappearance of the ice. Much waste has, therefore, been transported by ice across existing divides. Boulders carried in this way from one valley system to another, and, in general, those deposited by ice in positions to which they could not have been transported by normal agencies, if they are recognisable as such owing to the rock composing them being of a kind foreign to the districts in which they are dropped, are termed *erratics.* The perched block shown in fig. 332 is an erratic.

Glacial Drift.—Ice sheets are most active in eroding near the centres of accumulation, and most active in depositing waste near their margins. In the intervening areas they erode in some places and deposit in others. The discontinuous sheet of waste thus spread over a great part of North America and northern Europe by the ice sheets of the Glacial Period is termed generally *drift;* but as commonly understood "drift" includes not only morainic, or glacier-laid, material but also debris of glacier origin which has been carried a short distance and then deposited by water—*fluvioglacial* (or "glaciofluvial") drift. Much of the glacier-laid material has originated as a subglacial deposit; it is *ground moraine,* and often contains much sand and clay, as well as rock fragments, being then termed *till* (also "boulder clay"). Mixed with it are more or less worn pebbles, cobbles, and boulders, some of them "soled" (rubbed flat on one side), rounded on the edges, polished, and striated.

In some places the ground moraine forms a sheet of fairly uniform thickness, reproducing subdued topographic forms of the underlying surface; but elsewhere it varies irregularly in thickness and produces new landforms with weaker or stronger relief than those of the floor on which it lies.

Drumlins.—Elongated mounds or short ridges, generally of smooth and symmetrical form and built of rather clayey till, are termed *drumlins.* Typically they are elliptical or half-egg shaped with moderate surface slopes (fig. 331). Most of them result from irregular deposit of thick ground moraine; but some may have been shaped out of earlier-formed till deposits. All have been moulded and streamlined by the advance of ice sheets or large valley glaciers over them. They are elongated in the direction of movement of the ice. In some northern parts of the United States vast drumlin swarms cover great areas of lowland. In the European Alps zones of drumlins lie just within some large end-moraine loops and ridges.

Some drumlins have bedrock cores, the ground moraine having been plastered down apparently on an uneven rock floor. These *rock drumlins* (fig. 332) grade into *crag-and-tail* forms. The latter consist of ice-smoothed knobs of solid rock which give place leeward to tapering streamlined tails of ground moraine instead of termin-

Fig. 331.—A drumlin, near Newark, New York.
U.S. Geol. Survey: *G. K. Gilbert, photo.*

ating in plucked surfaces of rock like typical roches moutonnées. Crag-and-tail forms are common on the Scottish lowland.

Kames.—Unlike drumlins *kames* consist of water-laid sand and gravel of glacial origin, and generally form somewhat irregular terraces, *kame terraces* (fig. 333), which have been deposited commonly by streams of water flowing at the sides of glaciers near the snout. Where deposited against stagnant ice they may retain "ice-contact" faces which have been moulded on irregular ice margins. Somewhat similar terraces may have been deposited as deltas in standing water ponded beside stagnant slabs of ice. Where isolated blocks of ice have been buried by the gravels, subsequent melting of the ice has caused large, deep, bowl-shaped pits (*kettles*) to be

Fig. 332.—Rock drumlins of somewhat irregular form and a very large perched, erratic block, Arrow Flat, Queenstown district, New Zealand.

J. Park, photo.

Fig. 333.—Kame terrace, near Somers, Connecticut.

R. F. Flint, photo.

formed in these and other deposits of fluvioglacial gravel. Very irregular surfaces have resulted where the deposits of sand and gravel have been spread over sheets of stagnant ice which have subsequently melted.

Lone kames are isolated mounds of stratified material possibly deposited originally in embayments of the margin of stagnant ice or in hollows of its surface from which they have been afterwards let down by melting.

In Ireland similar accumulation of deltaic sands and gravels seems to have taken place in lakes impounded among the wasting remnants of an ice cap which had occupied the central lowland. This is an explanation given of the origin of extensive clusters of low hills of irregular form, composed of fluvioglacial material and known as "eskers"—though they are not eskers in the technical usage of the term conventionally accepted in geomorphology.

Fig. 334.—An esker in Minnesota.

Eskers.—True *eskers* (fig. 334) are long sinuous ridges, even-crested and as symmetrical in cross profile as railway embankments. They are superimposed, however, on other features of the landscape, passing up and down over gentle declivities. They are composed of rather regularly stratified sand and gravel, generally with deltaic bedding, and the running water from which the beds were deposited was either in or just emerging from the mouths of ice tunnels. Some eskers may be in part moulds of tunnels in which they were deposited; but probably their commonest mode of growth was as deltas in standing water (proglacial lakes) into which the melt-water streams from tunnels discharged below the surface. As the margin of the ice melted back, deposition of a tunnel-mouth delta followed it so as to build a continuous ridge like a long "squeeze" of toothpaste. Another mode of formation is responsible for producing some esker-like ridges, however, which are moulds of crevasses in stagnant ice. Such crevasse-fillings have been formed in the manner suggested above for lone kames.

An ice front which is delivering melt-water and debris through a tunnel into a proglacial lake may remain stationary for some time, so that it may build a quite large delta (perhaps a considerable fraction of a square mile in area) consisting of inclined ("back-set" and fore-set) and also top-set beds. It has a flat, gravelly top-set surface and a steep fore-set-sloping front with lobate margin—a lobe built forward by each distributing branch stream. Melting of the ice has left some such deltas isolated as mesa-like forms. They may be pitted on the top and on the proximal ("back-set") slope by kettles; and are attached flower-like to esker stems.

Some fluvioglacial gravel and sand is built also into marginal deltas and beach deposits that fringe and make the outlines of temporary proglacial lakes.

Outwash Plains.—Where glaciers and ice sheets discharge not against the regional slope (so as to impound lakes as they shrink back) but in the direction of slope of the land surface, melt-water flows away from them freely and carries with it much of the debris delivered by the ice at the terminal face. In general much of this fluvioglacial debris is deposited by the melt-water rivers as they are compelled to aggrade down-valley from the ice front. So abundant is the gravel in most cases that the off-flowing rivers require steep gradients to carry it, and must therefore deposit gravel to build such gradients up. For this reason aggraded plains, termed *valley trains,* were built down-valley from many glacier termini even at the height of a glacial epoch.

During slow shrinkage of glaciers, accompanied by retreat of the ice fronts, enormous loads of debris have become available for river transport and have been deposited in progressively abandoned glacial troughs. Dwindling of glaciers exposes much bare-rock surface and thus greatly accelerates the supply of frost-riven fragments, which stream down as rock talus on to the diminished glaciers so that they become filled with and buried under the load of angular debris they transport—as in the case of the surviving glaciers in New Zealand (figs. 283, 335). All this rock debris is available as a load for the melt-water rivers, and if there is more of it than they can carry away it must be deposited as moraines.

Absence of very conspicuously piled end moraines—and in most cases in New Zealand absence of any such deposits at the present ice fronts—suggests that much debris is laid down as ground moraine under progressively rising glacier snouts, and that this becomes covered by layers of outwash gravel as the glaciers shrink back.

Especially where reversed slopes have existed on bedrock floors, and shrinkage of glaciers has not been so rapid as to leave open the

Fig. 335.—The Mueller Glacier, New Zealand, covered with ablation moraine from side to side. This provides abundant gravel for building a valley train.
C. A. Cotton, photo.

trough-floor hollows as lake basins, much deposition of ground moraine must have taken place.

In the case of a glacier supplying but little debris, so that it shrinks back without depositing moraine under it and thus rising to a higher level, the maximum aggraded plain of outwash gravel may be trenched and terraced during the wasting-away of the glacier. In many cases, however, deep trenching of the outwash (which has very commonly taken place) is the result of dissection in the postglacial cycle, when final melting of the glaciers has been followed by a falling-off of the supply of waste from the mountains or the debris of postglacial weathering is trapped in up-valley basins yet unfilled. The rivers of the Canterbury alluvial plain in New Zealand, the great confluent fans of which are built of glacial outwash gravel, have trenched the surface very deeply—600 feet in the case of the Rakaia River (fig. 205).

CHAPTER XXV

VOLCANOES AND VOLCANIC PRODUCTS

Igneous action. Volcanic contributions to the atmosphere. Steam jets and hot springs. Volcanic landscape forms. Destructive volcanic action. Constructive volcanic action. Rock-forming materials emitted from volcanoes. Lava flows. Scoria and bombs. Pumice and ash. Ignimbrite sheets.

Igneous Action.—*Volcanic action* is one phase of *igneous action,* the other phase being *intrusion.* While volcanic action consists in the emission of material from *volcanoes,* which are vents at the earth's surface, the term "intrusion" is applied to the injection of hot fluid rock into fissures and cavities, which are enlarged in the process, but in many cases do not lead to the surface as feeding channels of volcanoes.

The hot fluid rock in the interior of the earth is termed *magma.* When it emerges on the surface it is known as *lava.* When it has solidified either on or beneath the surface as a result of cooling and the loss of its more volatile constituents, such as water and certain gases, it forms *igneous rocks.* The magma which has solidified as the known igneous rocks, volcanic and intrusive, has probably come from fused spots at a depth of a good many miles, but not from a continuous liquid interior. There are reasons for believing that the substance of the earth beneath the lithosphere, though very hot, is kept solid for the most part by the enormous pressure exerted by the weight of overlying rocks. It is, at any rate, rigid and immobile.

There has been igneous activity throughout all stages of the earth's long history. Volcanic rocks similar to those emitted as lavas by present-day volcanoes are found interbedded with the sedimentary rocks of all ages, and large intrusive bodies of igneous rock, such as granite, are also of many different ages.

While it is known that volcanic action is a phenomenon that is not peculiar to the present period, there is no reason, on the other hand, to suppose that the igneous activity of the earth is dying out. For an immense period the activity seems to have been, on the average, about the same as at present.

Volcanic Contributions to the Atmosphere.—In addition to altering landscape forms and spreading new deposits on the surface of the lithosphere volcanic action supplies great volumes of gases to the atmosphere. Much water ejected as gas into the atmosphere is condensed and added to the ocean. Other gases—sulphur and compounds of sulphur, hydrochloric acid, and chlorides, for example—solidify or are soluble or are quickly oxidised to form soluble compounds, and are dissolved or washed out of the atmosphere by rain. Carbon dioxide, however, being soluble only to a limited extent, is added to the atmosphere unaltered.

The amount of carbon dioxide in the atmosphere is quite small—three parts in ten thousand. The amount of carbon locked up in the rocks in the form of limestone and coal, all of which is derived from atmospheric carbon dioxide, however, represents a quantity tens of thousands of times as great as the volume of carbon dioxide now in the atmosphere. According to an old theory, this enormous quantity of carbon dioxide is regarded as having been all in the atmosphere at one time in an early stage of the earth's history. Before the removal of the greater part of the carbon from the atmosphere, however, the earth was clothed with vegetation and inhabited by animals differing but little from those now living, and it seems impossible that these could have existed in an atmosphere so different from that in which plants and animals are now adapted to live. Moreover, the nature of the sediments formed during past geological periods indicates weathering under atmospheric conditions similar to those now ruling. We are therefore compelled to believe that volcanic action, which is to-day supplying carbon dioxide to the atmosphere, has in the past supplied in this way, little by little, all the carbon that is now present in the limestone and coal of the lithosphere. The proportion of carbon dioxide in the atmosphere, while it has, no doubt, varied from time to time, may never have been very markedly different from what it is to-day.

Steam Jets and Hot Springs.—In many volcanic districts *fumaroles* (steam jets) and *hot springs* occur abundantly. Hot springs are not in all cases of volcanic origin; many, which are related to deeply extending fault fissures, supply water of surface origin which has flowed through underground channels at such a depth that it has become heated by contact with hot rocks. The source of heat in volcanic districts, on the other hand, is mainly steam coming from underlying igneous magma. A small quantity of this superheated steam is sufficient to heat up a considerable volume of ground water (fig. 336).

A volcano the activity of which has waned to the emission of steam and sulphurous gases from points within the crater is termed

Fig. 336.—A boiling waterfall in a stream fed by hot springs, Waimangu, New Zealand.

Rose, photo.

a *solfatara*. White Island, in the Bay of Plenty, New Zealand, is a volcano that has reached the solfataric stage (fig. 337). The last vestige of activity may be the presence of a crater lake kept warm by emission of steam, as in the case of the New Zealand volcano Ruapehu.

The water of hot springs brings to the surface quantities of mineral substances in solution, among which is silica. Silica is deposited around some vents as an incrustation of *siliceous sinter,*

Fig. 337.—White Island, Bay of Plenty, New Zealand (a volcano at the solfataric stage). Rock mounds on the crater floor are relics of a recent small volcanic mudflow.
Stewart and White, photo.

Fig. 338.—Cone of siliceous sinter surrounding the orifice of a small geyser, the Crow's Nest, near Taupo, New Zealand.
N.Z. Tourist Department, photo.

protecting the ground from erosion and sometimes building conspicuous mounds (fig. 338). Sinter deposits form the surface in parts of the Rotorua and Taupo districts of New Zealand, and the celebrated Pink and White Terraces, at Rotomahana, which were destroyed by the Tarawera eruption (1886), were also built of this material.

Where the conduits are lined with sinter hot springs emerge as clear streams. In other cases steam bubbles through mud formed

Fig. 339.—Mud volcano at Waiotapu, New Zealand.
F. G. Radcliffe, photo.

from volcanic rock decomposed by hot acid water and ground to an impalpable paste by the constant stirring due to uprise of steam through the mud. Around some springs this mud is built into cones, which are termed *mud volcanoes* (fig. 339).

A hot spring from which a column of water is shot out at regular or irregular intervals is a *geyser* (fig. 339A). The giant geyser Waimangu, which is now no longer active, made its appearance beside one of a linear series of small explosion craters formed by the Tarawera eruption of 1886, in New Zealand (fig. 340). Being a new geyser it had not lined its pipe with sinter, and it therefore threw out a column of dark and muddy water. This attained a maximum height of considerably over 1000 feet. Smaller geysers remain in operation in the Rotorua-Taupo volcanic district of New Zealand, as well as in Iceland and the Yellowstone Park (U.S.).

Volcanic Landscape Forms.—Those materials which are ejected from volcanoes in the solid state, together with the fluid rock which

Fig. 339A.—The Wairoa Geyser, at Whakarewarewa, New Zealand, emitted clear water from a sinter-lined orifice.

J. R. Blencowe, photo.

after flowing out quickly cools and solidifies, build new landforms. Large areas of the earth's surface owe either the actual forms they now exhibit or the initial relief from which those forms were sculptured to the accumulation of material of volcanic origin. In many of these regions volcanic action is now extinct, but the source of the material and the origin of forms built of it are quite clear from analogy with the products of volcanoes that are still active.

Destructive Volcanic Action.—Volcanic activity is mainly constructive as a geomorphic agent; but locally it is destructive in the same sense as gully erosion is destructive, in that it produces hollow forms such as craters and crater-like chasms by explosion, subsidence, and engulfment. Full consideration of these may be deferred; but the effects of the Tarawera eruption of 1886, in New Zealand, may be cited as an example of explosive volcanic action, without attempting to develop a theory to account for the origin of the phenomena.

Fig. 340.—A volcanic explosion crater adjoining the throat of the Waimangu Geyser, New Zealand. *F. G. Radcliffe, photo.*

The eruption blew out a line of craters and elongated pits (fig. 341), forming a nearly continuous trench about nine miles long, with a mean width of about an eighth of a mile and a depth varying from 300 to 1400 feet. This "rift" passes across the top of Mount Tarawera (fig. 342), which is a dome or mesa of volcanic rock, and continues in a south-westerly direction for some distance, becoming wider and shallower, and forming the basin of the present Lake Rotomahana, which is larger than the lake of the same name existing before the eruption. Farther south-westward it is continued by a line of small craters (fig. 340). Much fine material was ejected to a great height and carried away by wind to be deposited as a widespread ash shower; but coarser fragments blown out in smaller

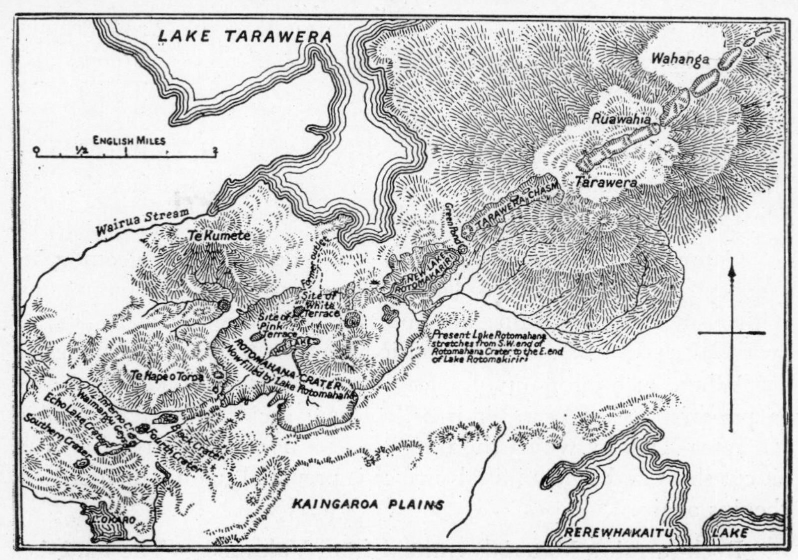

Fig. 341.—Map of the Tarawera volcanic rift soon after the eruption of 1886. After Bell (*Geographical Journal*, vol. 40, 1912).

Fig. 342.—Mount Tarawera, showing the "Chasm," part of the rift opened by the explosion of 1886, in New Zealand. Nearer at hand is the pumice-mud deposit of material ejected from Lake Rotomahana. *C. A. Cotton, photo.*

amount by the explosion came to rest round about. Around Lake Rotomahana there is a deposit of a mixture of rock fragments and mud derived entirely from the pre-existing landscape. This buried and destroyed the vegetation over a large area, and wrecked several villages. More than a hundred persons were killed, and the loss of human life would have been much greater but for the fact that the district was very sparsely peopled.

Constructive Volcanic Action.—Considered as a geomorphic agency volcanic activity is largely constructive. Great mountains, either singly or in groups, are built up, and large areas are flooded with lava (fig. 350) or deeply buried beneath fragmentary material.

Where such piling-up of volcanic lava and debris takes place over a pre-existing landscape it is a "volcanic accident," referred to in Chapter XVI, by which the progress of a normal geomorphic cycle it cut short and a new initial surface is prepared upon which erosion begins again.

Rock-forming Materials emitted from Volcanoes.—The materials emitted from volcanoes (in addition to the gases mentioned above) are both liquid and solid. The liquid material, or lava, consists of a mixture of minerals, chiefly silicates, in a state of fusion, or of solution the one in the other. It varies widely in mineral and hence also in chemical composition, and so forms on solidification a considerable variety of rocks. By the time the lava flows out on the surface it has lost a great part of the gaseous constituents which formed an integral part of the magma within the lithosphere, and most of the remainder escape during cooling.

Lava Flows.—The temperature of lava when emitted is generally between 1000° and 1500° C. and not far above the solidifying point. It is still sufficiently liquid to flow, but the liquidity is very variable, varying to some extent with the temperature, but depending to a greater extent on the chemical composition of the lava. In general lavas that have the composition of the rock basalt[1] are liquid when emitted and flow very freely; while most other lavas, and especially those richest in silica (the "acid" lavas) are relatively viscid,

---

[1] Considered chemically basalt is a "basic" lava—poor in silica and rich in iron and magnesia. It is dark-coloured and heavy. "Rhyolite," at the other extreme, is rich in silica—an "acid" lava—and is specifically lighter and also light in colour. "Trachyte" and "andesite" lavas are "intermediate" in every way between basalt and rhyolite.

congealing generally as thick convex-surfaced tongues even on rather steep slopes.

Some free-flowing basalt lava flows, which spread out widely and thinly, freeze over with a smooth satiny skin, beneath which liquid lava still runs. This gives rise to the *pahoehoe* type of lava surface (fig. 343). The skin before it is hard and brittle assumes inflated, billowy forms, or is wrinkled or drawn out into a "ropy" surface. This lava advances as a succession of small freely-flowing tongues each of which freezes over, so that it becomes a tube through

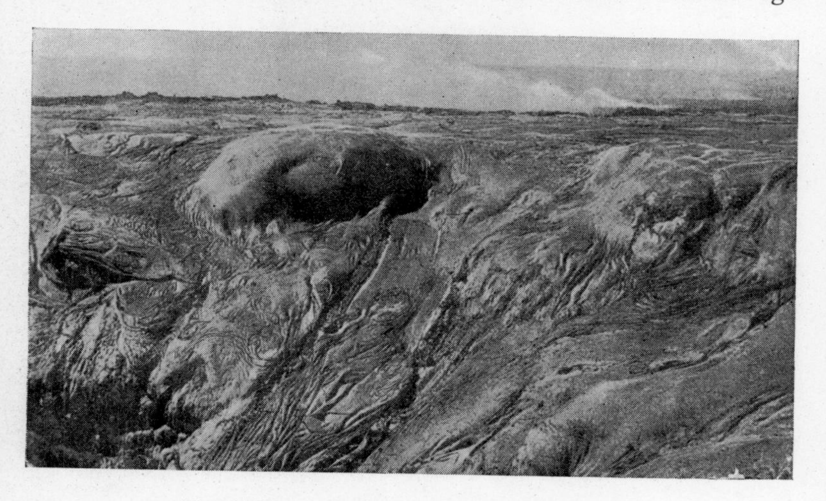

Fig. 343.—A pahoehoe lava flow, Savaii, Samoa.

which liquid lava runs to form a new frontal extension of the flow. Where the lava has run out and left such a tube empty it may remain open as a cavern or tunnel (fig. 344), and such caverns are common wherever there are pahoehoe lava flows. Collapsed tunnels also remain as trenches separating parallel ridges on some lava plains.

Another feature of minor relief is the *lava blister*. A blistered surface has been formed when a rather thin flow has invaded low, wet ground and pockets of steam have been generated under it. The blisters remain as permanent hillocks on some lava plains (fig. 345). Pressure domes and ridges also are rucked up; these are generally cracked along the top.

Other lava flows, including some composed of basaltic lava of the same chemical composition as pahoehoe, advance and cool with a

Fig. 344.—A lava tunnel in Hawaii.

Fig. 345.—Lava blisters, which have been developed where basalt has spread out over a wet valley bottom, near Poroti, New Zealand.

C. A. Cotton, photo.

blocky or cinder-like surface of *scoria* lumps (fig. 346). Where this scoria is very much inflated (vesicular) and has been drawn out into spinous projections by escape of gas from it the lava flow is typical *aa*.[1] In Hawaii aa flows are sluggish as a whole, though rivers of freely-flowing liquid lava rush over their surfaces. They come to rest with steep fronts. Scoria blocks on some lava flows become rounded by rolling as forward movement of the flow continues. Falling down the steep front they may be overridden by

Fig. 346.—Blocky, scoriaceous, or aa surface of a lava flow on the summit of Mount Tongariro, New Zealand. *R. Speight, photo.*

the flow, so that there is a layer of scoria blocks under as well as over the lava. The advance of such a flow is very noisy.

Scoria and Bombs.—In addition to lava poured forth in the liquid state there is a vast amount of rock material of similar origin ejected explosively as fragments, large and small, which have cooled sufficiently to be solid or nearly solid when they fall to the ground. In some cases the fragments are scoria in a general way similar to that which is formed by solidification on aa lava surfaces. Typical

[1] "Pahoehoe" and "aa" are Hawaiian terms.

scoria is basaltic in composition. Mixed with scoria—amongst that, for example, forming the volcanic hills near Auckland, New Zealand—*volcanic bombs* are sometimes found. Some probably originate as fragments of the skins of enormous gas bubbles which rise to the surface of lava in a crater and there burst. The fragments of lava are hurled through the air, rotating meanwhile and assuming a spheroidal form with twisted, corkscrew-like ends. By the time they fall to the ground they have cooled and solidified sufficiently to retain their shape, except that they are generally somewhat flattened by the impact of their fall.

Some scoria may be lava that has solidified as a crust on the free surface of a lava column in an open crater and has been afterwards ejected explosively. The origin of much basaltic scoria, however, is attributed to "fire-fountain" phenomena such as have been observed at vents in which basalt lava rises in Hawaii. Continuous jets of gas from the lava are emitted under such pressure that they carry up with them columns of large lava blebs, which solidify and fall round about as cinder-like scoria.

Some volcanoes, in the "vulcanian" phase of activity, named from Vulcano, in the Mediterranean, eject only blocks and fragments of lava which has frozen over in the crater. Common among the fragments are "bread-crust" bombs, named from their cracked-crust appearance. Eruptions of such material are spasmodic. Explosions which renew activity in previously dormant volcanoes eject at first only solid fragments of old rock, but generally some derived from new lava soon make their appearance.

Pumice and Ash.—The more viscid—that is, generally non-basaltic—lavas become much inflated owing to liberation of gas throughout the body of material in the conduit through which lava is rising to the surface. Expansion of the gas owing to relief of pressure as the surface is approached provides the motive power for the explosive ejection of material. It also converts some lavas into a foam which when solidified makes *pumice*. Pumice may be ejected in large lumps; or the process of gas-emission may reduce the material to small pellets (*lapilli*) or practically to a powder consisting of tubular shreds of glass and isolated minute crystals of minerals in course of separation from the cooling lava. Such fine *ash* (not "ash" in the sense of being a product of combustion, however), mixed in varying proportions with the coarser grades of material, is ejected very abundantly from some volcanoes, and when it comes to rest and is consolidated into a compact material becomes *tuff*. When newly fallen much of it is like mud.

The finest ash forms part of some of the smoke-like clouds emitted from volcanoes, and these may rain down volcanic mud.

Layers of pumice and ash scattered and distributed very widely by volcanic explosions cover the landscape surface as *shower* deposits

Fig. 347.—Ash beds of widespread "shower" origin, at Tiroa, near the centre of the North Island of New Zealand.
H. T. Ferrar, photo.

over many thousands of square miles in the central part of the North Island of New Zealand from the east to the west coast (fig. 347). The successive ash showers that cover this region have come from different sources, which are not all known with certainty, but some late showers, consisting of acid pumice and ash, are traced to an origin in craters within the area covered by Lake Taupo, and some other explosion pits are known (fig. 348). Among the shower layers are some of very fine material which have accumulated very slowly ("ash layers of intermittent origin") and may very well be called volcanic loess. Other layers have resulted from single great eruptions ("ash beds of paroxysmal origin"). The Taupo shower, referred to above, is one of these. Pumiceous material of Taupo origin (30 or 40 miles from the source) forms the upper layer in fig. 348. It is more than 6 inches thick over an area of 8800 square miles, and near the source consists of large pumice lumps. Compared with this paroxysm the explosion of Tarawera in 1886 (p. 354) was a small affair, for the shower which resulted from it was more than 6 inches thick over an area of only 600 square miles. It is recognisable, however, over about 4000 square miles, and attains a thickness of 170 feet on the brink of the Tarawera rift from which it was emitted, consisting there of coarse scoria lumps and bombs

Fig. 348.—The Tikitapu explosion crater, near Rotorua, New Zealand, from which pumice and ash have been widely distributed as a "shower."

C. A. Cotton, photo.

of a sort consisting of fragments of the white rock forming the walls of the rift (fig. 342), coated with skins of a dark lava into which they have fallen.

Ignimbrite Sheets.—Glowing lava has sometimes been ejected in fine shreds and clots of liquid, accompanied in some cases by larger solidified fragments, all of which are still giving off vapour, so that they do not become cooled by contact with the atmosphere but form a sort of gaseous emulsion that flows very freely down land slopes and will spread out widely on a lowland if produced in sufficient quantity. A great "sand flow," as it has been termed, in the Valley of Ten Thousand Smokes, near Katmai volcano, in

Alaska, which was emitted in 1912, had such an origin. There are indications that this volcanic sand was still at a red heat when it came to rest. It was emitted probably from a number of vents, and was produced in sufficient quantity to fill a very large valley.

"Glowing clouds" (*nuées ardentes*) of similar material driven out horizontally by the explosive force of their own generation during periods of activity from bodies of hot, viscid lava squeezed out at the summit of Mt. Pelée, in Martinique, rush with great

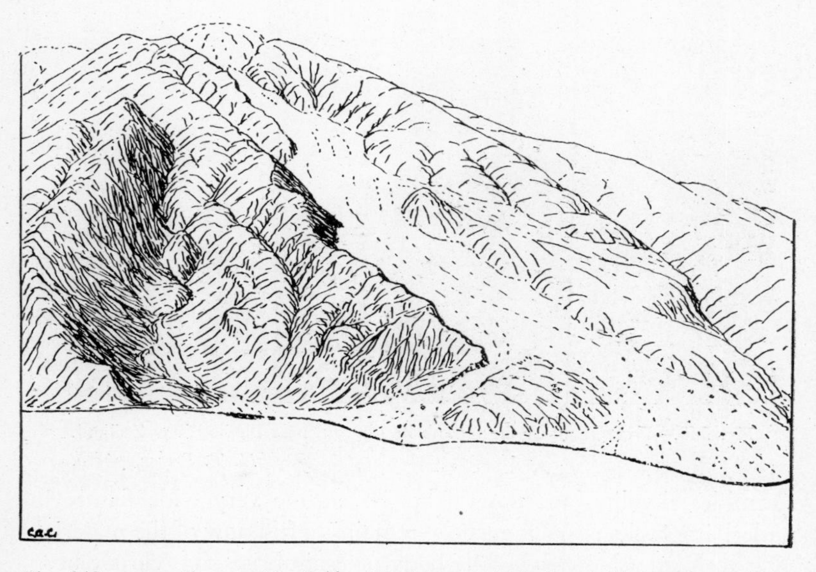

Fig. 348A.—A valley on Mt. Pelée, Martinique, which has guided *nuées ardentes* down the mountain-side and has become filled with lava rubble derived from them. (From photographs.)

velocity as fiery avalanches down the mountain-side into the sea. So well lubricated by cushions of expanding gas are the hot solid fragments which make up a part of the glowing clouds that the rush of these avalanches is quite silent. As a result of the emission of very numerous *nuées ardentes* during the eruptions of 1929-32 not only has a great valley been filled to the brim with debris but a delta-like salient has been built out from the shoreline (fig. 348A), and there is an enormous submarine accumulation of the finer ash, which has travelled far from the source.

Though loose and sandy at the surface, the material of the Katmai "sand flow" may be welded into firm rock below. Such welding of red-hot rock particles of glowing-cloud origin is believed to have produced the rock of the *ignimbrite* plateau, a feature of wide extent in the central and north-east central districts of the North Island of New Zealand, the rock of which in some places

Fig. 349.—Escarpment of the ignimbrite plateau, near Piopio, New Zealand.
H. T. Ferrar, photo.

resembles rhyolite lava flows (fig. 349). One very wide fissure in underlying rocks near Ongarue[1]—remaining full now of the material, so as to form a large dyke-like body of ignimbrite—has clearly been a source of the *nuées ardente* material; and there may be many others. Low-lying at first, probably, the ignimbrite sheet has been upwarped and block-faulted. It was in existence before most of the other volcanic features of the region made their appearance.

---

[1] Made known to the writer by courtesy of Dr. P. Marshall, who has described and named "ignimbrite."

CHAPTER XXVI

LAVA FLOODS AND BASALT DOMES

Lava plateaux and plains. Dissection of lava sheets. Inverted relief. Volcanic lakes and river diversion. Basalt cones. Scoria mounds. Basalt domes. Dissection of basalt domes.

Lava Plateaux and Plains.—Widely extending piles of lava sheets with the nearly horizontal surfaces which are common where the lava has been of a free-flowing basaltic kind may bury pre-existing landscapes entirely (fig. 350). They build initially high-level plains,

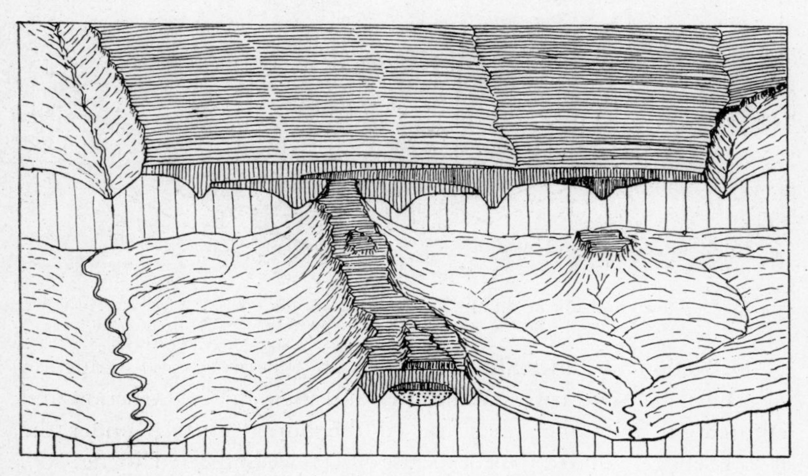

Fig. 350.—Early (rear) and late (front) stages in the erosional destruction of a lava plateau.

which have become typical *lava plateaux* where they are now in course of dissection. Rather less extensive sheets, or complexes of sheets, spreading over wide valley plains and lowlands make *lava plains*. Ignimbrite accumulations may take a similar form. Examples of extensive lava plateaux are the Columbia River and Dekkan plateaux of north-western United States and south-western India respectively. Examples of lava plains are common in northern New Zealand and south-eastern Australia—and, indeed, throughout the world.

The lava built up to form the great basalt plateaux is believed to have poured out as floods from numerous fissures or networks ("swarms") of fissures not associated with volcanic mountains; and the locus of emission must have changed from time to time. Smaller complexes of lava sheets ranking as basalt plains may have originated similarly in some cases; but in other cases the lavas have flowed from fissures that have opened on the flanks of large volcanic mountains (figs. 352, 354 and 382).

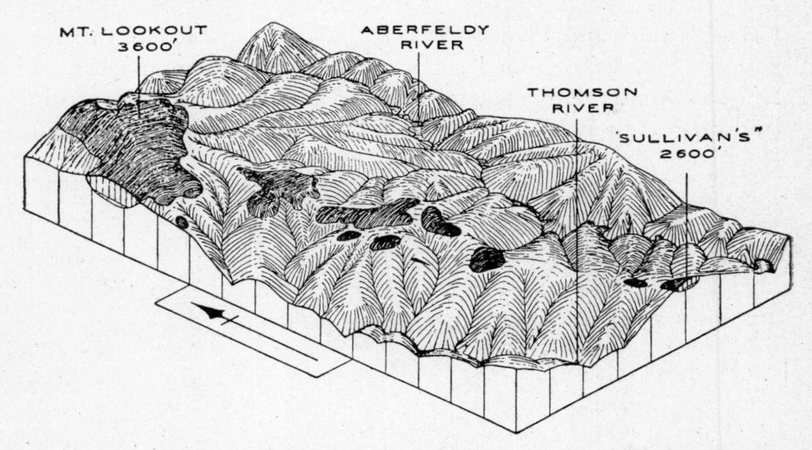

Fig. 351.—Lava residuals marking the line of a former valley, Victoria, Australia, an example of inversion of relief. (After E. S. Hills.)

Dissection of Lava Sheets.—Stages in the process of reduction of lava plateaux to mesas and buttes and their final destruction and elimination from the landscape (if the buried surface under the lava is entirely above the local base-level) are indicated in fig. 350. Dissection by rivers of consequent and insequent origin takes place essentially on similar lines to that of other plateaux of regional extent (Chapter VII) except that the process may be slow because of the tendency of volcanic landscapes to swallow water and convey it in underground channels, thus robbing the surface of rivers.

Inverted Relief.—The last remnants of a lava-made plateau or plain in a penultimate stage of destruction generally linger along the axes of valleys of the lava-buried landscape (figs. 350, 351). Very early in the history of a lava plain—even in early stages of its accumulation (shown in fig. 350)—lava commonly forms divides over the sites of former valleys, affording examples of *volcanic* *inversion of relief.* As a result new valleys are formed as rivers are forced to take new courses (perhaps one on each side of a lava tongue—fig. 352) and such valleys may be perpetuated in the landscape when the lava is almost destroyed (figs. 350, 351) and even wholly removed; in such a case the inversion has become permanent.

Volcanic Lakes and River Diversion.—Small outflows of lava, insufficient to change the whole aspect of a landscape (fig. 352), are yet capable of introducing important modifications into the course

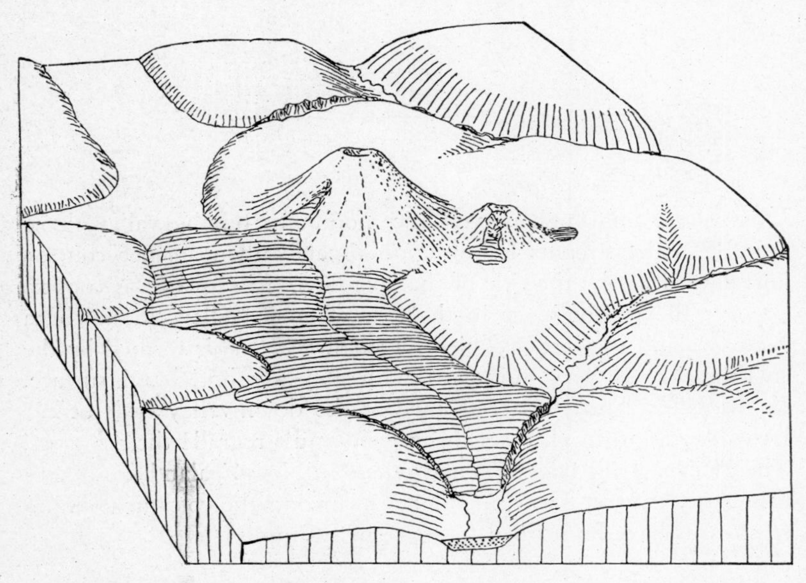

Fig. 352.—A lava stream ponds lakes and diverts rivers. (After W. M. Davis.)

of the normal cycle. The lava makes its way into valleys, which it blocks, ponding streams and in some cases compelling them to spill over divides and take new courses (fig. 352). Lake Omapere, in northern New Zealand, has been formed owing to the blocking of a river valley (Waitangi River, fig. 353) by lava, and the lake now spills over through an ungraded channel into the head of the Utakura River. Thus the main divide between drainage to the east and west coasts has been shifted several miles.

In some cases, where river courses are blocked either by the spilling of lava into the valleys (fig. 352) or by actual outbreak of

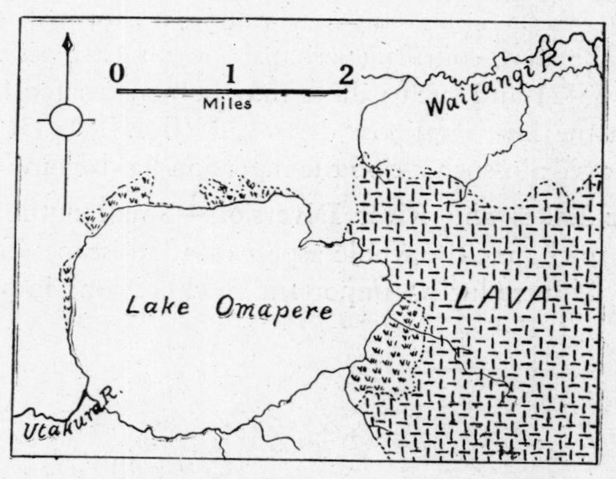

Fig. 353.—Lake Omapere, New Zealand, impounded in the upper Waitangi valley by a lava dam.

activity and upgrowth of volcanic mountains on the valley floors (fig. 354), the streams follow approximately their former courses, and flow either by the side of the lava flow, if its surface is convex, or over the top of it, as in the case of some valleys in northern New Zealand that are occupied by small *lava plains* formed by the solidification of very fluid lava with a nearly horizontal surface. In the latter case falls are formed at the down-valley ends of the lava sheets, and in all cases the streams must regrade their courses. The Wairua Falls (fig. 355) and others in New Zealand are due to this cause. A great many small lakes formed by the volcanic ponding of streams have been filled up to form swampy flats.

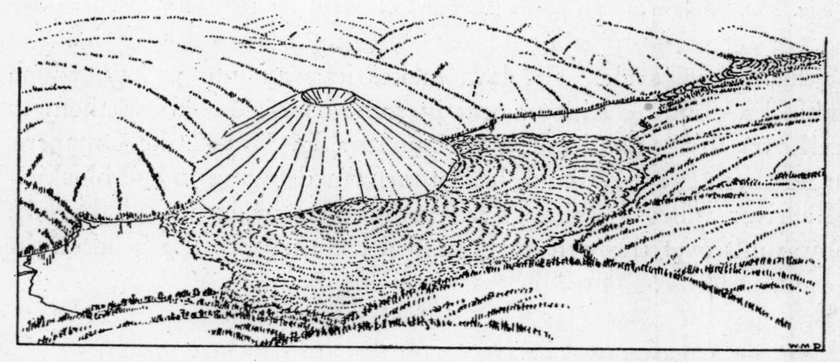

Fig. 354.—Growth of a volcano and outflow of lava have obstructed a valley, forming lakes. (After W. M. Davis.)

Fig. 355.—The Wairua Falls, New Zealand, formed where a ponded river has spilled over the level surface of a lava plain.

C. A. Cotton, photo.

Fig. 356.—Whatitiri, a basalt "cone," or low dome, surrounded by a lava plain, in the North Auckland district of New Zealand.

N. H. Taylor, photo.

Basalt Cones.—Widely spreading basalt floods pour generally from localised vents, which may be somewhat enlarged parts of fissures or systems of rifts; and over the vents arise low broad lava hills of flatly conical or rather domed shape (fig. 356). In some regions where much basalt lava has been emitted none of these have grown to the dimension of mountains.

Scoria Mounds.—Though quiet outpouring is the ruling method of basalt eruption, quite frequently mounds of scoria are built over vents. Little fine ash is formed—pumice and ash being pro-

Fig. 357.—Mt. Maungatapere, a scoria mound, Whangarei district, New Zealand.
N. H. Taylor, photo.

duced in quantity only by non-basaltic volcanoes. Great explosions do not generally occur in basalt volcanoes, and even small explosive eruptions are rare and are developed only as a result of superficial contact of lava with sea-water or ground water. "Fire-fountaining" (p. 360), is rather common, however, at vents emitting basalt, and very probably most of the very numerous scoria cones and mounds in basaltic volcanic districts have been built by this process. The scoria mounds—Mt. Eden and others—in and around the city of Auckland, New Zealand, are classic examples. There are numerous others (figs. 357, 358) in northern New Zealand, however, and in all regions in which recent outpouring of basaltic lava has taken place.

Basalt Domes.—In some cases free-flowing abundant basalt builds mountains instead of spreading out horizontally to form built-up plains or plateaux. Such mountains assume the form of domes with circular, oval, or elliptical ground plan, and the dome-building habit is perhaps related to persistence of intermittent outflow through one swarm of fissures over a long period as contrasted with a repeated shifting of activity from one place to another, which may lead to plateau-making instead of dome-building.

Fig. 358.—Te Ahuahu scoria cone, 400 feet high, surrounded by the basalt plain which blocks the Waitangi valley to form Lake Omapere, New Zealand (fig. 353.) Note the single erosion gutter leading down from the rim of the crater.
C. A. Cotton, photo.

A vast number of flows each a few feet thick contribute to the growth of a *basalt dome* (which is alternatively named a "shield volcano"). In the Hawaiian Islands, which consist of basalt domes, some young and still growing but others dissected by erosion (fig. 359), the internal structure of some domes can be seen. The edifice consists almost entirely of flows of basalt, intercalations of fragmentary materials being rare. The lava sheets are nearly always parallel to the dome-shaped surface—that is, nearly horizontal under the broad summit and steeper on the flanks. This disposes of the theory that the dome form is accidental and due to piling up of successive horizontal sheets of diminishing diameter.

In the case of very high domes, such as Mauna Loa, in Hawaii, and Etna, in Sicily, both of which are still growing, lava is now

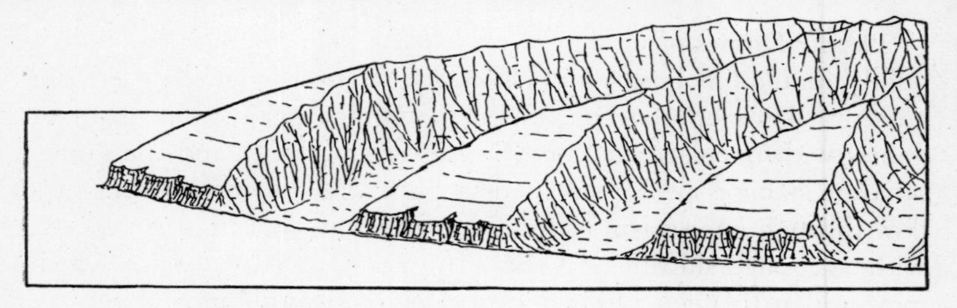

Fig. 359.—Submature dissection of an island initially a basalt dome.

poured out from fissures on the flanks of the mountains, instead of at the summit (as formerly). The lava breaks through, apparently, as a result of the enormous hydrostatic pressure in the lava column reaching to so great a height. Lateral outpouring tends to build buttresses around the original symmetrical dome.

Basalt cones (p. 370) may perhaps be regarded as embryonic domes. The very symmetrical cone Rangitoto, at Auckland, New Zealand, is surmounted by a scoria mound (fig. 360), but such features are common on some large lava mountains also. Hundreds

Fig. 360.—Rangitoto Island, Auckland, New Zealand, a basalt cone surmounted by a scoria mound.

Home Studios, Takapuna, photo.

of such "adventive" cones are dotted over the great dome of Etna, and there is a cluster of them on the broad summit and others on the flanks of Mauna Kea, in Hawaii.

Dissection of Basalt Domes.—Basalt mountains are known in various stages of dissection and destruction by erosion. Like all conical and dome-shaped initial landforms they are drained by

Fig. 361.—Mature dissection of a basalt dome, Maui Island, Hawaiian group. *Tai Sing Loo, photo.*

systems of consequent valleys arranged radially like the spokes of a wheel. There is little run-off from new surfaces of basalt or scoria, for they absorb water thirstily and drain it away underground, but when weathering has proceeded to some depth rivers are formed and radial ravines are cut, perhaps dissecting the dome very deeply. They gnaw back headward into the heart of the mountain.

Maturely dissected basaltic mountains not only occur among the domes of the Hawaiian group (fig. 361), but are common also among other "high" islands of the central Pacific. Tahiti and Rarotonga (fig. 362) are examples. Where dissection is not yet

Fig. 362.—Rarotonga Island, a maturely dissected basalt dome with a fringing reef of coral.

C. A. Cotton, photo.

quite mature some lower spurs preserve remnants of the constructional surface (fig. 359). Submaturely dissected constructional slopes are seen on Banks Peninsula, New Zealand, which consists of a pair of basalt mountains dissected, cliffed by the sea at the margin, and partly submerged (fig. 363).

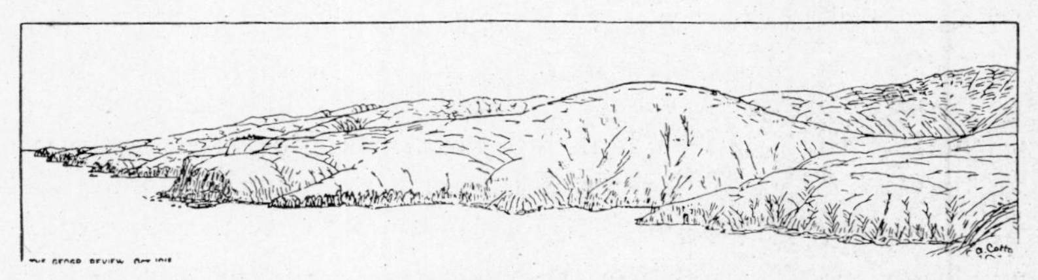

Fig. 363.—The north side of Banks Peninsula, New Zealand—the flank of a basaltic mountain submaturely dissected, cliffed at the sea margin, and partly submerged.

Inevitably the central part of a dome becomes hollowed out by long continued erosion (fig. 364). This is quite apart from the possible presence initially of a central crater, which may have resulted from explosion or subsidence. When stream heads gnaw

Fig. 364.—A basalt dome with centre hollowed out by erosion.

back headward so as to occupy the central area, escarpments of eroded lava sheets retreat from the centre, allowing the streams to enlarge headwater basins. Perhaps one such stream becomes a master, and thus a single headwater basin comes to occupy the centre. The stream draining this is invigorated and increases in volume as the headwater basin is enlarged, and therefore cuts its valley down deeply, developing an easy gradient in its gorge through the flank of the dome.

The whole centre has thus been removed from the main volcano of the island of Tahiti and replaced by the Papenoo Valley, which is surrounded by a ring of high residual peaks. In New Zealand, each of the two contiguous domes forming Banks Peninsula has been eviscerated by stream erosion so as to form the great hollows now occupied by Lyttelton and Akaroa harbours (figs. 365, 366). The great hollows are contained within almost continuous escarpments—but in the case of Lyttelton Harbour the escarpment slope is obscured by a flow of new lava at one place (fig. 365) and broken down by erosion at another.

Great hollows excavated in the centres of volcanic mountains by erosion may be termed *erosion calderas,* as they present some resemblance to the over-size craters termed "calderas" (see next chapter). The great "Caldera" of La Palma (Canary Islands) appears to have been opened out in this way. Though it has not been invaded by the sea it is very similar to the valley systems that have been drowned to form the harbours of Lyttelton and Akaroa, but is enclosed by a higher escarpment. This example is of particular

Fig. 365.—Port Lyttelton, New Zealand, a valley system eroded in the heart of a basalt volcanic mountain and then submerged. The even slope down to the water in the centre is the surface of a lava flow of later date than the erosion of the valley system.

Fig. 366.—The harbour of Akaroa, Banks Peninsula, New Zealand, similar in origin to that of Lyttelton (fig. 365). It is ringed around by a well-defined, nearly continuous lava escarpment. *V. C. Browne, photo.*

interest as its origin was for long a subject of controversy among vulcanologists. Some have considered that the stream which now flows through the "Barranca," or outlet gorge, and has succeeded in excavating the central hollow by extension of its headwater basin must have gained its mastery as a result of being favoured by taking a consequent course initially through a lateral hollow in the volcanic mountain such as might owe its origin to explosion or subsidence.

CHAPTER XXVII

VOLCANIC CONES

Central eruptions. Volcanic cones. Ash cones. Maars and tuff rings. Volcanic mountains. Concave slopes. Lava cones. Domes of viscid lava. Forms of craters. Dissection of cones. Volcanic skeletons. Laccolithic mountains.

Central Eruptions.—The eruptions of volcanoes in which lavas other than basalt rise to the surface are generally in the strict sense "central," as the term is used in contrast with "fissure eruptions," in that the materials erupted—a considerable proportion of them fragmentary—are distributed symmetrically around the *crater* or orifice of a vertical conduit, the volcanic *pipe.* Symmetrical distribution of basaltic scoria around a vent takes place also, of course, but the building of scoria mounds is a local and temporary phase of basaltic activity.

The pipes through which non-basaltic lavas rise are no doubt developed from fissures; they have been thought to be situated where fissures or fissure systems intersect. Enlargement of the orifice by melting of fissure walls certainly takes place; but pipes seem to be opened and kept open continuously for long periods largely by the explosive emission and blowing-off of gases, which are commonly loaded with lava fragments.

Volcanic Cones.—Typically the accumulation of volcanic material about a central vent produces a mountain with the conical form (fig. 367) that is generally regarded as typical of volcanoes. Volcanic cones vary in shape according to the nature of the material ejected and the nature of the eruptions that have taken place—whether relatively quiet or paroxysmal. Typically there is a pit or cup-shaped hollow, the *crater,* truncating the apex of the cone. This is the opening of the volcanic pipe through which the ejected materials have come to the surface. Typically, also, the lower slopes of the cone—below a summit convexity near the crater—are concave in radial profile, the slope becoming gentler with increasing distance from the crater, around which the coarser ejected fragments are steeply piled up (fig. 367).

Some volcanic mountains are very bluntly truncated, owing to the whole top of the original cone having been blown away by an explosive eruption. In New Zealand Mounts Tongariro and Ruapehu (fig. 368) are described as having suffered in this way. Tongariro has now a summit area of about twenty square miles, diversified by explosion craters, some of them occupied by lakes, small cones of more recent growth, and small lava flows from these (fig. 346). Truncation has resulted in other cases from collapse and engulfment of summits (p. 389).

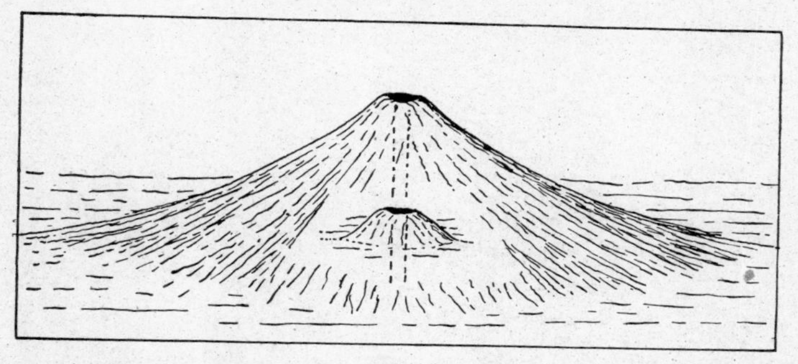

Fig. 367.—Infant and adult stages of the same volcanic cone, to illustrate the development of a concave profile.

The steepness of volcanic cones varies within wide limits. The steepest are the mounds built entirely of scoria of coarse grade (fig. 357). Where there is a proportion of finer material, either scoria or ash, the summit convexity is less prominent, and gentler and concave outer slopes develop the conical form (fig. 358).

Ash Cones.—Small *ash cones* are built locally where basaltic lava produces ash as a result of contact with surface water; but the majority of ash cones surmount the pipes of non-basaltic volcanoes, which intermittently produce ash in large quantities, as described in Chapter XXV. If the grade of coarseness of material is the same there is no essential difference of form between these and the cones of basaltic scoria and bombs built by fire-fountaining. The average steepness of the ash slopes of Ngauruhoe (fig. 368) is 35°. Generally, however, there is a relatively large proportion of fine material, which is thrown farther away from the crater and accumulates to form gentler slopes. Large blocks and bombs accumulating at the summit of the cone may make the summit resemble a scoria mound (fig. 367).

Over pipes fed with lava of the viscid kind that gives off its gas explosively a continuous or intermittent supply of pumiceous ash results in the growth of cones to large dimensions. The pipe does not necessarily increase in diameter meanwhile, and so a symmetrical and almost pointed cone may be built up to a great height by this process (figs. 367, 372).

Fig. 368.—A general view of the volcanic mountains in the centre of the North Island of New Zealand. In the distance is Ruapehu; in the middle distance the still-growing symmetrical cone of Ngauruhoe; and in the foreground the diversified irregular plateau truncating the top of Tongariro.

V. C. Browne, photo.

Maars and Tuff Rings.—The first stage in the history of an individual volcano of the central kind is an explosive outbreak the immediate cause of which in some cases is contact of lava with water. The first explosion may be the last also, and there are many examples of nearly circular explosion cavities containing lakes, which have thus originated as embryonic volcanoes, and are termed *maars* (fig. 369). They are surrounded in most cases by low, broad rings of ash consolidated to form tuff.

Tuff rings of wide radius (fig. 370) in the Auckland city vicinity, New Zealand, resulted apparently from rather intense but short-

Fig. 369.—Pupuke Lake, Takapuna, New Zealand—a maar.

J. A. Bartrum, photo.

Fig. 370.—Faulted beds of tuff in the ring around Pupuke Lake (fig. 369).

C. A. Cotton, photo.

lived explosive activity at points where rising basalt encountered water. This was followed by the building of scoria mounds and outpouring of basalt to form small lava plains.

Volcanic Mountains.—Where ash is emitted abundantly by eruptions of moderate intensity—not great paroxysms, which would distribute the material as more widespread "showers" (Chapter XXV)—an ash cone may grow in height to many hundreds of feet in the first day or two of its existence, as was the case at Monte Nuovo, near Naples, in 1538, and in the new cone Vulcan, at

Fig. 371.—The new volcanic cone Vulcan, at Rabaul, New Britain, built in a few days in 1937. *Turner, photo.*

Rabaul, in the island of New Britain, in 1937 (fig. 371). Growth to the dimensions of a mountain usually takes many thousands of years, however; for it is intermittent. With many periods of dormancy or slight activity and with variation in intensity of activity during paroxysms, a cone is built which is layered or stratified in coarser and finer ash layers parallel to the outer slopes. Thus large ash cones have been classed as "stratovolcanoes." In most cases tongues of lava pour down the ash slopes from time to time, breaking out through ("breaching") the weak ash wall of the crater or bursting forth at some lower level on the cone (fig. 352). The tongues of lava (not continuous sheets around the cone) solidify, at least in part, on the slopes, though some lava may run off on to lower ground, as shown in fig. 352. A stratovolcano with such intercalated lava layers is sometimes described as a "composite" cone. The feeding channels of lateral lava outflows are radial cracks reaching out from the central pipe, and when lava solidifies in these they become dykes, which strengthen an edifice otherwise very weak. If explosive activity develops at a lateral vent it may become a permanent branch from the main pipe, and a *parasitic cone* may grow up over it (figs. 352, 372). Activity may be trans-

Fig. 372.—Mount Egmont, a New Zealand volcano, with a parasitic cone on its flank.
F. G. Radcliffe, photo.

ferred entirely to the new crater, and the parasitic cone may grow so as to overtop or completely envelop the original volcano.

Concave Slopes.—Concavity of profile on outer slopes is a characteristic feature of debris-built (including composite) cones. Being universally present, it must be ascribed, in part at least, to a very simple cause, namely, the building up of the higher slopes to the angle of rest of coarse material while finer ash travels farther afield and comes to rest where it falls.

There are other causes, however, which contribute to produce the broadly concave infilling of the re-entering angle at the base of the debris slope, especially in the case of large cones. Filling of this angle by lava flows is suggested in fig. 352. Without such lava filling, however, ash and debris slopes themselves flatten out and pass gradually into the nearby level plains of accumulation of wide extent which surround large volcanoes—the Ruapehu-Tongariro group, for example, in the centre of the North Island of New Zealand; and also Mount Egmont, farther west. The material of which the outer, gentle slopes and the surrounding plains are built is by no means all air-borne ash, but contains a large proportion of coarse boulders. Some blocks, as well as ash, are carried from the mountains by streams and deposited as alluvial fans; but much of the material in question is not of alluvial accumulation.

Other processes which are of great importance in distributing coarse volcanic material widely are mass movement by landsliding (affecting mainly steep slopes of fine ash), the hot avalanching of *nuée ardente* material (p. 363), and volcanic "mudflows." The high velocity and mysterious mobility observed in the hot avalanches of Martinique indicate that the material might travel many miles over nearby level ground. It contains abundant large boulders.

Volcanic mudflows, termed in Java *lahars,* have originated especially where outbursts of renewed activity have taken place through craters that have been occupied by lakes. The so-called mud is a mixture of water and ash with blocks of all sizes. This material after rushing down a mountain-side travels to a great distance and when it comes to rest eventually may cover a large area with tumbled heaps of boulders somewhat resembling glacial moraines (fig. 373; compare also fig. 337). Not only is this process responsible for supplying coarse material to build up plains but it explains the presence of great swarms of hillocks west of Mount Egmont, New Zealand, as well as the lahar hillocks in the Tongariro National Park, the materials of which are obviously derived from Mount Ruapehu (fig. 373).

Lava Cones.—Where lava greatly predominates over ash in the construction of a cone of mixed materials the result may be termed a *lava cone*. In this case the slopes assumed by lava surfaces determine the steepness and form of the cone. In contrast with the smooth and gentle slopes of basalt cones (figs. 356, 360) those of other lavas are steeper (fig. 374) and commonly much less symmetrical.

Fig. 373.—Stranded debris of a lahar, forming mounds on the Waimarino Plain, New Zealand.

C. A. Cotton, photo.

Fig. 374.—Mt. Edgecumbe, New Zealand, a steep, but symmetrical lava cone of intermediate (dacite) lava.

C. A. Cotton, photo.

Intermediate (andesite) lavas flow fairly freely and the piles they build are recognisably conical (fig. 375), though individual flows are thick and convex and a cone built of them commonly appears corrugated.

Fig. 375.—An andesite lava cone, Mt. Tauhara, Taupo, New Zealand.

Domes of Viscid Lava.—The more viscid (acid) lavas are piled up irregularly in forms that may have little resemblance to cones. An example of such a pile is Mayor Island in the Bay of Plenty, New Zealand (fig. 376). This pile, though irregular in form, is more a dome than a cone. Such is possibly the origin of some rather old mountains of rhyolite in the Rotorua-Taupo volcanic district of New Zealand—for example, Tarawera (figs. 341, 342) and Ngongotaha (fig. 377) which have been converted by long-continued

Fig. 376.—Mayor Island volcano, New Zealand, showing four of the thick flows of acid lava of which the irregular dome is built.

erosion into mesa-like forms. Mt. Haparangi is described as a much newer rhyolite dome. Very commonly, indeed, the more acid and very viscid lavas build steep-sided "mamelons" immediately over the pipes from which they are exuded, and these are sometimes referred to as "lava domes" though they are very different from the basalt domes already described. Some of them, exuded within large craters, are also called "plug domes." Some outpouring takes place; but some mamelons grow in size as viscid lava is

Fig. 377.—A mesa-like rhyolitic mountain, possibly a "dome," Ngongotaha, Rotorua, New Zealand.
C. A. Cotton, photo.

injected within a solidified crust. Pushing piston-like through this crust, high but short-lived "spines" arise. The best-known example existed for a few months on the summit of Mt. Pelée, in Martinique, during the eruptions of 1902. All such domes are relatively small landforms. Ancient examples are known, notably in Auvergne, central France; and small new domes have appeared within the craters of volcanoes in recent years. These commonly crumble rapidly away, and in Martinique they give off the remarkable *nuées ardentes* already described. Some new islands, which have appeared as a result of sub-oceanic volcanic eruptions have been of this nature; but others are the summits of ash cones rising from the sea floor. They are quickly demolished and reduced to shoals by marine erosion; but outflow of lava in considerable volume might convert any of them into a more permanent volcanic island.

Forms of Craters.—The craters of central volcanoes are nearly always approximately circular (fig. 378). Their size is determined not by the size of the cones formed around them, but rather by the

Fig. 378.—The crater of Ngauruhoe volcano, New Zealand, which is externally an ash cone (compare profile in fig. 368), but exposes lava flows in the crater walls, showing that the cone is of composite construction.

V. C. Browne, photo.

diameter of the pipe beneath. The craters of scoria mounds and ash cones of small dimensions are thus relatively large. They are also bowl-shaped, for some of the ejected blocks and bombs fall within and some without the crater rim, the former building up the inner slope of the crater while the latter are adding to the outer slope of the cone. Ash is thus stratified parallel to the outer slope and also to the crater slope. During moderate activity fragmentary material is deposited within the craters of large volcanoes also, forming layers sloping inward, but when there is a particularly violent explosive eruption, and the whole apex of the cone is blown away, the crater thus enlarged has precipitous walls in which the edges of the strata parallel to the outer slope are exposed (fig. 378). An explosion crater is larger in diameter than the pipe below it, which opens out funnelwise. Within large explosion craters that have been refilled new craters are opened (fig. 378). Thus "nested" craters originate. The larger the diameter of a crater developed by explosion the more bluntly is a cone truncated (fig. 368). Many large explosion craters contain lakes (fig. 379).

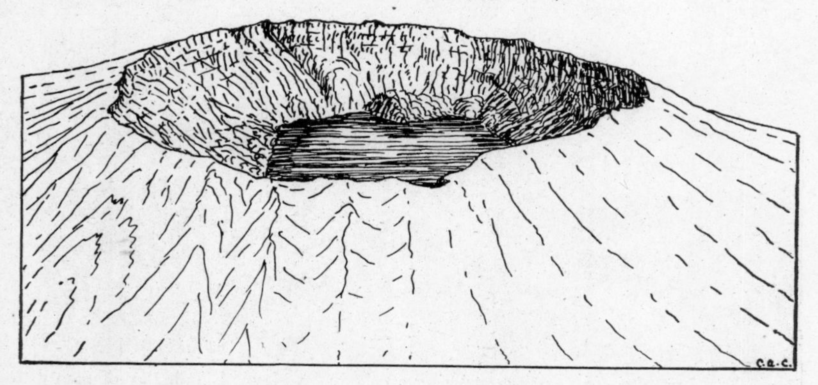

Fig. 379.—A crater lake, Coseguina volcano, Nicaragua. (Drawn from a photograph.)

Explosion may occur on such a large scale as to demolish a summit and enlarge a crater to excessively larger dimensions converting it into a *caldera*. Most crater rings which are similarly steep-walled and are of such great diameter as to enclose calderas have been found to be the results not of explosion, however, but of collapse and in-sinking of the tops of volcanoes, caused possibly by blowing-off or drawing-off of lava formerly filling reservoirs beneath the mountains. Solid material engulfed a little at a time may in some cases be re-incorporated in liquid lava. Absence of a sufficient quantity of fragmentary debris round about which is obviously derived from a demolished mountain-top will discredit the theory that a caldera has been formed by simple explosion. The subsidence hypothesis is favoured in explanation of the broad caldera occupied by Crater Lake, in Oregon.

An enlarged crater, five miles in circumference, on Mayor Island, New Zealand, which is shown in fig. 380, may be classed as a caldera. As is commonly the case, subsequent activity has partly filled this cavity with pumiceous ash and has built a new dome of acid lava within it. The caldera is excentric in the lava dome which forms the original volcano. Thus the wall is low on one side (shown in fig. 380).

So-called craters, better termed *sinks,* and also some smaller pits, on and near the summits of basalt domes are steep-sided and generally level-floored hollows which may have originated as small cavities as a result probably of local re-melting of lava, but have

Fig. 380.—Part of the crater ring enclosing a caldera on Mayor Island, Bay of Plenty, New Zealand. To the left rises a new lava dome built within the caldera.
C. A. Cotton, photo.

been in some cases very greatly enlarged by foundering. Their walls are now fault scarps, commonly showing the features of splintered faults, and the floors consist of lava which has run in from fissures in the walls and has spread out as pahoehoe flows. Large active sinks of the dimensions of "calderas" are situated on the summits of the Mauna Loa and Kilauea domes on Hawaii Island.

Dissection of Cones.—Slow-growing cones of ash are seen to be already dissected by very numerous radial consequent ravines (fig. 381). (The smooth, undissected surface of the infant cone Vulcan may be noted in fig. 371, however.) Radial drainage systems are developed on lava cones also and on cones of coarse scoria, though much more slowly, because the material is more resistant and also because the scoria or the scoriaceous surface of lava is so porous that water sinks quickly underground, and so few surface streams are formed. On Te Ahuahu scoria cone, shown in fig. 358, for example, only one small consequent gutter has been cut by erosion, and that only where the whole of the overflow from the shallow crater

Fig. 381.—Erosion by consequent ravines on a growing ash cone, Ngauruhoe, New Zealand. *H. Winkelmann, photo.*

depression has poured out at one point in a single wet-weather stream. Apparently there is no other concentrated run-off from this cone.

On composite volcanoes lava tongues flow into and fill the radial ravines. Being convex, they become divides, displacing the

Fig. 382.—Convex-surfaced lava flows become radial consequent divides on the flank of Mount Egmont, New Zealand.

F. G. Radcliffe, photo.

water streams, which then must take courses between radial lava flows. Thus "inversion of relief" (p. 366) is constantly in progress on many growing cones (fig. 382).

At an advanced stage of dissection of a cone the number of consequent streams is generally much reduced by the process of abstraction, and those that survive in the struggle for existence cut large and deep valleys. Little-dissected sectors of the constructional surface of a volcanic mountain, if they survive, separated by a few

Fig. 383.—Hogback-making dyke of igneous rock, North Canterbury, New Zealand. *C. A. Cotton, photo.*

deeply-cut master consequents in bottle-necked valleys, have been termed *planezes*. One or more of the large consequent valleys may extend headward so as to hollow out the centre of a cone in the manner described in connection with the dissection of basalt domes.

Volcanic Skeletons.—After the cone of an extinct volcano has become maturely dissected it is progressively destroyed by erosion, and as the geomorphic cycle proceeds towards old age, the land surface may be worn down to a level beneath the base of all the volcanic deposits. Even when this takes place, however, some indications of former volcanic action will remain, for the pipe by

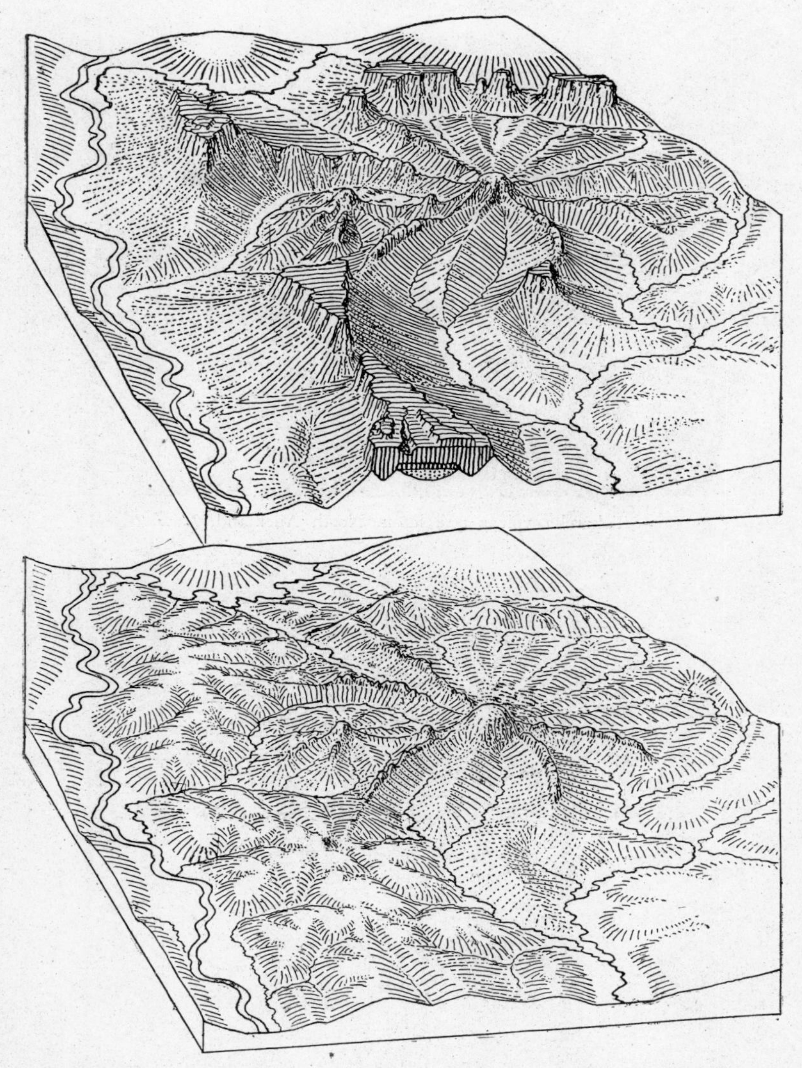

Fig. 384.—Volcanic skeleton as exposed before (above) and after (below) final removal of all superficial volcanic accumulations by erosion. (After W. M. Davis.)

Fig. 385.—Tokatoka volcanic skeleton, North Auckland, New Zealand.
C. A. Cotton, photo.

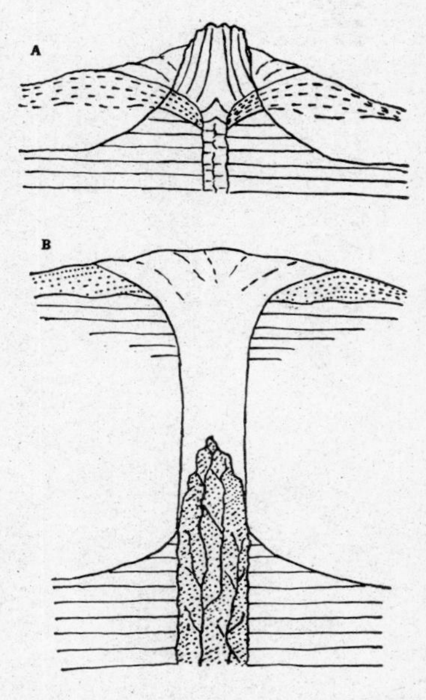

Fig. 386.—Two types of volcanic neck exposed by shallow (A) and deep erosion (B) respectively. (After H. Williams.)

way of which lava formerly reached the surface will be plugged with either compact solidified igneous rock or with agglomerate, a mass of blocks of lava. The plug is commonly resistant, and where left in relief by selective erosion becomes a *neck*, which may be a prominent rugged peak. Dykes also may remain intersecting rocks below the bases of former volcanoes and later stand out in relief above surrounding weak rocks as hogbacks (fig. 383).

Dykes may be radially arranged around a neck, supporting it as buttresses. Such dykes were probably feeding channels for lateral outflows of lava on a cone of which the neck was the axis. Neck and buttressing dykes together form a *volcanic skeleton* (figs. 384, 385).

In addition to necks exposed by deep erosion possibly continuing through successive erosion cycles (the "Navajo" type: fig. 386, B), some are merely plug domes left standing after the removal of easily eroded cones of ash which have surrounded them (the "Hopi" type: fig. 386, A) and have themselves been reduced but little by erosion.

Laccolithic Mountains.—Sheets of intrusive rock of uniform thickness intercalated between sedimentary strata or lava sheets are termed *sills*. In some cases intrusive sheets swell into thick lens-shaped masses, lifting the rocks above them so as to form dome-shaped uplifts of the surface. Such intrusive bodies are *laccoliths*. Laccolithic domes occur in greatest perfection of symmetrical development in the Henry Mountains, in southern Utah, where formerly horizontal strata have been up-domed. "Salt domes" are similarly raised by injection of bodies of rock salt. Each such dome will be eroded and go through a geomorphic cycle independently of its surroundings. In common with all dome-shaped structures of stratified rocks it will generally be characterised when mature by the presence of concentric arcuate homoclinal features. In the case of some of the Henry Mountains laccoliths erosion has exposed the igneous cores and maturely dissected them; and the mountains thus formed are surrounded by curved homoclinal ridges on the upturned edges of the more resistant members of the domed covering strata.

CHAPTER XXVIII

MARINE EROSION

Shoreline sculpture. Waves. Size of waves. Waves impelled by wind. Breaking of wave crests in deep water. Waves running into shallow water. Breakers. Undertow. Deflection of waves. Sheltered waters. Waves as eroding agents. Transportation by currents.

Shoreline Sculpture.—The outline of the land, or form of the shoreline,[1] and the profile of the coast[2] are practically everywhere the result of the work of waves assisted by currents. Waves are energetic eroding agents, making use, as do other eroding agents, of rock fragments as tools or abrading material to attack and grind away solid rock; while currents are effective chiefly as transporting agents, moving waste that is stirred up by wave action.

Waves.—Wave motion is set up on the surface of water as a result of brushing by wind. Waves, however, travel to great distances from the region in which they originate, and so the ocean surface is frequently found to be in motion without apparent cause; and, indeed, except in landlocked waters, the surface is never at rest. Waves within the area in which they are impelled by wind are termed *forced waves,* or "sea"; when unaccompanied by wind they are termed *free waves,* or "swell." Wave motion consists in an orbital motion of the water particles. In the case of free waves on the surface of deep water the orbits, or paths, in which the particles move are closed and circular, the orbits (immediately at the surface) being all of the same size. In a wave all particles in a line at right angles to the direction in which the wave travels move together (are "in the same phase"), while

[1] The *shoreline* is the line traced by the sea-margin. As this changes its position with the tides, it is sometimes necessary in detailed descriptions to speak of the *high-water shoreline,* or *high-water mark,* and *low-water shoreline,* or *low-water mark.* The "shore" is sometimes defined as the zone over which the line of contact between land and sea migrates.

[2] "Coast" is sometimes defined as the margin of the land, a zone of indeterminate width, but in geomorphological study it is convenient to include under this head the "shore" also, and a zone of the neighbouring sea floor, also of varying width.

successive particles in the line of propagation of the wave are (as regards their phase, or position in their orbits) a minute distance behind each other.

If the orbits of a number of superficial particles in the line of propagation of a wave be drawn in a diagram, and the position of each particle in its orbit at a given instant marked, a line drawn through the points so obtained will indicate the profile of the undulating surface at that instant with a fair degree of accuracy (fig. 387).

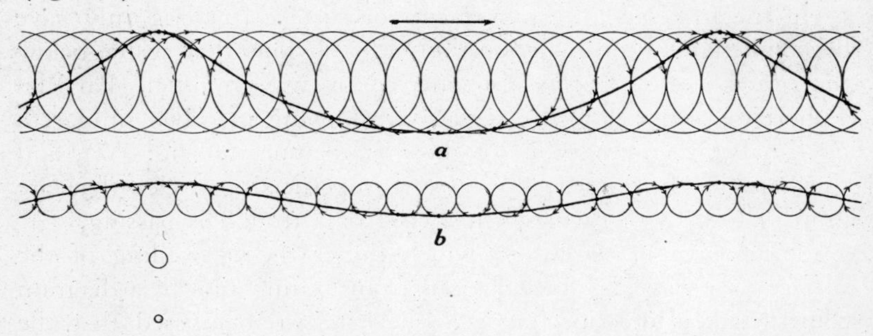

Fig. 387.—Diagrams of the orbits of a number of surface particles (or small elements) at intervals in the line of propagation of a wave, showing simultaneous positions of the particles in their orbits, and the profile of the water surface at that instant. The large arrow shows the direction in which the waves are travelling, and the small arrows the direction of movement of the water particles in their orbits. In *a* the height of waves relatively to the length is exaggerated; *b* represents a normal profile of ocean waves on a natural scale; at the left side of *b* the small circles show the diminution in the size of orbits with increasing depth below the surface.

If attention is confined to the movement of a single particle during the passage of a wave (fig. 388), it will be seen that, as the crest of a wave is approaching (*B*), the particle is on the side of its orbit nearer to the approaching crest, and is rising (*b*). When

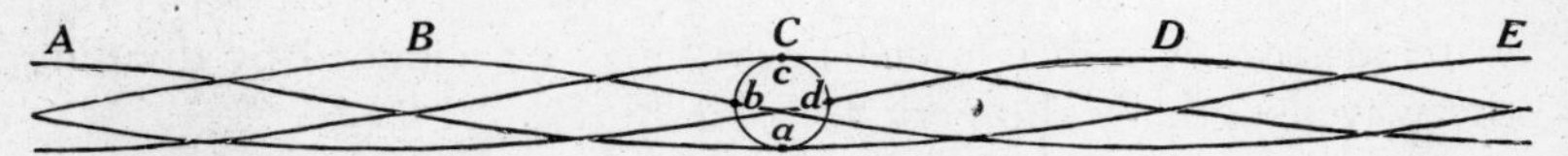

Fig. 388.—Diagram showing the movement of a particle (or small element) of water during the passage of a complete wave. The letters *a, b, c, d* mark the positions of the water particle in its orbit as a wave-crest occupies the positions *A, B, C, D* respectively.

the crest arrives (*C*) the particle is at its highest position (*c*) and is moving forward; when the crest has passed (*D*) the particle is again on that side of its orbit nearer to the now receding crest, and is sinking (*d*); and when the wave has moved so far that the particle is at the next trough (wave profile, *AE*) it is at its lowest position (*a*), and is moving backward to go through a similar series of motions as each succeeding wave passes. These motions are readily verified by watching the movement of a small object floating on agitated water.

In the foregoing the movements of surface particles only have been taken into consideration, but it is obvious that water below the immediate surface is also affected by wave motion. Particles a short distance below the surface are moving in orbits similar to but smaller than the orbits of those at the surface (fig. 387), and they are in the same phase as the superficial particles that are immediately above them when a crest or a trough is passing.

The source of the water which causes the upswelling of the surface in a wave becomes obvious from examination of a diagram constructed as described above, when it is remembered that the water below is moving in the same manner as that at the surface. Every particle is on the side of its orbit nearer to a crest and farther from a trough, and thus the water is heaped towards the crests, while there is a deficiency in the troughs.

Size of Waves.—The height of waves from trough to crest (i.e., the diameter of the orbit of a water particle at the surface) varies in the open ocean from about 6 feet (low swell) to 30 feet (heavy sea), and exceptionally much greater heights are attained. The *wave-length,* or distance from crest to crest, varies in the case of forced waves in the open ocean from 200 to 600 feet, but the wave-length of a swell may be considerably greater. The *period* or time occupied by a complete orbital movement(i.e., the time that elapses between the passing of the crest of one wave and the crest of the next), is commonly between six and ten seconds. The *velocity* of a wave (to be distinguished from the *orbital velocity* of a water particle, which is much lower) may be obtained by dividing the wave-length by the period.

Waves impelled by Wind.—In waves impelled by wind the movements of the water particles are similar in a general way to those in free waves, but, as the surface water has a slight forward movement (*drift*) due to the wind, particles after completing their oscillations do not return quite to the positions from which they started, and so the orbits are not quite closed and not quite circular.

The wind accelerates the movements of particles on the crests of the waves, and, as a result, the velocity of particles in the upper parts of their orbits (in which they move forward) becomes greater than in the lower parts (in which they move backward), so that the waves become asymmetrical—steeper in front than behind. The acceleration of the movements in the wave-crests by wind results also in an increase of the size of orbits, making the waves higher and higher until a limit (imposed by friction) is reached, the maximum size of waves (on a water surface of unlimited area) depending on the velocity of the wind. As the forward movement of the waves is accelerated by the wind the wave-length also increases. Thus, under the impulsion of wind, waves, beginning as mere ripples, grow in all their dimensions until they become full-grown "seas." When the wind ceases, or the waves run out of the region in which the wind is blowing, the height is diminished owing to friction, and so the waves (now "swell") become much flattened.

Distance from land to windward is necessary for the growth of waves of really large size. It is a familiar fact that only small waves—mere ripples compared with ocean waves—are formed in small lakes and landlocked harbours. Even in relatively large bodies of water the "fetch" is insufficient for waves to attain nearly as great a height as in the open ocean, and the same is true in those portions of the oceans near the windward shore. In the Mediterranean Sea, for example, the largest waves have a height of about 16 feet, compared with heights of considerably over 30 feet attained in the Southern Ocean and North Atlantic.

Breaking of Wave Crests in Deep Water.—The formation of white caps in deep water must be distinguished from the breaking of waves where they run into shallow water (on a beach, for example). In deep water if the increase in height (size of orbit) due to the action of wind is not accompanied by a proportional increase of wave-length its result is a steepening of the waves. The crests in particular become sharpened to such an extent that they are blown over by the wind and fall forward and "break." The tendency to break is increased by the greater steepness of a wind-driven wave in front than behind. It is only exceptionally—in the greatest storms—that the largest or primary ocean waves break in this way; but smaller, secondary waves on the flanks and especially near the crests of the larger waves rapidly attain the necessary steepness and break, forming white caps.

Waves running into Shallow Water.—Though the water to some depth is affected by wave motion, the size of orbits decreases rapidly from the surface downward (fig. 387), being reduced to half at a depth equal to one-ninth of the wave-length, to one-fourth at a depth equal to two-ninths of the wave-length, to one-eighth at three-ninths of the wave-length, and so on until at a depth equal to the wave-length wave motion is inappreciable. The depth at which wave motion becomes inappreciable is termed *wave-base*.[1]

The general account of waves given above applies to waves in water so deep that appreciable wave motion does not extend to the bottom. As waves run into shallow water, where the depth is less than the wave-length, the water in contact with the bottom is in motion; but it is impossible for particles at the bottom to move in vertical circular orbits, and so the water there loses one component of its motion and moves back and forth in a straight line along the bottom—generally in a line that is approximately horizontal. The influence of the bottom affects also water above that immediately in contact with it, and so, a little above the bottom, particles of water are moving in orbits that instead of being circular are vertically compressed and nearly elliptical, the orbital form becoming more and more nearly normal as the surface is approached, though even at the surface the orbits are now not quite circular.

In the case of waves running in on a steep coast the linear orbits of the bottom particles are inclined instead of being horizontal, and in the extreme case of waves meeting a vertical wall the movement of the water in contact with the wall is up and down in a vertical line. From a vertical or very steeply inclined shore waves are reflected. Such shores are, however, very unusual, and commonly the bottom slopes gently, and the linear orbits of the bottom particles are not far from horizontal.

---

[1] This term is best defined as the depth "at which wave-action ceases to stir the sediments" (Fenneman).

The friction of the bottom is distributed upward through the water, and, as the waves run into water that is shallow as compared with the wave-length, there are important changes in the wave form. The wave velocity is reduced, and, the period remaining the same, this diminution of velocity results in a reduction of the wave-length. A part of the energy of the waves is lost owing to the friction of the bottom; but the height of waves is not generally reduced owing to this cause, because there is in operation an opposite tendency towards increase in the size of orbits due to "the transmittal of the motion of a larger amount of water to a small amount" (Fenneman).

Fig. 389.—Swell breaking on a rocky coast, near Wellington, New Zealand.
C. A. Cotton, photo.

This commonly results in an actual increase in the height of waves. Since the wave-length is decreasing and the height increasing, the waves as they run into shallower water increase in steepness.

Where waves run a long distance in very gradually shallowing water so much of the energy is absorbed by friction that the increase in height above referred to does not take place, and instead the waves are very much reduced in size before reaching the shore. This is the case on the coast of Holland.

Breakers.—The breaking of waves owing to shallowing water (fig. 389) occurs commonly in a depth about equal to the wave height. As the waves have been advancing across shallow water all the water under each trough has been moving backward and all the water under each crest forward. The backward motion in the one case and the forward motion in the other are retarded by the friction of the bottom, but, as the depth of water under a trough is considerably less than that under a crest, the back-moving water is retarded to a greater extent than is that moving forward. In other words, the velocity of water particles in the upper parts of their orbits is greater than in the lower parts. The result is a steepening of wave fronts. When now a wave runs into water with a depth about equal to the height of the waves there is insufficient water in front of the wave to rise and build up the crest as the wave advances. The crest is built up to the normal form behind owing to the usual crowding of water towards it, but at the crest the normal form ends abruptly. The forward motion carries the water in the crest onward so that it falls over in front of the wave, the wave breaks, and the wave form is destroyed. Though it is the absence of water in front that is the chief cause of breaking, a contributing cause is the steepening of the front that has already taken place owing to friction of the bottom.

Landward from the line of breakers on a steep beach the water surges up and down the slope, being piled up after the arrival of each breaker and receding again before the arrival of the next. When waves break far out on a very gently sloping beach or on a shoal, breaking does not quite destroy the waves, though considerably reducing their size. The reduced waves continue to roll forward to break again in shallow water. Within the breaker-line on some shelving shores each plunging crest forms a *wave of translation,* which travels across otherwise still water to the shore. (During the passage of a wave of translation water particles move upward, forward, and downward again without a compensating backward movement.) In other cases there is a confused medley of reduced ordinary waves (waves of oscillation) and waves of translation.

Undertow.—Where waves are driven in at right angles to the shoreline by wind the slow landward drift of the surface water is compensated in part by a return movement along the bottom setting away from the land. This is the *undertow*. The water streams back seaward also as rapidly-flowing narrow tongues reaching to the surface, which are called *rip currents.* If driven in obliquely the water escapes along the length of the shore.

Deflection of Waves.—The crests of waves in deep water trace straight lines at right angles to the direction of propagation, which is also a straight line. As land is approached, however, those parts of a wave that first run into shallowing water are most retarded by friction. Bending of the line of the wave crest results, the parts of the wave that are still in relatively deep water pressing on in advance of those parts that are in shallower water.

Owing to this effect a swell approaching a coast obliquely tends to swing around until the wave crests are parallel with the shoreline, or, in other words, the waves run straight in on the beach. This has an important effect in reducing transportation of material alongshore by wave action, for the water rushing up and down the beach inside the line of breakers travels to and fro in the same line.

When waves are driven by wind, however, their directions are not changed to so great an extent by retardation in the shallow water. They meet the shoreline obliquely; and the water rushes up the beach obliquely, curves around, and runs back down the slope of the beach. On a steep gravel beach the alongshore movement, both of the water and of pebbles which are swept along with it may be distinctly seen not only during the landward rush but also during the return, for there the alongshore momentum is not yet exhausted when the returning water meets the uprush from the next breaking wave. The water surging up and down the beach always carries with it sand and gravel in a zigzag path along the shoreline. Thus in the littoral zone (i.e., along the sea-margin, in very shallow water) much waste is transported alongshore by wave action alone.

Another very important effect of the bending or refraction of waves in water of uneven depth is seen where waves approach an indented coast such as is produced by partial submergence of a dissected land-surface (p. 214 and Chapter XXXI). Off points there is, in general, shallower water than there is off bays. Waves approaching the coast are retarded—their velocity and wave-length decreasing—to a greater extent in the shallower water lying off points than they are in the deeper water opposite bays (fig. 390). The crests of the waves are now closer together opposite points than opposite bays, and the crest-lines become more and more curved as the waves approach the shore (fig. 390, 1, 2, 3, 4, &c.). Since a wave is always propagated in a direction perpendicular to its crest-line, the lines of propagation, (e.g., *aA, bB, cC, dD,* fig. 390) bend towards the points and away from the heads of the bays. As the energy of a wave is transmitted in its direction of propagation, there is thus a great concentration of energy on the projecting points of the coast, which may be likened to the convergence of light through a convex lens (the energy of the portions of the waves between *c* and *d* being concentrated on the portion *CD* of the shoreline); and there is a corresponding spreading of the energy away from

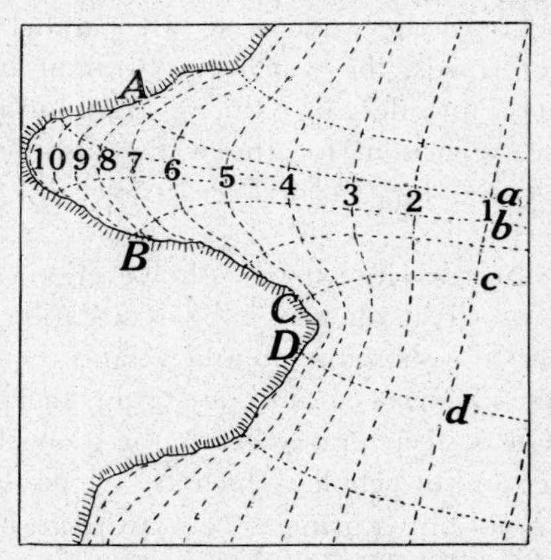

Fig. 390.—Concentration of wave-energy on headlands by refraction of waves in water of varying depth. (After Davis, modified.)

the heads of bays (the energy of the small portion of the wave *ab* being spread over the shore-line *AB*). Thus headlands are vigorously attacked by marine erosion, while comparatively smooth water is found at bay heads, even though the bays are open to the direction from which a swell comes. As wind-driven waves are less refracted than free waves, the concentration of energy on points is less marked with storm waves than with swell.

Sheltered Waters.—With the exception of the influence of varying depth of water (where the water is so shallow that friction of the bottom becomes important), there is nothing that tends to change the direction of propagation of waves. They do not turn corners—in other words, they cast "shadows," just as light does. To leeward, therefore, of a promontory or island there is smooth water, though on account of the shallowness of the water in proximity to land there is a certain amount of bending around the points, and so the "shadow" is not perfectly sharp. Landlocked harbours are thus affected by no waves except those developed within their own limits; and bays that are open on one side to the sea are protected from all ocean waves except those that enter them directly, and even these, except when driven by gales, are much weakened, as previously shown, by deflection towards the sides.

Waves as Eroding Agents.—Since the strongest movements of the water (those resulting from wave action) do not extend to the bottom except in shallow water, marine erosion takes place only in shallow water and is almost confined to coast lines. In the very shallow water, where waves break, the to-and-fro movement is sufficiently energetic to move large boulders, and also the impact of the waves, sometimes amounting to several tons per square foot, may be sufficient to loosen blocks of rock, and fragments are prised off owing to the suddenly increased pressure of either water or imprisoned air in crevices as a wave strikes an exposed surface of rock. Most of the erosive work of breaking waves is done, however, with the aid of rock fragments, either derived as just described or by falling from undercut cliffs or supplied by neighbouring rivers. These are dashed against the solid rock, and drawn to and fro across it. The gravel of the beach is thus itself worn down and rounded, and where the layer of gravel is thin it abrades the solid rock beneath it, and undercuts slopes at the shoreline, causing the unsupported rock above to slip down, so as to form cliffs fronting the shore. The material thus supplied is worn down and disposed of by the waves, and thus the cliffs are further worn back and steepened.

As beach pebbles are ground down by mutual abrasion the minerals in them become reduced to fine mud. Sand grains present along with gravel are pounded into mud, removal of which leaves clean-washed gravel. Where no debris coarser than sand results from wave attack on the land or is supplied by rivers, the particles, on the other hand, after being reduced to a certain minimum size, are not worn smaller, being protected from further attrition by the surface tension of the films of water between them. Grains of sand thus remain somewhat angular. White sand is composed chiefly of grains of quartz, with some of other light-coloured minerals, along with which there is commonly a varying quantity of flakes of white mica. Black sand is composed chiefly of grains of magnetite. Grey sand is a mixture of quartz grains with magnetite and other rock-forming minerals or with rock fragments not yet broken up into their separate minerals. The longer sand remains on, and the farther it travels along, beaches, the greater becomes the concentration of relatively imperishable quartz grains in it as more destructible mineral grains decay chemically. Thus, Dr. P. Marshall has found that the proportion of quartz grains increases from one-third to two-thirds of the whole in sand of acid volcanic origin as it travels from the mouth of the Waikato River to the northern extremity of New Zealand and as feldspar grains are progressively eliminated.

It is not only immediately at the shoreline that there is sufficient motion to cause erosion. As explained above, the orbital motion of the water in waves is interfered with by the bottom even at considerable depths, and converted into a to-and-fro movement. On a coast exposed to full-sized ocean waves this movement is sufficiently strong at depths of 10 and 20 fathoms or more to move to and fro coarse sand and even gravel,[1] and cause it to erode, or *abrade,* the bottom if bare rock is exposed, as is the case off the coast of Otago Peninsula, New Zealand. This is the process of *marine abrasion.* Though abrasion of a rock bottom may take place at these depths, it is possible only if the layer of waste on the bottom is thin and may be all moved. If the waste is at all thick, then only the upper layer of it can be stirred, and no abrasion of bedrock can take place.

The thickness of the waste layer on the bottom, which determines whether abrasion shall or shall not take place, is governed by the supply of waste, which in turn depends on the nature of the rocks and the energy with which the waves break at the shoreline, and also to a large extent on the loads brought down by neighbouring rivers. It is related also, of course, to the rate of removal of waste. Waste broken at the shoreline is removed in two directions—offshore and alongshore. Removal

---

[1] Some occurrences of gravel on the bottom under rather deep water have been explained as ancient beaches submerged by rise of sea-level. Such gravel must obviously now lie at a depth greater than that at which it can be moved about by wave motion.

offshore is effected by the to-and-fro component of wave motion, assisted by the undertow and rip currents, while movement alongshore is partly due to the zigzag path followed by the swash on the beach (p. 403). Alongshore movement is not confined, however, to the beach zone; it is also assisted by currents.

Transportation by Currents.—Ocean currents and tidal currents, though only rarely sufficiently rapid to erode even newly deposited sediment, actively transport fine silt that is held in suspension, and also coarser material such as sand and even gravel, when it is occasionally lifted clear of the bottom by wave action. Strong currents thus maintain a considerable depth of water by preventing accumulation of silt.

Tidal and ocean currents flowing along a coast attain their full velocity only at some distance offshore. Inshore they are much impeded by friction of the bottom and by irregularities of the shoreline which their momentum does not permit them to follow. A slower current following the shoreline more closely is dragged along, however, by the offshore current. The configuration of the coast determines whether this *littoral current* (as it is termed by Gilbert) shall follow the shoreline around the heads of open bays or sweep across bay mouths from headland to headland, leaving the water of the bay still, or perhaps generating an eddy in it.

While the offshore current can move the finer waste on the continental shelf when it is stirred by storm waves, it is the littoral current only which effects transportation of the coarser waste in the more agitated water of the littoral zone. The material thus moved, together with the gravel or coarse sand swept along (as explained above) by wave action within the breaker line, is the *shore drift,* which is built into beaches, spits, and bars when it reaches places favourable to accumulation (Chapter XXXIII).

CHAPTER XXIX

COASTAL PROFILES

Initial coastal profiles. Steep initial profile. Sea cliffs and the cut platform. Profile of equilibrium. High-water or shore platform. Profile and width of the graded platform. Marine terraces. Cover head. Profiles of progressively uplifted coasts.

Initial Coastal Profiles.—The initial forms on which the marine forces—waves and currents—begin to work are very varied in profile. The cycle of marine erosion may be initiated, for example, by a movement of regional subsidence or of regional uplift, in the former case a land surface being submerged to form the new sea floor in the shallow water zone, and in the latter case a portion of the floor of the deeper sea being brought into this position. In place of simple vertical movement there may be warping or faulting along the new shoreline. Thus the initial coast profile (including the portions above and below sea-level) may have any slope, from almost vertical to nearly horizontal and may be either smooth or irregular.

Steep Initial Profile.—The initial profile is rarely so steep that waves are reflected from the shore, but where it is vertical or nearly so waves have little or no erosive effect, partly because they are reflected without breaking, and partly because there is no resting-place for loose material at a convenient depth to allow it to be picked up and used by waves as tools, or weapons, in their attack on solid rock at the shoreline. Such material as is dislodged by the impact of waves on the initial shore slips immediately into deep water.

When, however, a slope initially too steep to cause waves to break has had its steepness reduced by slumping and subaerial erosion accompanied by accumulation of talus at the base (fig. 391, *b* and *b′*), waves will no longer be reflected, but will break, and will dislodge by their impact weathered and joint-bounded blocks of unweathered rock. This takes place also without any delay on shores which, though steep, have yet sufficiently gentle slopes initially to cause waves to break upon them.

Waves encountering a steep shore have lost but little energy owing to friction of the bottom before they reach the shoreline. They expend their energy at the breaker line. Most of this energy moreover, is available for the attack on the land, comparatively little being used up in grinding waste, for a steep coast is not encumbered with waste. Sufficient is present to act as tools with

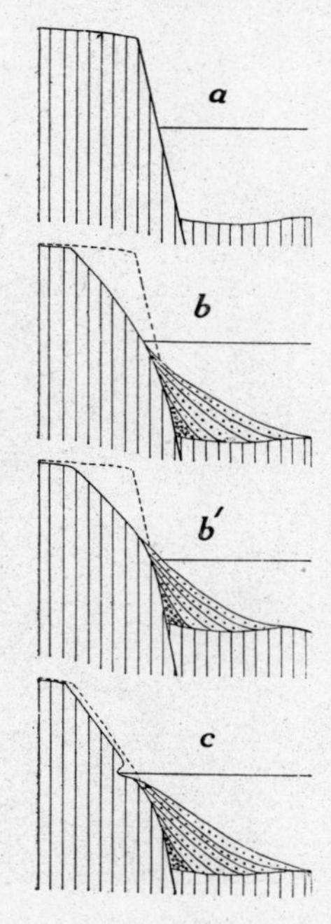

Fig. 391. — To illustrate the beginning of wave attack on a very steep initial coast. *a*, initial form; *b*, *b′*, forms after the profile is rendered less steep by accummulation of talus; *c*, sequential form, showing the beginning of wave work.

which the rushing and swirling water may batter and rasp the shore, but the bulk of the broken material is quickly drawn out into deep water and deposited there. Under these conditions wave action has its maximum efficiency as a destructive agency, and the shoreline recedes as a line of sea cliffs of increasing height.

Sea Cliffs and the Cut Platform.—Erosion may be so rapid that in cliffs of tough, unjointed rock a *nip* is cut—that is, a notch along the base, above which the cliff overhangs (figs. 391, 393). The material above slips down, however, before long, and the cliffs recede as the fallen blocks are themselves attacked by the waves, broken up, and removed, and the attack on the base of the cliff continues.

At this early stage in the development of the wave-cut profile, at which the shoreline is still rapidly receding, all cliffs are steep; but the steepness of any particular cliff depends largely on its structure. Cliffs may be vertical (fig. 392) or may overhang a nip (fig. 393), or, if a system of division-planes—stratification or joints—dipping inland is the only one present, they may slant outward for their full height. The presence of a nip indicates absence of joints in the rock of a cliff rather than any excess of vigour in the

Fig. 392.—Vertical cliffs and stack determined by the presence of vertical joints in horizontal stratified rocks ("flagstones"), Holborn Head, Caithness, Scotland. The cut platform developed by marine erosion is here far below high-water level.
H.M. Geol. Survey, photo.

attack by waves; for jointless rocks overhang a nip even on the shores of landlocked waters (fig. 394).

The retreat of young and steep cliffs takes place as a succession of rock falls and slides, which are particularly large where resistant strata overlie easily eroded formations along the shore.

At the foot of a line of receding sea cliffs there may be a gently-sloping wave-cut platform, in some cases smoothly worn, but in others accidented by many small unconsumed *stacks* (fig. 395). The base of the cliff is then generally at or near high-water level,

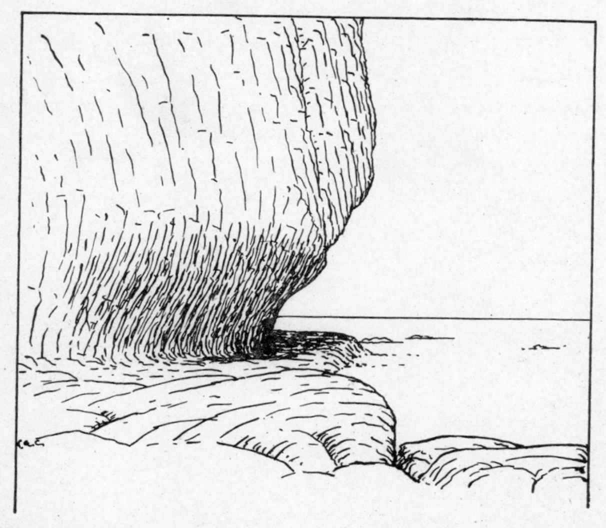

Fig. 393.—Nip at the base of a wave-cut sea cliff. Pillar Point, Washington, U.S.

Fig. 394.—Stack reduced to a mushroom shape by development of a nip in well-cemented jointless rock in the landlocked Whangaroa Harbour, New Zealand.
F. G. Radcliffe, photo.

for the material above that level is to some extent loosened by subaerial weathering, and thus prepared for ready removal even by weak waves. In some cases, however, where steep coasts are subject to very violent wave attack, the cliff base is below high-water level and the landward edge of the wave-cut platform is covered at high water to a considerable depth, which may be taken as an indication that subaerial weathering has failed to keep pace with marine erosion (fig. 392). On the other hand, the base of the cliff

Fig. 395.—Sea cliffs with wave-cut rock platform at their base, East Head, Kaikoura Peninsula, New Zealand. Above the general level stand numerous low stacks.

R. Speight, photo.

may retreat under the combined attack of weathering and the swash of breaking waves at some height above high-water mark (p. 413).

Farther out, at the line of breakers, where waves expend most of their energy, there is sufficient movement of the water to keep very coarse waste in motion. This material—boulders, gravel, and coarse sand—is dragged to and fro over the bedrock bottom, unless the supply of waste is excessive, in which case only the upper layers of waste will be moved and ground. The abrasive action of this material is such that a bottom consisting of solid unweathered and even unjointed rock may be rapidly worn down.

Still farther seaward to a considerable depth wave motion drags finer waste to and fro, and so abrasion continues, though less vigorously, on such parts of the rock floor as remain bare or are occasionally swept clear of protective waste. This continued offshore deepening by marine abrasion accounts for the fact that a cut platform generally slopes rather uniformly seaward; for the outer part, having been longest subject to wave action, has been most deeply abraded. The wearing down of the outer part of a broad platform from sea-level has taken a long time; but its abrasion will continue (though more and more slowly) as long as the waste on it continues to be moved to and fro over bare rock.

Profile of Equilibrium.—At an early stage in the erosion of a steep coast, after a certain amount of cliffing and platform-cutting has taken place and this has been accompanied by some seaward extension of the platform by deposit of rock waste as sediment, the

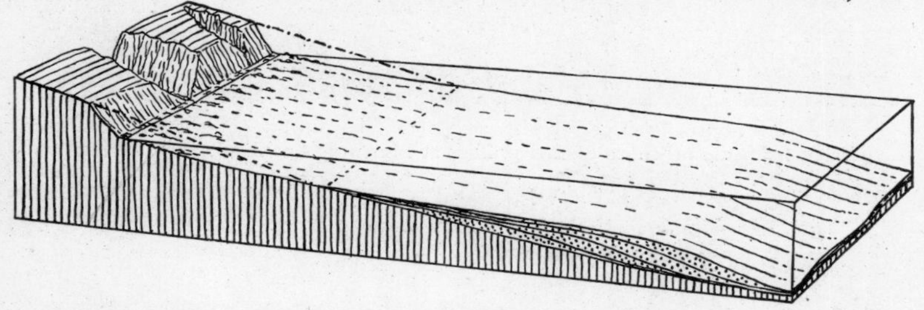

Fig. 396.—Cut-and-built platform, or continental shelf, with graded profile, in front of wave-cut cliffs developed from the initial profile indicated.

slope of the platform to its outer edge becomes smooth and nearly uniform owing to attainment of a state of balance between erosion and deposition at all points on it (fig. 396). The profile of the offshore platform is now *graded,* or a *profile of equilibrium* has been developed across it. Landward the profile is concave and steepens considerably at the inner margin, which may be (but is not necessarily) at the base of the land cliff.

High-water or Shore Platform.—Between the shore end of the concave profile of equilibrium and the base of the cliff there is quite commonly present a level bench, the *high-water* or *shore platform,* the origin of which is distinct from that of the graded surface farther seaward. From this it may be separated by a steep descent, almost a nip, just as another nip may be present in its rear at the cliff base (fig. 397).

At first sight it would appear that a shore such as that shown in fig. 397 had been uplifted and that the higher-level bench was a remnant of an older graded platform in course of removal and

Fig. 397.—An unusually broad high-water rock platform, separated by a scarped descent from the off-shore graded profile, at Muriwai, Auckland, New Zealand.

Douglas Johnson, photo.

Fig. 398.—Destruction of a probably older and uplifted rock platform is in progress and a newer platform is developing. East coast of Marlborough, New Zealand.

C. A. Cotton, photo.

replacement by a newer one adjusted to the present sea-level. Such may well be the correct interpretation of the history of the two platforms shown in fig. 398. High-water rock platforms, however, are still in course of development as is indicated by the bare, freshly worn rock surface and the cleanly scoured nature of the cliff-base angle or nip at the rear (fig. 397). The feature is distinct from the graded profile of equilibrium, which is developed mainly under water.

Apparently there are various ways in which erosion may make a horizontal "saw cut" into the land at or about high-water level which is able to keep ahead of the general process of marine erosion.

Fig. 399.—The "Old Hat," Bay of Islands, New Zealand. A small island of a drowned landscape reduced to a stack by development of cliffs and a high-water platform around it. *F. G. Radcliffe, photo.*

Within landlocked embayments, where wave action is feeble and inefficient in its attack on solid rock, a high-water platform of considerable breadth may be developed as practically the only modification of the steep initial profile that has resulted from drowning of land slopes (figs. 399, 400). In such cases feeble wave action has removed the products of rock-decay (chemical weathering), which has affected the rocks only above the level of saturation —that is, high-water level. This plane, therefore determines a surface of fresh rock exposed in the platform.

The foregoing is not applicable, on the other hand, to coasts exposed to heavy surf (that shown in fig. 397, for example) and fringed by broad platforms farther seaward that have evidently been worn by vigorous marine erosion. Yet a high-water platform is so commonly present on such shores that it must be regarded as a normal feature developed by the cliff-making processes. The horizontal "saw cut" near high-water level may or may not keep ahead of the general process of platform-cutting and grading going on in the zone of breakers and farther seaward. If it keeps well ahead, a cut rock platform of considerable breadth is developed

Fig. 400.—High-water rock platform at Greenhithe, upper reaches of Auckland Harbour, New Zealand.
C. A. Cotton, photo.

and maintained; if it fails to keep ahead at all, the high-water platform has zero width—that is, is locally absent. As for the origin of the "saw cut" in this case, it may be in part similar to that described above in the case of sheltered waters; but it appears also that the swirling impact of masses of water driven landward when great waves break in severe storms is particularly effective in developing a cliff or nip at the rear of the higher platform and in cleanly scouring this platform itself. The landward part of this platform, moreover, is frequently dry and is subject to disintegration at the surface owing to wetting and drying. When storm waves wash away rock debris thus loosened they sometimes even hollow

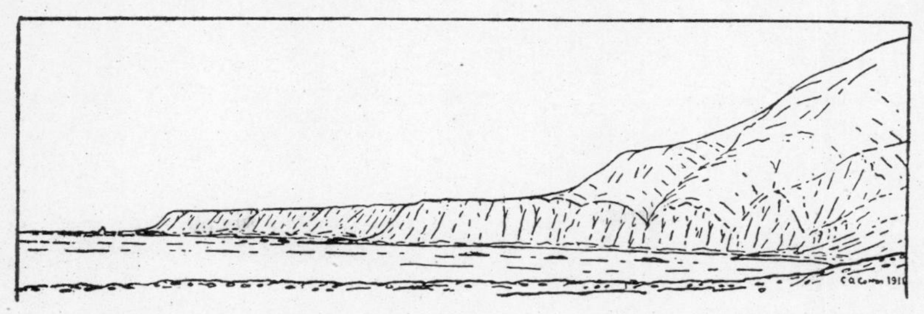

Fig. 401.—Remnants of uplifted marine platforms forming a narrow, upper, dissected bench and a broad, well-preserved, lower marine terrace at Tongue Point, Wellington, New Zealand. The lower bench exhibits the profile of a graded off-shore platform sloping rather steeply seaward.

out a landward strip of a high-water platform to some extent, leaving a residual rampart at the seaward edge.

Profile and Width of the Graded Platform.—A seaward slope developed under water on a cut platform is shown in fig. 401. Two benches are here seen, but the upper one is narrow and submaturely dissected. The lower bench displays its broadest remnant at this point, which is seen again in fig. 402 and (along with the west-

Fig. 402.—The Tongue Point marine terrace, Wellington, New Zealand, showing thin beach deposits over a cut surface of bedrock.

C. A. Cotton, photo.

ward continuation of the terrace) in figs. 403, 404. It is smoothly graded, but slopes somewhat steeply.

Marine Terraces.—The platform referred to above has emerged to become the Tongue Point *marine terrace*. Because of warping which has taken place since the emergence its elevation varies from

Fig. 403.—View westward along the Tongue Point marine terrace, Cook Strait, New Zealand. *V. C. Browne, photo.*

point to point along the coast, but at Tongue Point the ancient shoreline is about 220 feet above sea-level. The terrace is everywhere strongly cliffed at the margin by modern marine erosion. It is such cliffing that converts a narrow coastal plain or emergent platform into a terrace. This bench, like most marine terraces, is discontinuous along the shore, having been cut away altogether by modern marine erosion at some places.

Fig. 404.—Another view of the marine terrace shown in fig. 403.
C. A. Cotton, photo.

Fig. 405.—A boulder-covered and very recently emerged cut platform forming a narrow coastal plain at Cape Turakirae, near Wellington, New Zealand. (A beach ridge appears in the left upper corner of this view.)
C. A. Cotton, photo.

Such benches are generally thinly veneered with beach gravel. During slow emergence deposits that have been laid down in rather deep water far out on a platform are liable to be reworked, largely removed, and replaced by beach material. This is not invariably the case, however, and the thin landward edge of a wedge of "coastal-plain" marine deposits containing fossil shells may be present. It is found on a marine terrace at Motunau, for example, on the east coast of the South Island of New Zealand. This terrace was cut rapidly on soft rocks, and slopes very gently seaward.

Minor irregularities, including prominent stacks, were probably very numerous originally on the Tongue Point platform (shown in figs. 401-404) if one may judge from the rough relief of reefs of rocks now fringing the adjacent shoreline. The smoothness of the terrace surface in its present condition indicates that such stacks have crumbled down and been destroyed by subaerial weathering. A recently emerged cut platform, or narrow coastal plain not yet cliffed to convert it into a terrace, at Cape Turakirae, which is also near Wellington, New Zealand, has an extremely rough floor of stacks and large boulders as yet unaffected by weathering (fig. 405). During very recent retreat of the sea from this platform several successive beach ridges were piled in parallel lines along the emerging sea-floor. The retreat continues intermittently.

A pavement of fresh boulders indicates very recent emergence in the case of the Hawaiian uplifted platform shown in fig. 406.

The cliff-base angle at the rear of marine terraces is in most cases somewhat obscured by talus from the weathered cliffs (fig. 407), but even where such cover is present it may be trenched by ravines which reveal beach gravel under it.

Cover Head.—Some marine terraces have a very thick accumulation of *cover head* over them, consisting of talus cones and alluvial fans—material which has been spread over them during and after emergence. This produces the Southern Californian type of marine terrace (fig. 408), bordering high and steep coasts that consist of weak rocks subject to rapid erosion.

An enormous accumulation of such cover head on a marine abraded platform of vast extent forms a very extensive piedmont alluvial plain fringing the Santa Monica Mountains at Los Angeles, California; and its margin, cliffed now by the sea, forms the "Palisades" (fig. 409). Similar but less thick cover head is present

Fig. 406.—Sea cliff and fresh boulder-strewn rock platform upraised 550 feet on the island of Lanai, Hawaiian group.

H. T. Stearns, photo.

Fig. 407.—A cut platform, new cliff, and marine terrace with a cover head, which obscures the form of an ancient cliff, Polhawn Cove, Whitsand Bay, Cornwall.

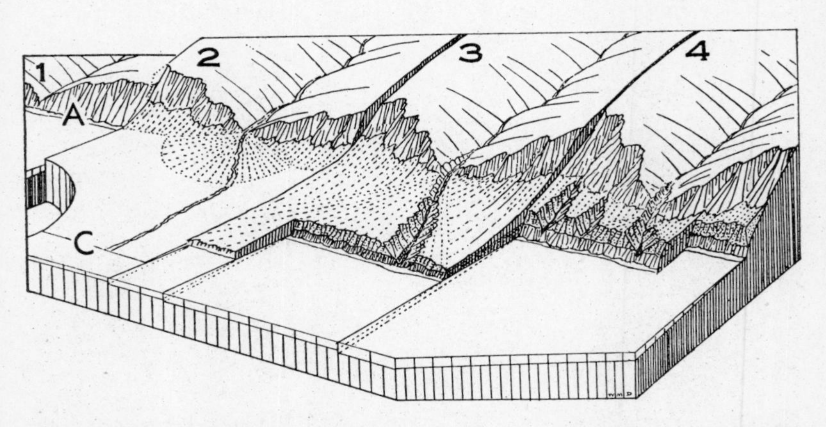

Fig. 408.—A marine platform bordering a coast (1) is uplifted (2) so that the sea withdraws form *A* to *C*. It is then deeply buried under a "head" of cover, cliffed at the margin by the sea (3), and reduced to a marine terrace (4). (After W. M. Davis.)

Fig. 409.—Cliffs of an alluvial cover head on a marine-cut platform, Palisades, Santa Monica, California.

C. A. Cotton, photo.

over an extensive platform at the head of Palliser Bay, in New Zealand (fig. 410).

Profiles of Progressively Uplifted Coasts.—Three marine terraces of the coast of Southern California have been ascribed[1] to a slow (and possibly continuous) emergent movement of the land, an uplift which might have caused continuous negative movement of the shoreline but for the contemporaneous occurrence of period-

Fig. 410.—Marine-cut bench at the head of Palliser Bay, New Zealand, with alluvial cover head.

C. A. Cotton, photo.

ical advances (positive movements) of the sea, which must have been caused by the melting of the ice of successive glacial epochs. All the advances except the latest have been followed by withdrawals. To these intermittent advances of the sea is assigned the cutting of platforms, each of which after it has subsequently emerged has been cliffed at the margin by the sea during its next advance.

It does not seem necessary to assume that sea-level rises during the cutting of every marine platform; but deepening water on a platform will certainly keep wave action vigorous while the platform is extended landward and will thus speed up the process of

[1] By W. M. Davis.

platform-cutting and cliff recession. Steepness of the seaward slope of a cut platform, such as that shown in profile in fig. 401, may perhaps be an indication that sea-level was rising during this cliff-cutting episode.

Fig. 411.—Marine terraces near Cape Viscaino, on the coast of northern California. (After W. M. Davis.)

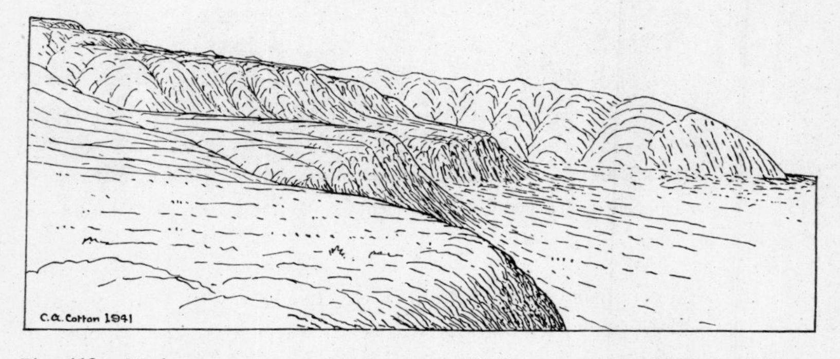

Fig. 412.—Marine terraces at Orongorongo, Wellington, New Zealand. Tilting towards the observer has affected this whole flight of terraces (compare fig. 458).

The attack of the sea during either pauses or reversals in progressive emergence has caused the development of flights of terraces reaching up considerably more than 1000 feet above present sea-level on the coasts of Southern and Northern California (fig. 411) and central New Zealand (especially Wellington—fig. 412); but in the latter region the terraces have been strongly warped by later movements (fig. 458).

CHAPTER XXX

COASTAL PROFILES (*Continued*)

The built platform. The continental shelf. The beach. Organic accumulations: coral reefs. The continental slope. Submarine canyons. Plains of marine erosion. Progradation. Offshore bars. Progradation controlled by supply of waste. Sedimentation in landlocked waters.

The Built Platform.—Far out on the platform developed by wave action at the margin of the land the waste that results from marine erosion, together with that brought down to the sea by rivers, is moved about in various directions on the bottom by the to-and-fro movement of wave-agitated water and by chance currents, some of it becoming very finely comminuted in the process, but, as the undertow gives the bottom water a preponderating seaward movement, the waste is worked slowly outward. Though the upper layer of this comminuted waste is in motion, there is generally a sufficiently thick accumulation of it on bottoms considerably shallower than the depth of wave-base to protect the bedrock floor from abrasion. The cut platform does not then extend out to the level of wave-base, but is flanked seaward by a bank of sediment consisting in its deeper parts of waste that has travelled out into water too deep to be stirred to the bottom by wave action—that is, deeper than wave-base—and has come to rest there, and in its upper part of sediment above wave-base, the upper layer of which is subject to movement and is in process of transportation. This bank of sediment forms the *built platform* (fig. 396). The equilibrium of the sediment forming that part of the built platform above wave-base depends on continuance of the supply of waste, for, if the supply were to be cut off, transportation due to movement of the bottom water would continue, the sediment lying above wave-base would thus be gradually removed, and if bedrock were exposed by the stripping away of the sediment it would be subject to abrasion as long as any fragments large enough to act as tools remained upon it. The depth at which the cut platform ends and the built platform begins thus depends on equilibrium between waste supply and transportation. So also (within limits) does the depth to which abrasion can lower the platform.

The Continental Shelf.—The off-shore profile, once graded (fig. 396), remains so unless the cycle of marine erosion is interrupted by earth movements; but the width and slope of the whole platform (*continental shelf*) may change considerably. As long as wave action remains vigorous and waste is removed the shoreline retreats, and at the same time the built portion of the platform generally continues to grow seaward as additional waste is deposited. The outer margin of the platform remains at the depth of wave-base (a depth of about 70 fathoms off exposed coasts), for sediment sliding over the edge of the existing shelf or settling from suspension accumulates in the still water up to this level. Thus, the shelf increasing in width and its edge remaining at the same depth below sea-level, the slope of its surface becomes more and more gentle.

Such a shelf surrounds the lands and has generally a width of many miles. It narrows, however, where—on the west side of Palliser Bay, New Zealand, for example, and on parts of the Californian coast—the initial coast profile has been steep on account of recent earth movements of great magnitude.

The sediment on the surface of a normal, gently-inclined shelf is principally fine sand, passing into coarser sand and in some cases gravel as the shoreline is approached, and into muddy sand or sandy mud towards the outer edge.

The Beach.—Along such parts of a coast as are not at present being actively cut back—more especially opposite bays, but frequently also, as a temporary condition, in front of cliffs the form of which shows that they have been recently attacked at the base—a cut platform is overlaid by a continuous or nearly continuous sheet of waste, the graded profile of the surface of which is continued above high-water level, where sand or gravel has been piled up by the breaking waves. Between tide marks the surface of this waste sheet is the *beach,* while the portion above high-water level may be piled into the form of a ridge—a *beach ridge,* or *storm beach* (fig. 413). The beach and beach ridge are not permanent accumulations but are liable to be cut away rapidly by wave action in response to changing conditions of weather or currents. So also (though it is less visible and obvious) is the layer of waste which may temporarily overlie a cut platform.

Organic Accumulations: Coral Reefs.—The hard parts of marine organisms, principally molluscan and other shells, are entombed within the sediments as fossils, and in places where the supply of land-derived debris almost fails, and where marine life is particularly abundant, the remains of organisms, sometimes ground to fragments by mutual abrasion, accumulate in the shelf deposits as layers which afterwards become beds of limestone.

In very warm seas calcareous deposits accumulate in quite shallow water as *coral reefs,* which consist of a great variety of calcareous

Fig. 413.—Storm beach in front of a cliff which has recently been steepened by marine erosion. This beach ridge was abandoned by the sea after the 5-feet uplift in 1855, at Wellington, New Zealand, and afterwards overgrown in places by vegetation.

C. A. Cotton, photo.

remains (including some of marine-plant origin) but are strengthened and bound together by "reef-building" corals. These coral growths, which are the skeletons of clustered and branching colonies of attached animals (polyps) budding and branching from one another, but individually resembling the soft-bodied sea anemones seen in rock pools, can live only in pure sea-water the temperature of which does not fall below 68° F., and at depths not exceeding 20 or 30 fathoms.

When a coral reef becomes established along a shore (as a *fringing reef*) it affords complete protection from further marine erosion, offering nearly as great resistance as compact limestone would to wave attack and having moreover the faculty of regeneration when partly demolished by waves (fig. 414).

The continuity of a fringing reef is broken by passages (fig. 414) opposite the mouths of streams, the fresh water from which stunts the coral or completely prevents its growth. A *barrier reef* differs from a fringing reef in that it is separated from the land by a strip of fairly deep water (Chapter XXXI).

Fig. 414.—A fringing reef, Niue Island, South Pacific Ocean, protecting a steep shore from marine erosion. *S. Taylor, photo.*

The Continental Slope.—Beyond the edge of the continental shelf there is a steeper slope (the *continental slope*) leading down into the ocean depths. This is the front of the accumulating bank of sediment forming the built platform of the shelf. As it is of the same nature as the steep front of a delta, it may like it be called a *fore-set* slope. The subaqueous portions of the deltas of large rivers are, indeed, merely salients of the continental shelf. The material on this slope, and also that underlying the coarser material on the top of a shelf built out while sea-level remains stationary, is principally mud that has settled down and come to rest in the still water below wave-base. Accumulation of this fine material cannot take place where there is any motion of the water in contact with the bottom.

Submarine Canyons.—Exploration of the sea-floor by means of recently developed methods of rapid sounding has shown that unlike continental shelves, which are generally flat, continental slopes have considerable relief and are trenched commonly by submarine valleys, some of which are thousands of feet deep and extend very far down the slopes to great ocean depths. The origin of these *submarine canyons* presents problems as yet unsolved. The canyons may be eroded features of submerged lands; but this is almost incredible, for what could have become of the oceans while these slopes were undergoing erosion above sea-level? They may, on the other hand, be of submarine origin, perhaps eroded by currents of water streaming down the sub-ocean slopes because heavily laden with mud. This hypothesis requires an explanation of the mud-laden water, which has been ascribed to stirring of sediment along continental shelves that had become partly emergent owing to withdrawal of water from the oceans to be piled up as ice to make the continental glaciers of the Ice Age. Another hypothesis explains the canyons by postulating that underground water derived from the continents has passed through permeable strata of a built shelf and emerged far down the slopes as voluminous springs; these have gnawed back by a headward sapping process so as to open the canyons. There are also various subsidiary hypotheses of submarine slumping and mudflow phenomena which may be appealed to as possibly contributing to the development of under-sea relief.

Plains of Marine Erosion.—The slope of the surface of the continental shelf becomes more and more gentle as the width of the shelf increases. As a result, the waves running shoreward over it are affected more and more by the friction of the bottom, and so reach the shoreline with diminishing energy. Retreat of the shoreline becomes slower and slower. The wave-cut cliffs, at first nearly vertical, later assume more and more gentle slopes as the subaerial processes grading the slopes are able to keep pace with the slower retreat of the cliff bases. At last wave energy will become so reduced that it will be almost completely used up in grinding and transporting seaward the waste brought down by streams. The rate of retreat of the shoreline thus falls off rapidly, and in the case of land with strong relief it will become so slow as to be negligible. When later, however, the relief of the land has been destroyed by subaerial erosion and the supply of waste derived from it falls off almost to zero, even much enfeebled waves can attack the shoreline again and abrade the cut platform. Thus marine planation is theoretically capable of ultimately cutting a platform of unlimited width—i.e., of cutting the land away altogether—but the process demands an extravagantly long period of still-stand for such development of a *plain of marine erosion*.

During progressive submergence, on the other hand, there is no retardation of the rate of marine planation by increase in the width of a shallow-water zone. As the land and continental shelf sink relatively to sea-level, the depth of water over the cut platform constantly increases, thus allowing the waves always to reach the shoreline with sufficient energy to erode vigorously, and so to extend the cut platform rapidly landward. Such a cut platform, unlike that formed while sea-level is stationary, does not owe its seaward slope to continued abrasion of the bottom in the moderately deep water offshore but to continued submergence of the successive strips cut down to the level of the line of breakers at the shoreline. A plain so formed is buried, however, beneath sediment progressively as it is cut, and where sedimentary deposits are thick and extensive they are not entirely removed or reworked by the action of waves if the shoreline later retreats over them.

Among the broad areas in various parts of the world which are shown by the survival of plateau remnants to be erosion surfaces of little or no relief uplifted and dissected, though some are certainly peneplains, others appear to have originated as plains of marine erosion; and this is certainly the case with large areas of fossil plain on which marine covering beds still rest. Considerable portions of the resurrected fossil plains now forming conspicuous plateau features in New Zealand (Chapter XII), notably those in northern Nelson, were smoothed finally by marine erosion, as is shown by the fact that remnants of cover surviving here and there on the plateaux consist of marine deposits and have a layer of beach-worn pebbles at the base, which lies on a smoothly abraded surface of unweathered rock.

Deformed structures of the rocks underlying a fossil plain often indicate that the region was mountainous in a far distant past, and therefore that a vast amount of erosion has been necessary to destroy its relief; but it is by no means obligatory to assume that the whole or even a great part of the planation was the work of the sea. The amount of waste that has to be removed during the levelling down of a mountainous land is enormous, and the movement of submergence that must be postulated to explain the formation of a broad plain by marine erosion from such an initial form is extremely slow and must go on evenly and continuously throughout a vast lapse of time. It is more probable therefore, that few regions except those of small relief—that is, regions that have already been reduced by subaerial erosion to peneplains—have been completely planed off by the sea over wide areas. The soil on the low relief forms of a peneplain is deeply weathered and offers little resistance to marine erosion. So planation of such a previously prepared surface may be effected by the sea during a movement of submergence occupying a comparatively short time.

Progradation.—Besides the case of initially steep coasts (*a*), as already discussed, two other cases may be recognised in which the initial profile is (*b*) already approximately of the declivity required for a graded under-water profile or (*c*) less steep—that is, very nearly horizontal. Either of these conditions may follow if the shoreline has moved to a new position as a result of emergence of a strip of the former sea-floor as a coastal plain or if the sea has advanced over a partly submerged delta or piedmont alluvial plain.

In the former case (*b*) waves cannot attack the gently sloping initial land, for a very slight attack upon it will supply sufficient waste to overload the waves and the debris will be thrown up again as a protective beach. The coarser part (sand and gravel) of the load brought down to the sea by rivers must indeed be thus built into beaches and the shoreline is thus progressively built forward *pari passu* with the deposit of layers of finer waste as "top-set" beds, which are added to the underwater surface of a built platform or continental shelf extending seaward (fig. 415, *B*). This shoreline advance is *progradation,* in contrast with *retrogradation*—the cutting back of the shore in a line of cliffs as previously described. Prograded areas are *forelands,* and if continuous for some distance alongshore are *strand plains.*

If the material thrown up by the prograding sea is gravel successive beach ridges are distinguishable in profile, but if it is sand these are destroyed by wind, and dunes are built. Parallel dune ridges, fixed by vegetation, may be built as foredunes marking successive positions of the shoreline (p. 267).

Offshore Bars.—The remaining case (*c*) of nearly horizontal initial profile—insufficiently steep to provide a graded offshore profile ready made—necessitates for its development vertical erosion or excavation of the sea bottom seaward and deposition landward. If

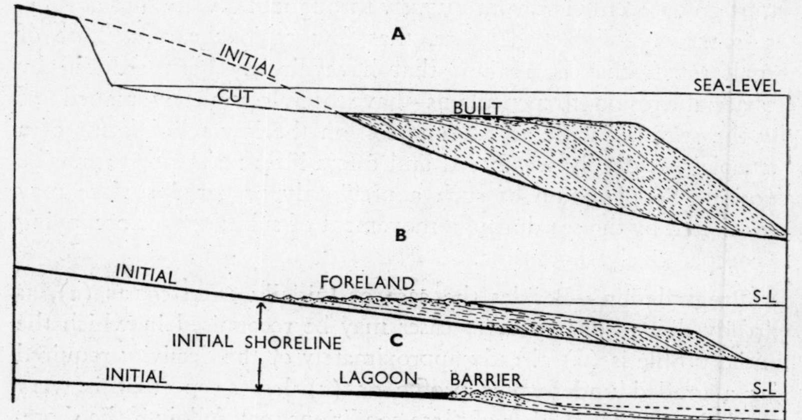

Fig. 415.—Retrogradation (*A*) contrasted with progradation (*B*) and the building of an off-shore bar (*C*). Vertical scale and steepness of slopes and beds exaggerated.

the bottom is eroded vigorously at and seaward of the breaker line, the sand thus stirred up is thrown up either on the beach or seaward of it, forming in the latter case an emergent ridge, termed an *offshore bar,* or *barrier,* between which and the initial shoreline a lagoon is enclosed (fig. 415, *C*).

The lagoon may remain connected with the sea by a few more or less permanent channels ("inlets"), which are kept open by tidal and river currents and may be scoured to some depth, making harbours behind the barrier (fig. 416). Lagoons become filled in, at least in part, however, by mud flats and peat-forming salt-marsh vegetation.

An offshore bar may be extended seaward by accumulation of successive beach strips in the same way as a prograded coast, and, indeed, the two kinds of shoreline may become indistinguishable where lagoons are filled in and perhaps buried beneath dunes of sand derived from the outer beaches.

Offshore bars may also be attacked and cut away by the sea if the waves become hungry as a result of a falling off in the supply of waste. Such must be their ultimate fate if sea-level remains long enough constant in one position. The first-formed bar having been thus cut away, waves will build a new one landward of the position of the first. The barrier may be thus thought of as pushed

Fig. 416.—The entrance to Tauranga Harbour, Bay of Plenty, New Zealand, which is enclosed by Matakana Island (left) and a sand isthmus (right) which have originated mainly as off-shore bars. The Mount Maunganui peninsula (upper left corner) is a "land-tied island." View looking seaward.

V. C. Browne, photo.

landwards, so that the lagoon or marsh behind it is progressively narrowed and eventually eliminated; after which even a very flat, low-lying shore may be retrograded as low cliffs.

The presence of offshore bars does not afford a definite proof, as has sometimes been assumed, that the latest movement has been a withdrawal of the sea to a lower level. In the case of the offshore bars of the Bay of Plenty coast of New Zealand (fig. 416), which fringe a drowned shoreline, it is highly probable that the bar-building resulted from a plentiful supply of air-borne volcanic ash brought to the Bay of Plenty by prevailing south-westerly winds from the Taupo-Rotorua volcanic field.

Progradation Controlled by Supply of Waste.—Progradation of a coastal strip may also be determined by an increase in the supply of waste while sea-level remains fixed. Quite commonly such an increase is a normal result of the "rectification" of an embayed shoreline in the course of the shoreline cycle (Chapter XXXI) which results in the development of a continuous beach, affording

Fig. 417.—Foreland developed by progradation in front of low cliffs, mouth of the Waipara River, Canterbury, New Zealand.

V. C. Browne, photo.

an easy path for the transportation of sand (or gravel) alongshore by waves. In this case forelands are built by progradation in front of previously cut cliffs (fig. 417).

A peculiarity of the Paekakariki prograded lowland (near Wellington, New Zealand) is that it includes features developed during alternating episodes of progradation and retrogradation (figs. 418, 419), the former of which may be assigned to phases in which the supply of sand brought down by rivers farther north (the

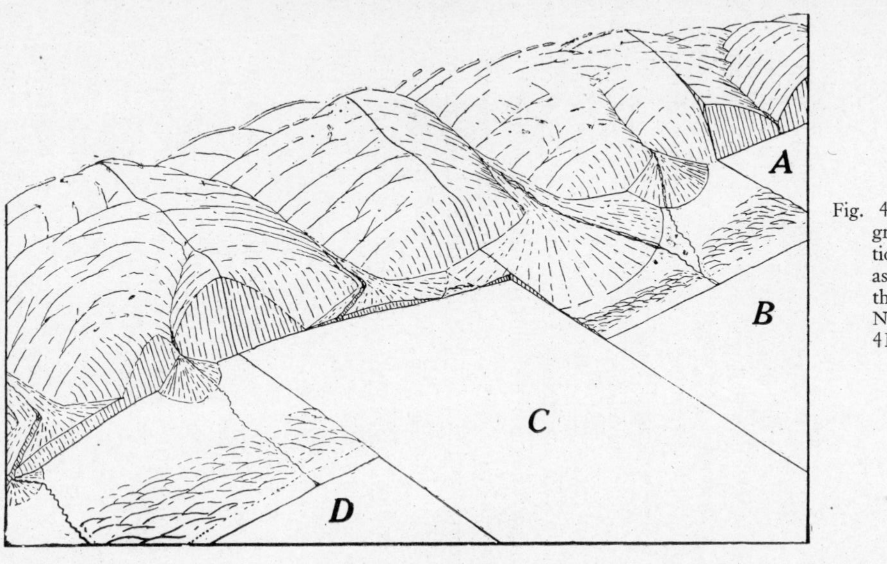

Fig. 418.—Successive stages retrogradation *A*, *C*, and progradation, *B*. *D*, affecting a coast, so as to produce features like those of the Paekakariki coast, New Zealand. (Compare fig. 419.)

Fig. 419.—The Paekakariki coast, New Zealand, viewed from fixed dunes on the modern foreland.

Wanganui River, especially) was greatly augmented by volcanic ash eruptions in the centre of the North Island.

The material composing the Paekakariki foreland (fig. 419) is of two kinds, gravel of local origin and sand which has been transported alongshore from the north. The abundance of the latter at certain times has been the cause of progradation, and reversals of the process appear to have resulted from failure of the supply. The sand thrown up by the sea in the first traceable progradational phase apparently formed a foreland, on which the gravel brought down by local streams accumulated as fans (fig. 418, *B*). Then came a phase of retrogradation, in which the foreland was almost completely cut away, *C*. A later extensive progradation has built a new dune-covered foreland several miles in width, *D*. The cliffs of the earlier retrogradational phase are now somewhat subdued and rounded, and pass by a smooth concave curve at the base into the talus slopes and alluvial fans of the next phase—progradation. These fans are irregularly truncated by the cliffs developed in the later retrogradational phase, which are cut back far enough in places to intersect the line of cliffs of the earlier retrogradation, *D*. In front of the newer line of cliffs lies the modern foreland, consisting of a belt of dunes, which on the landward side are fixed by vegetation, and a narrow strip of marsh between the fixed dunes and the cliffs. This seems to have been a lagoon enclosed during a phase of offshore bar-building in the latest progradation.

Sedimentation in Landlocked Waters.—In sheltered waters (that is, small lakes or enclosed bays) wave-base is at a shallow depth—perhaps 4 or 5 fathoms, but varying with the size of the sheet of water and the length of the waves which arise on its surface. Sediment sinking below wave-base is undisturbed except by strong tidal currents, which scour out and keep open channels through it. The waste carried by streams into landlocked embayments and broken by wave action around their margins is deposited in them, therefore, and little makes its way out to sea until the embayments are filled up nearly to sea-level. Indeed, the fact that such bays are generally so filled, though the stage of the shoreline cycle may indicate that the date of their formation by submergence of the land surface (fig. 420) was very recent, and the observed rapidity with which silt accumulates in sheltered waters make it clear that the tide carries into the initial embayments and deposits there a great quantity of fine waste from the outer coast. Much in-carried sand accumulates as rather conspicuous delta-like forms (below high-water level) within the openings of tidal channels through the barriers and bars of sand which have converted many bays into lagoons. They are called "tidal deltas."

CHAPTER XXXI

COASTAL OUTLINES: SUBMERGENCE

The shoreline cycle. Initial forms of coasts. Coasts of submergence and of emergence. Classification of coasts. Coasts of submergence. Development of minor irregularities. Rectification of the coastal outline. Spits and bars. Maturity. Bights and coves. Barrier (coral) reefs and atolls associated with coasts of submergence.

The Shoreline Cycle.—In the development of coastal features marine erosion plays a part analogous to that normally assumed on the surface of the land by rain and running water in producing those sequential forms which supply all the detail in a general

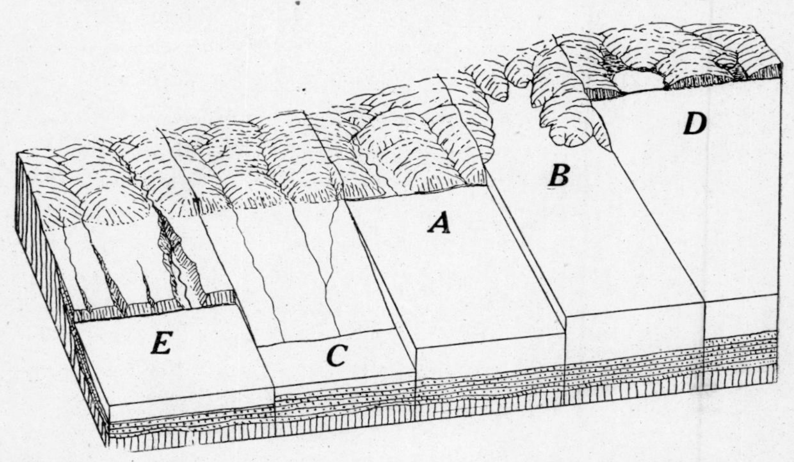

Fig. 420.—Coasts of submergence and of emergence (represented in the diagram as though due to rise and fall of sea-level). *B*, effect of submergence or subsidence, and *C*, effect of emergence or uplift; *A*, pre-existing coast; *D* and *E*, sequential forms derived from the initial forms *B* and *C* respectively.

view of either a coast or a landscape. When a broad view of a coast is taken, however, it is generally possible to distinguish more or less distinct traces of larger initial forms, as is the case also in many landscapes. Actual coasts are sequential forms developed by erosion, and in part by accumulation, from varied initial forms.

A succession of stages, or *shoreline cycle,* through which the coastal features normally pass, can be developed for each kind of initial coast.

Initial Forms of Coasts.—There is a strong contrast between typical coasts of submergence and coasts of emergence in the early stages of the shoreline cycle (fig. 420). The latter, bordering areas of newly exposed sea-floor, are straight and featureless, while the former, on account of the *drowning,* or partial submergence, of the features of diversified land surfaces, are generally highly irregular.[1] A striking imitation of the effects of partial submergence of a mountainous land is sometimes afforded by the view from above of fog or cloud banks lying in valleys and reproducing the outlines of bays and islands with great fidelity (fig. 421).

Besides initial forms due to submergence and emergence there are fault coasts, initially fault scarps descending into the sea; while another type of initial coast results from accumulation of volcanic material, where a growing volcano forms a salient of the coastal outline or is built up from the sea-bottom to become an island; and yet another distinct type is that found where the sea has entered troughs excavated by glaciers extending below sea-level.

Coasts of Submergence and of Emergence.—Movements of the ocean-level will produce results similar to uplift and subsidence of the land except that these eustatic movements will be world-wide and their effects of equal magnitude over large areas. The observed amount of submergence or emergence often varies, however, from point to point, and there is sometimes a rapid passage from a coast of submergence to one of emergence, indicating that movement of the land—generally diverse movement—has been responsible for some initial coasts and has elsewhere acted in combination with eustatic submergence, modifying and occasionally reversing its effects.

Some shorelines due to *warping* need not be considered separately, for there is no essential difference in form between shorelines due to regional depression or uplift and those in which the submergence or emergence is local and due to gentle tilting or warping. The actual tilting or warping movement may involve uplift inland and depression seaward, and yet at the shoreline it may result in either submergence or emergence according as the hinge line of the

[1] Some features resulting from alternating emergence and submergence may be traced on most coasts, but the latest movement has generally determined the major forms.

Fig. 421.—The mountains of south-western New Zealand (Mount Tutoko from the south-east) partly submerged in clouds, producing an effect resembling an embayed shoreline with outlying islands.

V. C. Browne, photo.

warping or tilting is landward or seaward of the pre-existing shoreline. Even warping so pronounced as to result in monoclinal flexure of the surface is almost indistinguishable in its effects from marginal faulting.

It is another matter, however, where deformation (whether warping or block faulting) takes place along lines transverse to the coast. Upwarping or emergence of upheaved blocks will result in the production of coastal salients, or, on the other hand, downwarping or subsidence of blocks will cause the formation of initial embayments. If such features are developed on a very large scale, the origin of the coast as a whole may be described as "composite," and in detailed description attention may be confined to the new shorelines bounding individual blocks—shorelines of submergence or emergence or fault shorelines as the case may be. If, however, deformation of this kind but of a smaller texture has affected a coast, the salients and re-entrants will be of such dimensions that they must be classed as initial features. Their combination may produce an indented shoreline in a general way similar to that of a submerged coast, and the course of shoreline cycle will then be similar in a general way also; while individual elements of the shoreline are emergent, submerged, or fault-bounded, and may be described under these heads.

Such coasts of *transverse deformation* must be given their place in the classification of initial coastal outlines. Few examples of them have been described; but at Wellington, New Zealand, Port Nicholson, one of the finest harbours in the world, has been produced by just this process.

Shorelines (of various origins) that owe their initial forms to causes other than emergence or submergence have been sometimes grouped as "neutral."

Classification of Coasts.—Classification according to the origin of the initial form presents difficulties because of the complicated history of most coastal regions. Coasts presenting forms combining features of diverse origin, due perhaps to successive earth movements, must often be described as "compound." Failing a full and complete classification, however, the following synoptic scheme has been found useful in bringing together coasts related either in their initial or sequential forms.

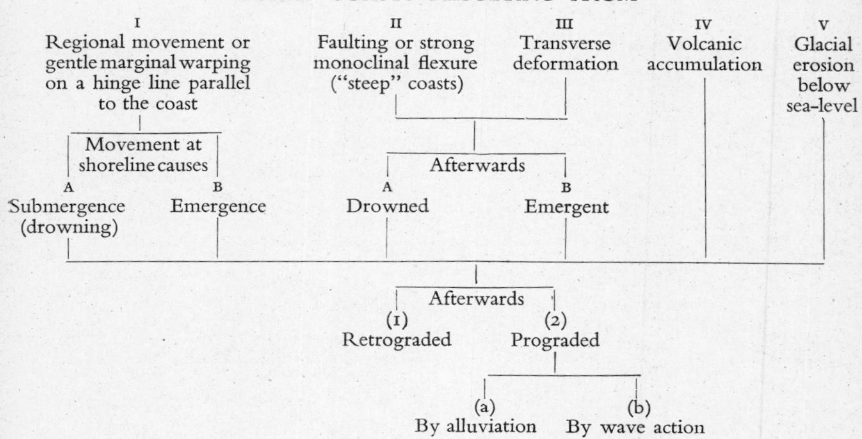

Coasts of Submergence.—Most deeply embayed coasts have been recently submerged as a whole. Submergence of the seaward margin of a dissected land surface allows the sea to enter the lower parts of valleys, converting them into *drowned valleys* (fig. 420, *B*). The rivers are *betrunked*[1]—that is, shorn of their lower courses—and the river systems are *dismembered*—that is, streams formerly tributaries of trunk rivers now enter the sea by separate mouths (fig. 420, *B*). It is by the drowning of valleys that estuaries and a great many of the most useful harbours of the world have been formed (figs. 218, 365, 366, 424).

Where before submergence the rivers run more or less parallel to the coast in open valleys (as where the strike of strata, folds, or blocks is parallel to the coast), and reach the sea by way of transverse gorges, very fine landlocked harbours of the Dalmatian type are produced by drowning. Where, on the other hand, the strike of structures is transverse to the coast, drowned valleys extending far inland and broadening at the mouth are formed, which are termed *rias*. Rias indent the south-west coast of Ireland, and excellent examples are afforded by Queen Charlotte and Pelorus Sounds, which are embayments of the Cook Strait shoreline in New Zealand (figs. 422, 423).

[1] Contrast with "beheading," which deprives rivers of their headwaters.

Fig. 422.—Deeply drowned branching bays, Pelorus Sound, New Zealand. View looking northward to Cook Strait.

Fig. 423.—Branching bays and drowned shoreline and islets in Queen Charlotte Sound, New Zealand. The town, Picton, is built on a bay-head delta.

V. C. Browne, photo.

Partly drowned ridges form projecting capes, headlands, and outlying islands, while islands are formed also within the embayments by the unsubmerged higher parts of spurs. Occasionally

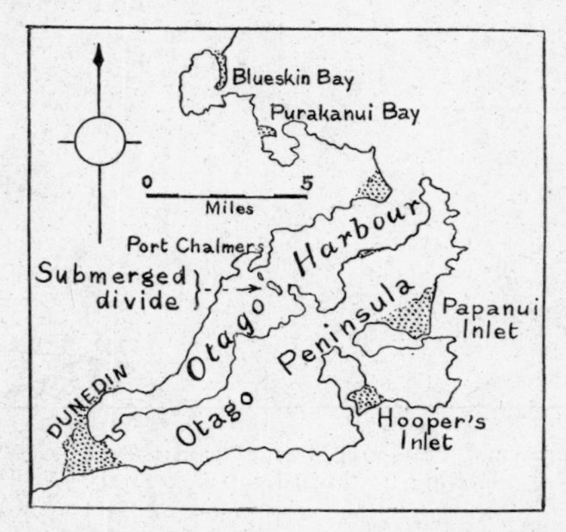

Fig. 424.—Map of Otago Harbour, New Zealand, showing drowned valleys, spits, bay-bars, and a submerged divide.

Fig. 425.—View looking across the submerged divide in Otago Harbour to Otago Peninsula (compare fig. 424).

F. G. Radcliffe, photo.

divides are submerged and large islands are separated from the mainland by narrow straits which result from the drowning of two or more neighbouring valleys. Otago Peninsula (fig. 424) was an island formed thus by the submergence of a divide (fig. 425), though it has been again joined to the mainland at another place by an isthmus of sand on which part of the city of Dunedin has been built (fig. 424).

Development of Minor Irregularities.—The initial offshore profiles along a coast of submergence are irregular, and are generally much steeper than a profile of equilibrium. Thus erosion begins at once along the shoreline, outstanding points being attacked by ocean waves, and the shores of enclosed and sheltered waters by the smaller waves that arise within their own limits. The initial

Fig. 426.—Young cliffed shoreline of submergence, Bay of Islands, New Zealand.
C. A. Cotton, photo.

outline, though it may trace an intricate pattern, is made up usually of smooth curves determined by the intersection of the plane of sea-level with the graded subaerial slopes; and the first effect of wave attack on such an outline is to introduce innumerable minor irregularities (such as those shown in figs. 426, 427), determined by differences of rock hardness and the presence of joints, crushed zones, and any other weak places. A young depressed coast at the sequential stage at which these small irregularities have made their appearance is described as *crenulate*.

Steeply inclined sheets of shattered or easily weathered rock—whether strata or dykes—outcropping at the shoreline are excavated

Fig. 427.—Crenulate stage of a young drowned shoreline, Motuketekete Island, Hauraki Gulf, New Zealand. *V. C. Browne, photo.*

Fig. 428.—Sea caves in easily eroded columnar-jointed basalt, Fingal's Cave, Island of Staffa, Scotland. *L.M.S. Railway, photo.*

to form sea caves along the cliff base (figs. 428, 429) or open clefts in the cliffs and rock platforms (fig. 427). A *blowhole* is formed where part of the roof of a deeply penetrating sea cave falls in, leaving an open funnel, up through which a blast of air and spray is projected as each wave enters the mouth of the cave. Many examples of blowholes are known which are connected with the sea by very long tunnels (fig. 430).

Fig. 429.—Caves and clefts in a low sea cliff cut prior to a recent withdrawal of the sea, Palliser Bay, New Zealand.

C. A. Cotton, photo.

The outcrops of strata or dykes of relatively resistant rock may remain projecting prominently beyond the general line of the shore (fig. 2). Some dykes, on the other hand, are more rapidly weathered than the enclosing rocks, and are excavated by the sea to form clefts and caverns.

Bodies of rock that offer resistance to erosion while quarrying and excavation go on around them as a result of wave action remain standing above the cut platform beyond a receding line of cliffs as steep-walled *stacks* (figs. 392, 431), and some of these remain connected to the cliffs for a time by *arches* (figs. 431, 432). Outlying stacks when worn down to sea-level become *reefs*.

Rectification of the Coastal Outline.—Though marine erosion develops minor irregularities—the crenulate features of youth—on rocky shores, yet its general effect on the initially intricate shoreline pattern of a submerged coast is to simplify it. Rectification of the outline of an initial shoreline embayed as a result of transverse

Fig. 430.—A blowhole and the entrance of a tunnel (200 yards long) which connects it with a cave in an outer cliff, Pourewa Island, near Tolaga Bay, New Zealand. *F. A. Hargreaves, photo.*

deformation must be effected in a similar way. Marine erosion proceeds to *rectify* a shoreline initially intricate by cutting back projecting headlands (figs. 426, 431) (and also outlying islands) upon which wave energy is largely concentrated by the refraction of waves (p. 404). Convincing evidence that the land has been cut back a considerable distance is often found in an inland slope

Fig. 431.—Progressive development of arches and stacks, Dyrholaey, Iceland.

Fig. 432.—Rock platform, wave-cut cliff, and arch, Amuri Bluff, New Zealand.
P. Marshall, photo.

Fig. 433.—Bay-head delta of the Hutt River, near Wellington, New Zealand. In the foreground is a miniature delta built by a small stream. (Compare fig. 213.)

C. A. Cotton, photo.

Fig. 434.—Pocket beaches and some bay-filling on the young coast of New South Wales, north of Sydney.

of the land surface from the edge of the sea cliff—so that further recession will reduce the height of the cliff. This indicates that a hill has been more than half cut away (figs. 434, 436).

Further simplification of the outline results from deposition in the re-entrants of waste resulting from erosion of the headlands or brought down by neighbouring rivers, which build deltas of the coarser portion of their load at the heads of the drowned valleys or estuaries (figs. 210, 213, 219, 433).

Open bays have curving beaches (*pocket beaches*) around their heads, built of sand or gravel carried in from the cliffed headlands at either side (figs. 434, 435). The material on a pocket beach is

Fig. 435.—Slightly cliffed headlands and curving sandy pocket beach across the head of a shallow bay, Bay of Islands, New Zealand

subject to constant grinding, and the resulting fine waste is drawn away seaward; but where the rate of supply is greater than that of loss due to grinding successive strips of beach are added, and the bay head is thus prograded. As a result the beach may extend laterally so as to protect cliffs formerly subject to wave attack (fig. 435).

Frequently bays are also bridged across at or near their mouths by ridges, termed *bay bars,* or simply *bars,*[1] of sand or gravel stretching from headland to headland (figs. 436, 436A). These also protect the sides of the bays from the further attacks of ocean waves.

---

[1] The geomorphic use of the term "bar" differs from the nautical, which applies it only to a shoal across the mouth of a river. Bars of the latter kind originate in the same way as bay bars, but the formation of a permanent and continuous exposed ridge is prevented by the outflowing current. Exposed bars are formed temporarily, however, across the mouths of some rivers.

Fig. 436.—Submature shoreline—rectification of an embayed shoreline by development of bay bars, which convert bays into freshwater lagoons and tidal inlets. Freshwater Lagoon, near Santa Rosa, California.

Patterson Pictures, photo.

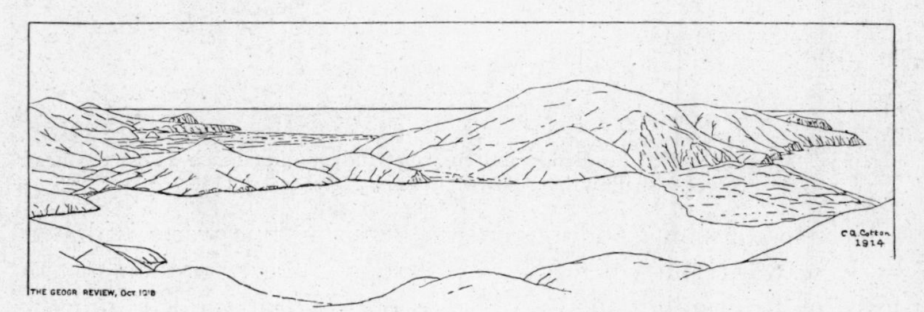

Fig. 436A.—Eastern bays of Otago Peninsula, New Zealand, enclosed by dune-covered bay-bars. (Sand drifts northward.)

Spits and Bars.—Bay bars are formed by the growth of spits across bays. A *spit* (fig. 437) grows outward from the lee side of a projecting headland if there is a sufficiently plentiful supply of coarse waste either broken from the headland itself by marine erosion or carried alongshore past it from some more distant source. Gravel or sand that is carried along by waves and by the littoral current at the beach line within the zone of breakers comes to rest when it passes the headland, because there it is carried into the deeper water of the bay beyond, and sinks to a depth at which there is insufficient motion to stir such coarse material. The accumulation of this waste builds at first a small salient to leeward of the projecting headland. More sand or gravel travels along in the shallow water bordering the seaward margin of this salient, reaches the end of it, and there sinks and comes to rest in deep water. The addition of this sand or gravel little by little causes the salient to grow in length and to become a spit. Sand or gravel carried over a spit by breaking waves comes to rest in the still water on the landward side, causing the spit to increase in width somewhat, and on the shoal so formed a beach ridge or ridges may be piled considerably above high-water level. Most spits have thus an

Fig. 437.—A spit growing across the mouth of a bay, Sandy Bay, Nelson, New Zealand

C. A. Cotton, photo.

exposed portion (fig. 437), and some have been much extended in width by progradation also.

Where the direction of alongshore drift changes with the winds the cliffed ends of headlands formed by drowned ridges are sometimes flanked by spits on both sides (*winged headlands*).

A spit that grows out far enough to encounter a transverse current or system of waves may have the debris travelling along its beach carried around the end—generally landward—so that growth continues in a new direction nearly at right angles to the proximal part of the spit, converting it into a *hook* or *hooked spit.* Most spits are somewhat hooked (fig. 437). Subsequently to the formation of a hook, a spit (after perhaps being modified considerably in form meanwhile by retrogradation or progradation due to wave action) may continue to grow in the original line. Thus a long spit may have a number of landward-projecting branches—relics of former hooks. These outline features have small relief however, and may be noticeable only at high water, when the greater part of a broad spit is submerged.

A mammoth spit, Farewell Spit, stretches eastward from Cape Farewell, South Island of New Zealand. It has a slightly hooked form convex to the north and is built of sand derived from the west coast of the island. It is broad and the emergent part is covered with dunes. The Boulder Bank, a natural breakwater which encloses the harbour of Nelson, New Zealand, is a spit of gravel and boulders (fig. 438) about seven miles long extending south-westward along the coast from a high cliffed headland of granitic rock.

Where a spit of sand has extended across a bay mouth so as to become a bay bar, a channel is generally kept open through it by tidal currents. Such an opening is so shallow, however, that it presents no permanent obstacle to the transportation of sand alongshore. The bar is therefore really continuous, though the emergent part of it is not. The last-formed portion of a sand-built bay bar, at the distal end of the spit from which the bar has developed, if it lies to leeward as regards the prevailing strong wind, may be much extended in width and also built up into dunes by wind-drifted sand (fig. 436A). This will cause the tidal channel over the bar to migrate to the proximal end of the original spit.

The drift alongshore—strictly the line separating the littoral current from the still water in the bay—guides the growing spit towards the next headland, and smooths its outline, when it becomes a bar, into a concave curve. The spit or bar "not only follows the line between the current and still water, but aids in giving definition to that line, and eventually walls in the current by contours adjusted to its natural flow" (Gilbert). The concavity in the line bounding the littoral drift where it crosses the mouth of an open bay may be so great that the bar which is eventually built across the bay is some distance from the mouth. Thus some bay bars are built near the heads of the initial bays instead of bridging the bay mouths.

As the headlands at each end of it are cut back, the seaward margin of the bar is cut away to a corresponding extent. Where

Fig. 438.—A long spit which makes a natural breakwater, the Boulder Bank, Nelson, New Zealand.

the exposed ridge on a bar is breached by the sea during this process the gap is soon mended with material thrown over the bar by breaking waves and coming to rest on the landward side, as is the case also with some offshore bars (p. 433). The bar is thus a relatively permanent feature, though the material composing it is subject to continual rearrangement.

The bridging of bay mouths by bars (together with the cutting back of headlands) shortens the shoreline very considerably, and simplifies it by substituting for the earlier intricate embayed outline one consisting of a few simple sweeping curves, such as may be closely followed by the alongshore currents that transport the

Fig. 439.—A tidal lagoon at low water. It is enclosed by a bar of sand and is silted up with mud banks, or flats. The Estuary, Sumner, New Zealand.
C. A. Cotton, photo.

beach-making waste. At this stage the coastal outline has passed through the stage of youth and has become *submature* (figs. 420, *D*; 436, 436A, 440).

In the still waters of bays enclosed by bars the fine waste brought down by streams and carried beyond the limits of the deltas at the bay heads sinks to the bottom and accumulates (p. 436). The small waves that arise in the enclosed bay and the scour of the tides (where a channel is maintained through the bar) prevent filling up to high-water level; and under their influence the superficial layer of the bay filling is moulded into shoals, or "banks," of sandy mud or sand with convex surfaces, lying between high-water and low-water level, separated by channels the beds of which may be slightly submerged at low water (fig. 439).

Within the extensive drowned-valley embayments of the North Auckland peninsula of New Zealand spits and bars built of molluscan shells are of common occurrence, these being sorted by wave action from the silt of mud banks and piled up to high-water level.

The higher parts of sand and mud banks may be converted gradually into dry land by the growth of salt-marsh vegetation or of

Fig. 440.—Straight, submature shoreline of submergence, as seen in Palliser Bay, New Zealand, where a bay bar encloses Onoke Lake. (Sketch diagram.)

mangroves, which prevent erosion and favour accumulation of silt. The low-lying parts of the Taieri Plain, in Otago, New Zealand, which are dead level, have originated in this way by the filling-in of a drowned valley (p. 234 and fig. 238). A very small movement of uplift is sufficient to place such flats beyond the reach of the highest tides. Thousands of acres thus emerged and became available as agricultural land when a 6-feet uplift caused the sea to withdraw from the mudflats of a large estuary at Napier, New Zealand, in 1929 (p. 164).

An example of a shoreline of submergence that has become straight at the submature stage is that across the head of Palliser Bay, New Zealand (figs. 203, 440). Retrogradation in a weak terrain has produced an even line of high cliffs broken by one large bay which a three-mile-long gravel bar has converted into Onoke Lake. The bay thus converted into a large lagoon originated as a result of drowning of the lower valley of the Ruamahanga River (fig. 203).

Maturity.—Retrogradation does not generally cease when the shoreline has been rectified as already described. It continues perhaps rapidly at places where weak rocks form the coast, though always more slowly elsewhere, so that the shoreline may retreat eventually

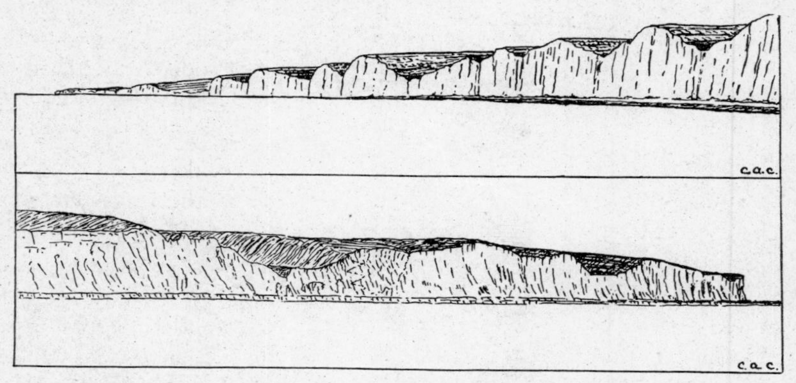

Fig. 441.—Valleys betrunked by cliff-recession facing the English Channel. Above: the chalk coast of Normandy. Below: the "white cliffs of Dover."

beyond the heads of the initial embayments and may become a line of eroded cliffs throughout its length. It is then described as *mature*.

Rapid retrogradation, especially in weak rocks, may destroy the lower courses of rivers, "betrunking" them by cliff recession. Large rivers thus shortened are rejuvenated; but smaller streams cannot deepen their valleys sufficiently rapidly to keep pace with rapid cliff recession, and their new mouths "hang" at various heights along the cliff front. On the chalk cliffs of Normandy such hanging valleys are termed *"valleuses."* They are well developed along both sides of the Strait of Dover, where the cliffs have receded a great distance in the soft chalk terrain (fig. 441); but they are by no means confined to this formation, being found wherever cliffs are rapidly retrograded. Commonly rejuvenation has proceeded to the extent of cutting a V-shaped notch in the lip of the coastal hanging valley. Where there has been much retrogradation the pattern of betrunked streams may indicate that they are the remnants of dismembered river systems.

A fully mature coast is not necessarily straight. Its outline consists rather of simple sweeping curves (see fig. 452, *DEF,* which might represent a mature coast developed from any type of initial form by retrogradation). The cliffs are cut back more easily and rapidly on areas of weak than on areas of resistant rocks not only because of the smaller resistance offered to marine erosion by the weaker rocks but also because in general the weaker parts of the terrain have already been reduced to somewhat low relief by normal erosion, so that a smaller bulk of rock has to be eroded and removed from the shoreline by the sea than from the resistant areas of the terrain.

Bights and Coves.—Selective erosion of the weaker areas goes on throughout the course of the shoreline cycle. By the time maturity is reached the curvature due to this cause will probably have reached its maximum. Differential erosion of the weaker rocks will not take place to such an extent as to produce a deeply indented coast. Rarely, indeed, does any marked irregularity of outline result from selective retrogradation. Open *coves* are cut out, however, where rather narrow belts of soft strata are transected by an initially less intricate shoreline, and also—rather characteristically—on locally decayed areas in some granite terrains, notably that of Cornwall. Such indentations do not penetrate far enough inland to enclose landlocked waters, however, for, when bays are thus formed, the land at the head of each bay is protected from erosion both by the headlands affording shelter from waves reaching the coast obliquely and also by the focussing of wave energy on the headlands and bay sides, rather than the bay heads, as a result of the refraction of waves as previously described (p. 403). Thus only broad *bights* on the larger areas of weak rocks and open coves on the smaller can result from marine erosion.

By the time shorelines are mature many of the smaller irregularities of steep, young coasts have disappeared, for with continued retrogradation the width of the continental shelf increases, waves running in over the shelving bottom lose energy, and the rate of cliff retreat becomes slow. Subaerial erosion is then not outstripped by marine erosion, but is capable of reducing the steepness of the cliffs and smoothing their outline by grading the slopes, and at the same time a more or less continuous beach takes the place of the earlier crenulate rocky outline.

The shoreline cycle need not be followed beyond maturity, for "old age" is not reached until the land is cut entirely away.

Fig. 442.—A barrier reef enclosing a small and shallow lagoon, Upolu Island, Western Samoa. The reef is defined by the line of surf, and the lagoon is on the left. The small outlying island is Fanuatapu.

J. Allan Thomson, photo.

Barrier (Coral) Reefs and Atolls associated with Coasts of Submergence.—Coral reefs superficially similar to fringing reefs (p. 427), but separated from the land by strips of water (*lagoons* or *moats*), which may be of any depth up to 20 fathoms and more, and of any width from a fraction of a mile to many miles, are termed *barrier reefs* (fig. 442). Barrier reefs surround many volcanic islands in the tropical part of the Pacific Ocean (Tahiti, for example, has, at Papeete, an excellent harbour thus enclosed), and an exceptionally large one, the Great Barrier Reef, extends for about a thousand miles along the coast of Queensland.

The observed fact that reef-building corals cannot live at depths much greater than 20 fathoms raises a difficulty as to the nature of the foundation on which the growth of barrier reefs began; for it is evident in most cases that the reef must be a great deal more than 20 fathoms thick, and that but for the presence of the reef the depth of water on its site would be very much greater than the depth at which the growth of a reef can begin.

There is the same difficulty as to the nature of the foundation on which the growth of coral began in the building of *atolls*—coral reefs of another type, also common in the Pacific, which form more or less regular rings, and occur isolated and surrounded by water of great depth, though the water in the lagoon within the encircling reef is relatively shallow. The only "land" associated with atolls is built of coral sand and fragments broken and piled upon parts of the reef ring by wave action. The "low" islands of the tropical Pacific, as distinguished from the "high," volcanic islands, are the exposed parts of atolls.

Theories postulating the existence of crater rings or steep-sided and flat-topped submerged mountains, with their summits at a depth of 20 fathoms as ready made foundations provided for atolls, seem scarcely worthy of consideration,[1] and it is generally considered that atolls and barrier reefs have so many features in common that they must have originated in the same way.

Among the theories put forward in explanation of atolls and barrier reefs the subsidence theory of Darwin accounts most satisfactorily for the majority of Pacific reefs, though it cannot be asserted that all barrier reefs and atolls owe their existence entirely to subsidence. According to this hypothesis continued upgrowth of coral takes place during slow subsidence on the site of what was originally a fringing reef, so that it becomes a barrier reef, or, in the case of a reef surrounding an island, becomes eventually an atoll when the island is completely submerged (fig. 443). The ring-like form of the reef, enclosing a lagoon, is accounted for by the more vigorous growth of the corals around the periphery, where there is a continual and abundant supply of pure sea-water and food. Inside this ring of growing coral the bottom is built up only by slower-growing organisms aided by the accumulation of waste, which is wholly derived from the reef in the case of an atoll, but from both reef and land in the case of a barrier reef.

---

[1] The existence of such a slightly submerged mountain beneath the atoll of Funafuti has been disproved by boring.

Strong evidence in favour of the subsidence theory is found in the fact that the coasts bordered by the barrier reefs are generally coasts of submergence—a confirmation of Darwin's theory that was first pointed out by Dana. When, also, uplifted barrier reefs (numerous examples of which are known) are examined, the basement on which they rest—that is, the bottom on which coral growth began—is always found to have been an eroded surface, which must have been cut at a higher level and have sunk progressively as the

Fig. 443.—Evolution of a barrier reef, and eventually an atoll, from a fringing reef during slow subsidence of a dissected volcanic island (the subsidence being shown as a rise of sea-level relative to the land). Front block, fringing reef; middle block, barrier reef; rear block, last stage of submergence of the island—the almost-atoll stage. (After W. M. Davis.)

thick reef was built up above it. Such indications of subsidence have been observed by Davis.

A postulate of postglacial rise of sea-level makes it unnecessary to assume actual subsidence of the basement to account for the submergence indicated by every up-growth of coral; but some subsidences have taken place also. Daly's "glacial-control" theory ascribes the preparation of extensive level rock foundations for many coral reefs to marine erosion during the Ice Age, when the ocean level was low and the prevailing low temperature reduced protective coral growths to a minimum.

There is much evidence of diverse movement in the Pacific region, some parts having sunk as others rose or remained stationary, while in other cases tilting occurred. There are even some crescent-shaped incomplete atolls, formed apparently by subsidence accompanied by a tilt so pronounced that it has carried down one side of the reef ring sufficiently rapidly to drown it. Acceptance of a theory of subsidence in explanation of barrier reefs and atolls does not, therefore, necessitate belief in universal subsidence of the bottom or a general rise of sea-level in the vast Pacific area beyond what is explained by the "glacio-eustatic" doctrine of augmentation of the volume of the oceans due to melting of continental glaciers.

Coasts of submergence bordered by barrier reefs are protected from attack by ocean waves. The headlands (partly submerged ridges and spurs) which project into the lagoon are, therefore, but little cliffed. When subsidence ceases, or there is a pause, deltas grow at the bay heads and smooth the outline of the shore. If renewed subsidence takes place it will, however, submerge these and restore the embayed outline. Practically all the waste of the land is entrapped in the lagoon, and in a long period of still-stand it is quite filled by outgrowing, confluent deltas.

Outside the reef there is generally a very steep slope down into deep water. This is a talus slope of fragments broken by wave action from the reef.

Darwin's theory of subsidence has not been accepted by all investigators as a satisfactory general explanation of the formation of coral reefs and atolls. Limitation of space precludes a full discussion of rival theories here; but a brief statement may be made of that favoured as an explanation of atolls by Murray, who failed to recognise any evidence of such submergence as might be attributed to subsidence of land or to a general rise of sea-level in the coral seas, and therefore refused to admit that *up*-growth of coral had contributed appreciably to the making of reefs. He postulated the initial establishment of a coral patch in the shallow water over the summit of a submarine mountain, followed by broad lateral outgrowth of the reef, which would extend progressively over a shelf built of wave-broken reef fragments. The opening and deepening of a lagoon within the outer reef ring he attributed to solution by sea-water of the original or central part of the reef, now dead because deprived of food.

CHAPTER XXXII

COASTAL OUTLINES: EMERGENCE, FAULT, AND TRANSVERSELY WARPED SHORELINES

Coasts of emergence. Initial and sequential outlines. Multicycle coasts. Uplift of small measure. Contraposed shorelines. Mature coasts of emergence. Ancient sea cliffs. Fault coasts. Monoclinal coasts. A coast resulting from transverse deformation.

Coasts of Emergence.—In regions of great crustal stability it might be urged that all shorelines must be derived from initially submerged coasts which resulted from the eustatic rise of sea-level at the close of the Ice Age. Near those continental regions which were heavily loaded with glaciers in the Ice Age, however, "isostatic" upheaval of the land has taken place as a result of the relief of load due to melting of glaciers.

Somewhat doubtful evidence has been presented of a small world-wide emergence in very recent times attributable to withdrawal of water from the ocean to swell the volumes of the Greenland and Antarctic ice sheets. Probably some high-water shore platforms, however, have been wrongly interpreted in favour of this theory as evidence of emergence. An emergent bench which is very continuous around south-eastern New Zealand— forming in some places a narrow coastal plain—the "42-feet raised beach," at Oamaru, for example—is quite possibly of isostatic origin, the result of relief of load due to the melting of the glaciers of the Ice Age, but it may be due, in part at least, to eustatic emergence.

Parts of the mobile belts of the world, including California and New Zealand, and volcanic islands such as the Hawaiian group, have been subject recently to diverse movements of considerable magnitude, and in these regions there are some emergent coasts which are really "uplifted" (fig. 406).

Initial and Sequential Outlines.—The initial shoreline of a coast of emergence is the usually simple line traced by the sea margin along an exposed sea-floor, which is the former continental shelf unless the amount of emergence is unusually great (fig. 420, *C*).

The succession of sequential forms developed from a shoreline so initiated is not the same in all cases, but varies with the steepness of the profile of the sea bottom seaward from the new shoreline. If the seaward slope is initially very gentle an offshore bar will be thrown up in the process of grading the profile (p. 432), and lagoons are thus enclosed, which may form serviceable harbours in the vicinity of river mouths, where channels—or "inlets"—of sufficient depth are scoured out and kept open by tidal currents. Many such harbours are drowned valleys in part, however, and the cause of formation of offshore bars is not always emergence (p. 433).

Where an offshore bar is built fringing an emerged coast, a deficiency in the supply of waste may later cause the waves breaking on the offshore bar to erode it, cutting away both it and the low and flat or dune-covered land of the partially filled lagoon and coastal plain behind. In that case a line of low cliffs is developed. The shoreline remains simple, for no conspicuous irregularities will be developed by erosion on the soft material forming the shore in such a case. If the seaward slope of the initial sea-floor in front of the uplifted coast is somewhat steeper, the development of the graded profile in the early stage of coastal evolution will demand erosion at the shoreline instead of offshore. Retreat (retrogradation) of the shoreline then begins at once, and cliffs are cut, which are low at first but increase in height as a sloping coastal plain is cut back (fig. 420, E). As long as only the soft material of the coastal plain is being eroded (the harder undermass not being exposed) the shoreline remains simple. A mature shoreline is early developed and may retreat rapidly and very far as such. Its features will then resemble very closely those of some mature shorelines developed from submerged coasts on weak terrains (p. 458). Valleys will be betrunked and the valley systems on the coastal plain will be dismembered. Larger streams will be rejuvenated, but the valleys of smaller streams will be betrunked and left hanging.

Multicycle Coasts.—Emergent coasts of such simple form maturely bordering broad coastal plains may be rare; but recent emergence of steep coasts has been of rather common occurrence. Generally such emergence has been intermittent, producing *multicycle coasts.*

Prior to emergence "coastal-plain" sediments on the platforms fringing steep coasts may not be thick. Towards the landward margin cut platforms are only thinly veneered with marine deposits, and these may be rewashed and redeposited as beaches during emergence, or a thin marine veneer may be buried beneath a thick head of alluvial cover (p. 420).

In any case a limited amount of cliff retreat from the new shoreline after emergence generally suffices to expose bedrock beneath the cover. Thus the cliffs of an emergent—two-cycle or multicycle—coast consist generally of bedrock at the shoreline, and unconsolidated cover may be confined to a veneer on the tread of the marine terrace which is developed when the toe of the seaward slope is cliffed. Examples of these have been cited in Chapter XXIX.

Uplift of Small Measure.—Uplift of small measure affecting an indented or crenulate shoreline may not expose a sufficiently broad strip of sea-floor to produce a new shoreline of simple outline. Parts of the still infantile shoreline which was exposed by the uplift of 1855 at Wellington, New Zealand, are thus parallel to the baseline of a slightly cliffed shoreline of former submergence (fig. 444).

An uplift of about 70 feet has exposed a steep, narrow, boulder-strewn cut platform at Cape Turakirae, near Wellington, New Zealand, shown in figs. 405, 458. In this case the emergence has been sufficient to simplify the still infantile shoreline, along which a gravel beach has developed, but no cliffs have been cut as yet.

Contraposed Shorelines.—Cliff retreat may be confined to the soft cover on an emergent coastal plain, or at any rate may be slowed down by the resistance offered to erosion by the undermass where this is exposed, so that a fossil surface is exhumed by the waves. Where this has taken place the shoreline is *contraposed* (fig. 445). Strictly the shoreline is still "contraposed" when cliffs have been developed in the undermass rocks and the shore is bordered by a marine terrace such as has already been described; but it makes for a better economy of terms to limit the use of contraposed to those shorelines on which the *surface* of the undermass has been resurrected from beneath marine cover. The term is particularly useful for the description of shorelines with some intricacy of outline due to resurrection of the relief of a land surface which has been buried (without marine planation) under

Fig. 444.—Raised beach, exposed rock platform, and new shoreline which resulted from a recent uplift of 5 feet, Breaker Bay, Wellington, New Zealand.

C. A. Cotton, photo.

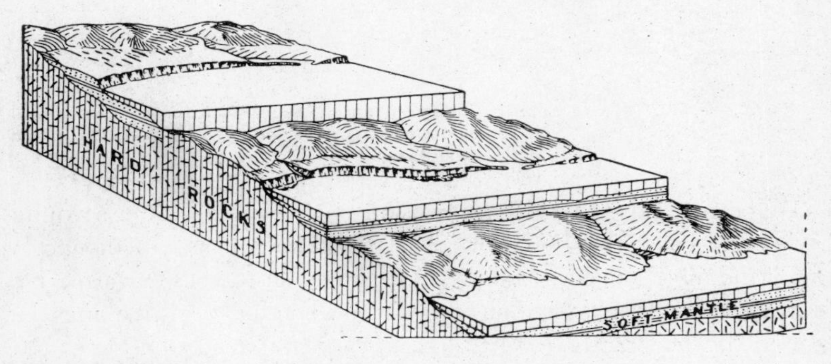

Fig. 445.—Diagram of a contraposed shoreline developed from a coastal plain of sediments overlying a former land surface of considerable relief. Earliest stage (upper part of diagram), cliffed coastal plain; second stage (middle part of diagram), contraposed shoreline developed; third stage (lower part of diagram), the sea beats against the irregular surface of the undermass after complete removal of the coastal-plain sediments by erosion. (After Clapp.)

coastal plain sediments, as shown in fig. 445. Perhaps the best examples of contraposed shorelines are those exposed on the recently emergent coast of Maine (fig. 446), where soft marine deposits laid down in embayments of a formerly drowned coast have been partly stripped away from the underlying surface of hard rock.

Mature Coasts of Emergence.—Though the shoreline of the cliffed margin of a coastal plain very early attains maturity of outline, it is advisable to restrict the application of the term "maturity" in the case of multicycle (or terraced) coasts to the stage at which marine terraces (characteristic of "youth"—see fig. 407),

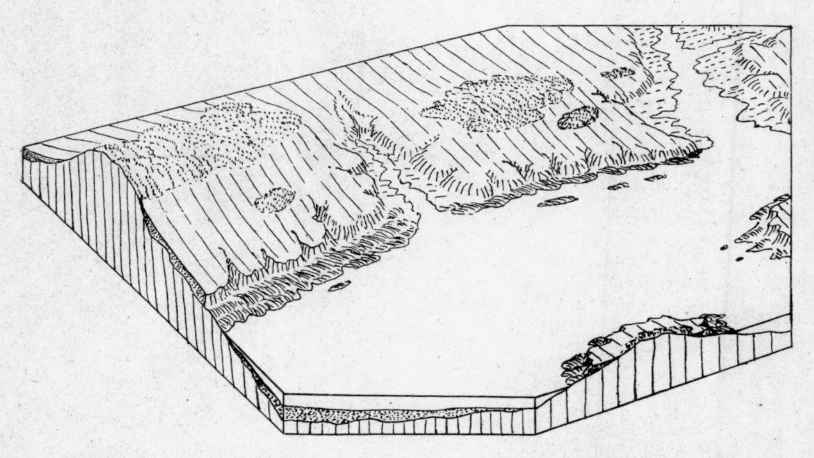

Fig. 446.—Features of the narrow coastal plain of Maine, showing a contraposed shoreline developed by stripping of weak marine covering beds from an uneven floor of hard bedrock. (After a diagram by W. M. Davis.)

have been removed by marine erosion (figs. 447, 448). On a young two-cycle coast the two stories of the cliffs are as yet distinct—with the more ancient, "fading" cliff fringed at the base by a marine terrace (fig. 449) and a newer, vigorously eroded cliff along the front of the terrace. When maturity is attained the new and ancient cliffs are merging into one, and the ancient cliff is in course of rejuvenation as the attack of the sea is renewed at a level below its former baseline (fig. 447).

In early maturity the shoreline may still be diversified by the irregularities of a crenulate shore (fig. 448); but more commonly the strength of the attack by waves is slowing down owing to the distance the waves must run in over a gently inclined built-and-cut platform (unless subsidence is in progress). Cliffs then become less steep as they are graded by normal erosion, especially in long intervals between intermittent attacks, during which the cliff base

Fig. 447.—The mature two-storied cliffs of Land's End, England—compare with fig. 407. (After W. M. Davis.)

Fig. 448.—Coast of emergence retrograded to a single line of cliffs (maturity), near Sinclair Head, Wellington, New Zealand.

is protected by a beach. By this time coves resulting from youthful selective erosion have disappeared or are bridged by beaches, and "crenulate" features, more characteristic of young shorelines, have generally been eliminated.

Ancient Sea Cliffs.—When emergence takes place the shoreline is withdrawn from the base of cliffs previously receding and, therefore, freshly cut, and the cliffs are subject henceforth to subaerial erosion only.

When cliff retrogradation is at an end, rejuvenation of streams discharging over the cliffs ceases also; and lowering of the local base-levels due to entrenchment of the streams extended across the emergent shelf, though it quickly affects the larger rivers of the

Fig. 449.—The two upper stories of a three-storied cliff, Tongue Point, Wellington, New Zealand. Both are dissected.

C. A. Cotton, photo.

hinterland (p. 217), is not much felt by the smaller streams arising on and dissecting the cliffs until perhaps the newly formed coastal plain has been narrowed considerably by recession of cliffs in the new shoreline cycle. Meanwhile dissection of the ancient cliff goes on on similar lines to the dissection of a fault scarp. The slope is reduced at first by weathering and crumbling of the cliff and accumulation of talus along the base. The minor irregularities, caves, and crenulations of a rocky shore are thus soon obliterated. The cliff is then dissected into a row of blunt-ended spurs separating steep-graded ravines, at the mouths of which fans are spread on the uplifted rock bench or coastal plain as cover head (fig. 449). At the same time weathering crumbles away projecting stacks on such portions of the rock bench below as are not buried by the talus and fans, making the undissected parts of it flat (fig. 449).

Cliffs from which the sea has been forced to withdraw owing to the building of deltas or the occurrence of marine progradation fade away in a similar manner (fig. 450), except that their ravines are not at all liable to be deepened by revived erosion of streams. In this case, on the other hand, accumulation of blown sand or of delta and alluvial deposits may bury the base of the cliff and cause some aggradation in the valleys of the streams that emerge on its face.

Fig. 450.—Ancient sea cliffs bordering the former extension of Cloudy Bay, New Zealand, now occupied by the delta of the Wairau River.

Fault Coasts.—The initial form of a fault coast is a fault scarp facing the sea. It is obvious, as indicated in fig. 451, that there must be transition forms between clear-cut fault coasts and coasts of submergence—probably of emergence also.

Initially a fault coast must trace a very simple if not quite a straight line—simpler than the line of a maturely retrograded coast, for it will pass indifferently across areas of weak and resistant rocks. As, however, the coast, being steep, will be exposed to energetic wave attack and will be rapidly eroded during the development of an offshore graded profile, it will quickly lose some of the peculiar characteristics of fault scarps on land surfaces, and will come to resemble other retrograded coasts more and more closely. A fault coast quickly passes through its stage of youth and becomes mature (figs. 452, 453). Fault coasts are recognisable in some cases owing to their cutting obliquely across the strike of the rocks (though all fault coasts do not necessarily do so), and also owing to captures and other disturbances in the drainage systems in the coastal districts due to subsidence of the former continuation of the land to seaward (fig. 454).

In New Zealand the coasts bounding Wellington, eastern Marlborough, and the west coast of the South Island, together with both

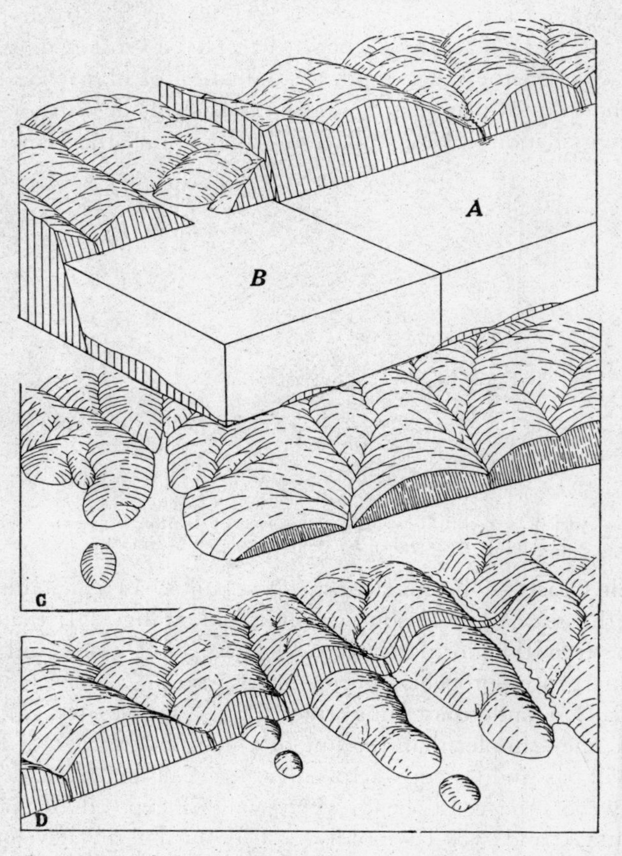

Fig. 451.—Initial fault coasts. *A,* a landward region has risen or remained stationary while a seaward strip has subsided entirely below sea-level. *B,* the same as *A* except that a landward strip has sunk far enough also to be partly submerged. *C,* the landward block is progressively submerged towards the left, so that the coast passes into a coast of submergence. *D,* a fault passes inland and dies out, and a fault coast merges into a coast of submergence.

the shores of the Firth of Thames, appear to be derived from fault coasts, though some parts are now prograded and most parts have been affected by later uplifts—as is shown by the presence

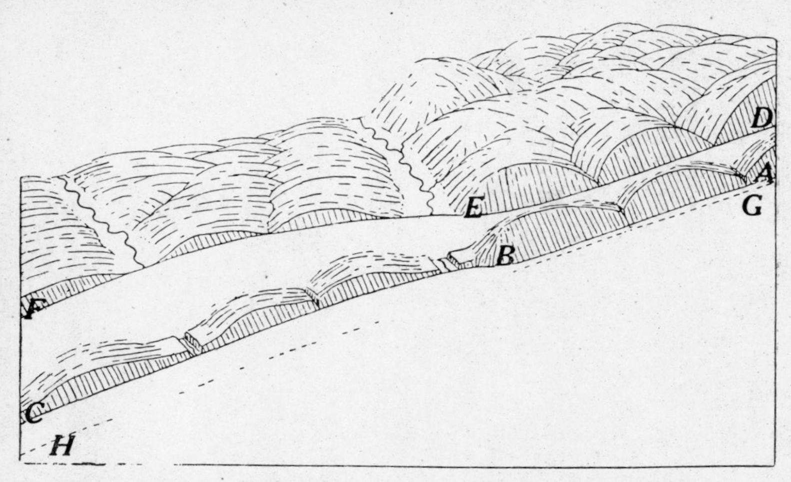

Fig. 452.—Development of an embayment of the shoreline of a mature fault coast in an area of weak rocks. *AB,* resistant rocks; *BC,* weak rocks; *DEF,* form of shoreline at a later stage; *GH,* line of initial shore, determined by a fault. In the prefaulting cycle of normal subaerial erosion the area of weak rocks had been reduced to much lower relief than the area of resistant rocks.

Fig. 453.—Mature coast north of Amuri Bluff, New Zealand, apparently a fault coast.

of marine terraces, so that they must be described as compound, or as fault coasts in a second (or later) cycle of marine erosion introduced by simple uplift (fig. 455). Coastal plains bordering fault coasts of a former cycle may be rapidly reduced in a new cycle to terraces by removal of the built platform, which is a thick mass of weak deposits on the seaward side of the fault (fig. 455). Fault coasts subsequently drowned are generally recognisable with less certainty.

The western, or Paekakariki, coast of southern Wellington, New Zealand, which is rather obviously of fault origin, cuts obliquely

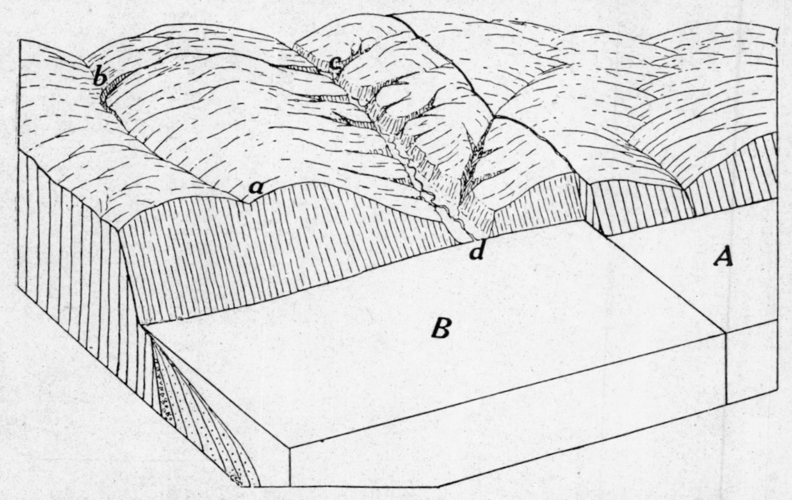

Fig. 454.—An early sequential form, block B, developed from an initial fault coast, block *A*. The inland-flowing stream *ab,* already beheaded by faulting, has been captured by a tributary *bc* of the revived seaward-flowing stream *cd*.

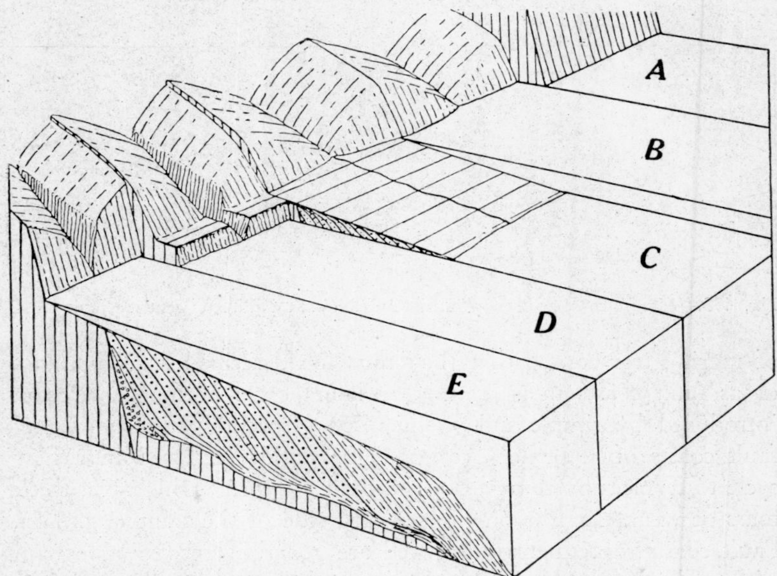

Fig. 455.—A fault coast affected by later uplift, so that it has become a two-cycle coast of emergence. *A, B,* first cycle (fault coast); *C, D, E,* second cycle (coast of emergence). Being both fault coasts and coasts of emergence such cases come under the head of "compound" coasts.

in a south-westerly direction (figs. 419, 463) across the more southerly trending grain of the landscape as a fault coast may be expected to do, and several small rivers flowing out on this coast (and also to the south coast of Wellington) reach the sea by very long roundabout courses like that shown in fig. 454.

The short strip of coast within the great Wellington Harbour embayment (see below) which is figured in Chapter XIV as a fault scarp is probably the only fault coast in the New Zealand region that may be claimed to be of such recent origin that it has not yet passed into a second cycle as a result of a more general emergence or submergence (fig. 456).

Fig. 456.—A fault coast on the line of the Wellington fault, within the Wellington Harbour embayment, New Zealand. (Compare figs. 178, 179.)

C. A. Cotton, photo.

Monoclinal Coasts.—Along with fault coasts must be grouped those resulting from monoclinal flexure at the shoreline; for they will be indistinguishable one from the other unless discovered in a very youthful condition. Such, however, is the case on a monoclinal coast at the north end of Fiordland, New Zealand (p. 480).

A Coast Resulting from Transverse Deformation.—Wellington Harbour (or Port Nicholson) has been formed by a great local subsidence which indents the southern coast of the North Island of New Zealand and has allowed the sea to invade it to a depth of twelve miles (fig. 457). The drowned area is bounded along the north-west side by a strip of fault coast (fig. 456), and elsewhere by warped surfaces resulting in coasts of submergence (figs.

Fig. 457.—Part of the Wellington Harbour (Port Nicholson) down-warped area in the transversely deformed southern coast of the North Island of New Zealand.
J. W. Jones, photo.

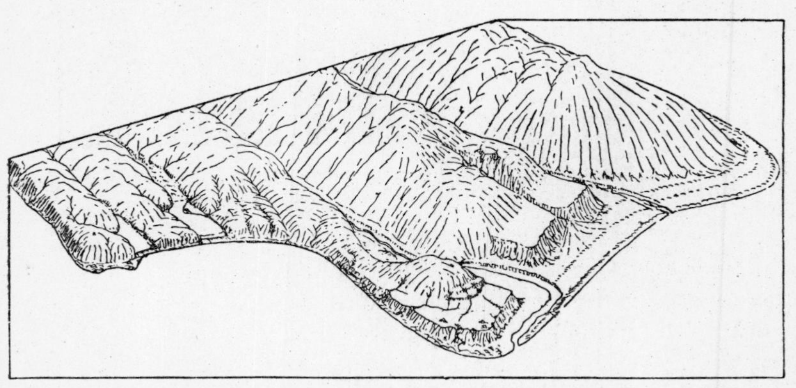

Fig. 458.—Transversely warped coast of southern Wellington, New Zealand. Marine terraces previously uplifted slant down evenly westward towards the area (left) with drowned shoreline, beyond which is the Port Nicholson down-warped area.

457, 465). The ocean coast flanking the great Port Nicholson depression on either side is, however, a multicycle coast of emergence, the marine terraces on which are warped on axes transverse to the shoreline. Those on the eastern side are tilted nearly uniformly down towards the axis of the great drowned area—the harbour

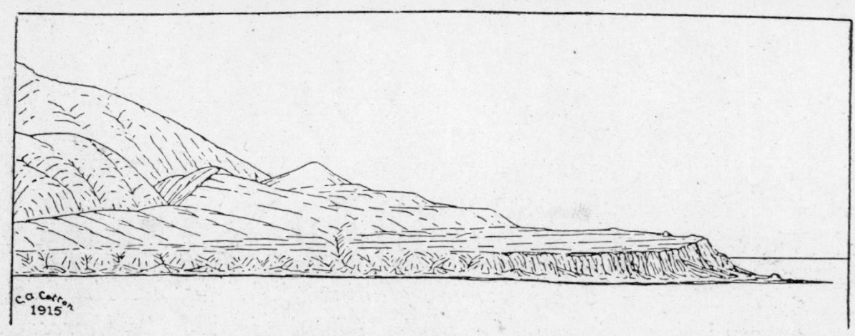

Fig. 459.—The downtilted marine terraces at Baring Head, Wellington, New Zealand, shown in the diagram, fig. 458.

embayment (figs. 458, 459). Farther east a much larger embayment of the same coast, Palliser Bay, is similarly of tectonic origin, though, being open to the ocean swell and having soft rocks across its head it has been greatly enlarged and modified by marine erosion. Its history is more complicated and probably dates farther back than the origin of Wellington Harbour, which, in geological terms, is an event of yesterday.

CHAPTER XXXIII

VOLCANIC, FIORD, PROGRADED, AND LAKE SHORELINES

Volcanic coasts. Fiord coasts. Prograded coasts. Alluvial prograded coasts. Progradation following grading of the outline. Artificial progradation. Cuspate forelands. Island-tying. Lake shores.

Volcanic Coasts.—Volcanic coasts, initiated by either accumulation of fragmental volcanic material or flows of lava with slopes descending into the sea, need not be discussed at length, for the general principles of shoreline development already outlined may

Fig. 460.—A volcanic coast with strongly cliffed headlands, which are cut back to an even line but are now separated by open bays, south side of Banks Peninsula, New Zealand. (The straight line of cliffs was developed before submergence initiated the current shoreline cycle, in which the shoreline is still young.)

C. A. Cotton, photo.

be applied to them. The initial profile will be somewhat steep, and so cliff-cutting will begin at once. Islands of volcanic ash, the summits of submarine cones, which occasionally emerge from the sea, yield so readily to erosion that, when accumulation ceases for a time, they are quickly reduced to shoals—the old-age stage of coastal development. Lava rocks are much more resistant to marine erosion. Small salients of the shoreline formed by lava flows may exist initially with bays between them, as on the southern side

Fig. 461.—Panoramic view of Milford Sound, a New Zealand fiord, showing Mitre Peak (left) and the northern side of the fiord. Angle of view, west to north.

of Lake Roto-a-ira, New Zealand, which is formed by lava flows from Mount Tongariro; but these will soon be smoothed out as the coast is cut back, and unbroken lines of steep cliffs may result, resembling those between the drowned valleys of the partly submerged volcanic island that now forms Banks Peninsula (fig. 460).

Fiord Coasts.—Where the sea enters a deeply excavated glacial trough after the melting away of the glacier a *fiord* results. A rise of sea-level may occur and allow the sea to enter glaciated valleys, or it may increase the depth of water in true fiords; but it is not necessary to assume such a rise to account for fiords. Indeed, along with or since the rise of sea-level that drowned the valleys of many coasts after the Ice Age, fiord regions rose isostatically as they were relieved of a great load of ice. It is clear that glaciers have excavated troughs far below sea-level; and it is in general such troughs that have been entered by the sea as the glaciers melted, forming fiords.

The peculiar features of *fiord coasts* are all within the fiords themselves. The outer coast, fronting the ocean, may be of any of the other types. In New Zealand, the indentations of the Fiordland coast, the south-western corner of the South Island, are true fiords greatly overdeepened by glacial erosion (figs. 461, 462). The outer coast of Fiordland, on the other hand is straight and descends into very deep water. In its northern part the structure of the coastal rocks indicates that this "steep" coast is a gigantic monoclinal flexure. Southward it may pass into a fault coast.

One of the finest New Zealand fiords is Milford Sound (figs. 461, 462). It is enclosed by nearly vertical walls rising 4000 feet above sea-level.

The sides of true fiords differ in no essential respect from those of glacial troughs cut entirely above sea-level. The profiles of their floors generally confirm also their glacial origin. Most fiords, like many of the lakes now occupying glacial troughs, but unlike the majority of rias and other arms of the sea, still preserve their underwater profiles but little altered by sedimentation. This is partly because of their great initial depth and holding capacity, and partly because of the shortness of the interval (since the melting-away of the ice) during which sediment has been accumulating in them. In the New Zealand fiords small deltas occur at the heads, but elsewhere depths of thousands of feet are commonly met with.

Almost identical floor profiles are found in other fiord regions, among which are, notably, Norway, Greenland, Alaska, and Patagonia. Towards the mouth the depth becomes less, the bedrock floor certainly rising in that direction, as it does in many of the glaciated valleys occupied by lakes (p. 331), though there is probably present some submarine terminal moraine on most fiord "thresholds."

Fig. 462.—View looking up Milford Sound, New Zealand, a typical fiord. The Stirling Falls (500 ft.) spout from the mouth of a hanging valley on the extreme left.

C. A. Cotton, photo.

The sides of fiords which, like those of Norway and south-western New Zealand, are cut in resistant, unjointed rocks and have nearly vertical walls exhibit the initial form very little, if at all, modified by marine erosion (p. 408). There is generally no trace of a nip in the base of the cliff, and indeed glacial striations on the rock walls have commonly escaped obliteration. Beaches are rare, and occur only where subaqueous talus slopes augmented by unusually plentiful supplies of waste brought in by streams accumulate up to sea-level. In Milford Sound two streams of considerable size plunge as falls from the mouths of hanging valleys which open at a height of 500 feet on the fiord walls—Stirling Falls (fig. 313A; also 461, left of centre; and fig. 462) and Bowen Falls. The Stirling Falls reach the sea in a single leap.

Fiord coasts may be expected to go through a cycle of shoreline development like that of coasts of submergence, the outline becoming graded, the embayments filled, and the coast being eventually cut back, if retrogradation continues long enough, to a mature outline. As noted above, however, most existing examples are in an extremely young stage of their shoreline cycle.

Prograded Coasts. — Progradation, which, as previously noted (p. 431), may occur where there is an over-abundant supply of waste and the offshore profile is not very steep, causes considerable changes in coastal outlines. A gently sloping profile of equilibrium may have been developed under previous conditions of less abundant waste-supply, and so progradation may take place in front of the sequential forms of coasts originating in various ways (p. 434).

In some cases progradation is caused by the outgrowth of deltas, either separate or confluent, forming *alluvial prograded coasts,* while in others the material built into forelands, though in part supplied by streams, is transported and sorted by waves and currents before being thrown up on an advancing shoreline.

Alluvial Prograded Coasts.—The shoreline of an alluvial coast built of coarse material is generally simple, the only irregularities being the salients formed by the fronts of deltas, which may be very broadly rounded off. A broad rounded salient is formed, for example, by the delta of the Waitaki River, New Zealand. This delta has been modified slightly in outline, however, by retrogradation, which has cut a line of low cliffs in the alluvium. The modern delta of the Clarence River (p. 206), small though it is, forms a more pronounced salient. The outline of the margins of the confluent deltas forming the Canterbury Plain (fig. 209) has been smoothed out by the movement of the shore drift. In the case of such deltas built of coarse material the off-shore profile remains sufficiently steep to allow energetic waves at the shoreline to prevent outgrowth of salients which would develop a lobate outline.

Deltas of fine material, on the other hand, may have very irregular shorelines (the well-known bird-foot delta of the Mississippi, for example), where the natural levees of many distributaries push out rapidly like fingers into the shallow water covering the broad subaqueous portions of the deltas, in crossing which waves have lost much of their energy, so that they are powerless to erode and smooth the outline of the shore. Deltas are commonly fringed also by sand bars built by waves either as spits or offshore bars and enclosing lagoons (the delta of the Nile, for example).

Progradation following Grading of the Outline.—When the outline of a portion of a coast becomes rectified and the shoreline submature, transportation alongshore is facilitated, and so great a supply of waste to some parts of the coast generally results as to cause progradation. Not all the material thrown up by waves and built into a prograded coast is shoreline drift, however. Some may have been moved by offshore currents along the continental shelf (at depths at which wave motion appreciably stirs the water in contact with the bottom). Where a very abundant supply of such waste necessitates rapid deposition to maintain the profile of equilibrium, accumulation may take place all over the surface as well as at the outer edge of the shelf. From the material thrown landward the finer particles are winnowed by wave action and carried away in suspension, to be redeposited seaward, leaving the coarser sand grains to be driven ashore by waves, especially waves of translation, and piled up as a beach along with the shore drift.

The outline of a prograded coast may be a smooth curve from one projecting headland to another, or a similar curve may end tangent to a retrograded coast, along which progradation encroaches as the foreland already existing increases in width (fig. 463). The curve of the shoreline is determined by the sweep of the littoral current, and where there are eddies or conflicting currents the outline is made up of two or more curves intersecting.

Artificial Progradation.—Walls, or groins (fig. 464), at right angles to a beach, are sometimes constructed to cause artificial progradation as a check to cliff recession where coastal towns are in danger of being engulfed. The shore drift cannot pass the obstruction until the shoreline has been built out in a sweeping curve to the seaward end of it, and a beach formed, along which transportation can take place.

At Timaru, New Zealand, harbour moles have acted in this way, forming a trap, southward of which an extensive strand plain has been built of gravel and much new land has been formed. Northward of Timaru the shoreline is now suffering retrogradation

Fig. 463.—The shoreline at the southern end of the foreland of western Wellington (Paekakariki coast), New Zealand, ends as a tangent to the cliffed shoreline farther south. In the distance the foreland is cuspate (p. 486).

C. A. Cotton, photo.

because the supply of waste formerly travelling northward along the beach has been thus cut off. The total cessation of the supply of gravel has caused the beach at Caroline Bay, immediately to leeward of the Timaru harbour moles, to be covered with sand,

Fig. 464.—Groins erected to promote artificial progradation at a point where the sea capriciously attacks the sand isthmus it had formerly built, tying Otago Peninsula to the mainland, St. Clair, Dunedin, New Zealand. *F. G. Radcliffe, photo.*

Fig. 465.—A cuspate foreland built in front of a submerged (and cliffed) shoreline within the Wellington Harbour embayment, New Zealand. *C. A. Cotton, photo.*

forming the only sandy beach for many miles and converting a hungry gravel foreshore into a seaside resort.

Cuspate Forelands.—Where conflicting currents meet—eddies, generally, of ocean or tidal currents—progradation commonly takes place, and a projecting foreland is built out, either as a local incident in an otherwise retrograded coast or as a salient of a continuous foreland. Though sometimes rounded at the end, such a salient is bounded typically by the two curves followed by the littoral currents, tangent to the general line of the coast some distance away from the projection at either side, and sweeping out to intersect each other in a sharp cusp at its extremity. Such a

Fig. 466.—Cuspate foreland and spit at the entrance to Otago Harbour, New Zealand. At the left a harbour mole has accelerated progradation.

cuspate foreland may form part of a barrier or may spring from the main shoreline (figs. 465, 466). It may be formed by the confluence of two spits, which enclose a lagoon, or may be built out solidly by the growth of successive beaches.

An outlying island seems sometimes to have caused the eddy currents which determine progradation. A large cuspate salient of the foreland forming the coastal lowland of western Wellington, New Zealand, points towards Kapiti Island (fig. 463).

Island-tying.—Outgrowth of a spit from a headland results sometimes in the formation of a bar or isthmus connecting a former island with the mainland; while in other cases similar *island-tying* takes place as a result of continued outgrowth of a cuspate foreland from the mainland (fig. 467); or the spit or foreland may grow from the island towards the mainland. A great many peninsulas are *land-tied islands,* each connected to the main-

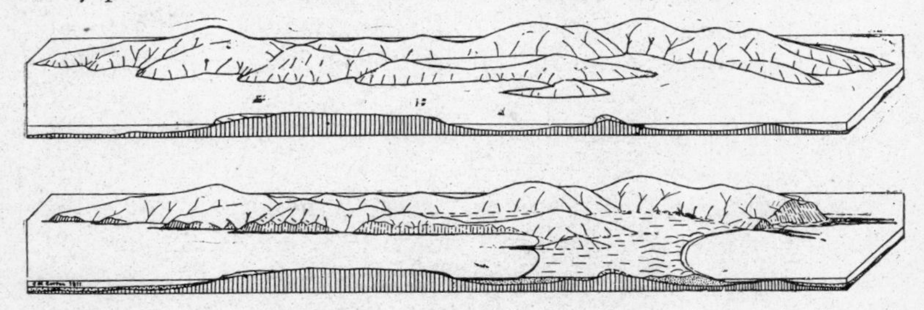

Fig. 467.—An island (above) has been tied to the mainland by the growth of a sand isthmus (tombolo), becoming Miramar Peninsula, Wellington, New Zealand.

land by an isthmus formed thus. A sand or gravel isthmus formed by the growth of a spit is also called a *tombolo* (figs. 468, 469).

Miramar Peninsula, at Wellington, New Zealand (fig. 467), serves as an example of a land-tied island. The sand isthmus connecting the former island with the mainland grew out either as a cuspate foreland or a narrow spit from the mainland at the western side, first converting the "island" into a peninsula, and then continuing on to form a bar across the mouth of a large bay, converting it into a lagoon which has since become dry land.

Fig. 468.—A sand isthmus, or tombolo, at Palm Beach, coast of New South Wales, north of Sydney, converting an island into a peninsula.

C. A. Cotton, photo.

Otago Peninsula, New Zealand, formerly an island isolated as a result of a submergence which drowned two valleys and the divide between their heads, forming a strait (p. 444, and figs. 424, 425), is now joined to the mainland by an isthmus which originated as a bar across the southern entrance to the strait.

Fig. 469.—A land-tied island in Lake Taupo, New Zealand. Note that the tombolo, narrow at first, is growing in width as successive beaches (recognisable as ridges) are added to it. *V. C. Browne, photo.*

Banks Peninsula, the most prominent protuberance on the shoreline of New Zealand, is doubly tied to the mainland by bars to north and south, both of which are outgrowths from the alluvial foreland formed by the confluent deltas of the Canterbury Plain. The tombolo on the southern side is built of gravel, that on the northern side of sand. With the exception of the portions remaining as Lake Ellesmere and the Sumner Estuary (fig. 439), the large lagoon enclosed by the bars, the Peninsula, and the alluvial plain has been filled and converted into low-lying land.

Lake Shores.—All the features of sea coasts are reproduced on the shores of lakes, those of large lakes like the North American

Great Lakes resembling those of the ocean, while the conditions in smaller lakes are more like those in landlocked harbours. Lakes in glacial troughs have shorelines initially like those of fiords. The majority of other lakes, however, those due to warping and to obstruction of drainage channels, spread over normally eroded land surfaces, and so their shores are shorelines of submergence (fig. 230). Fault coasts occur also. Lake Taupo, in New Zealand, for example, is bounded, at least in part, by fault scarps (fig. 470). Shorelines of

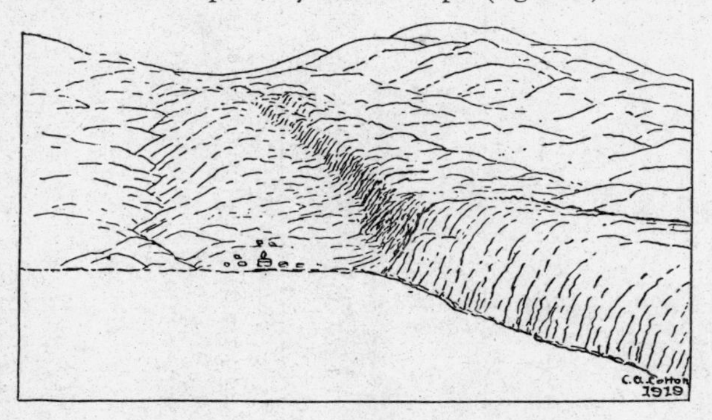

Fig. 470.—Fault scarp forming the shoreline on the west side of Lake Taupo, New Zealand, and running inland in a southerly direction.

emergence occur where the lake level has been lowered by cutting-down of the outlet, or, in arid regions, by shrinkage of the lake due to evaporation.

In small lakes lowering of the lake level generally cuts short the shoreline cycle before it has reached an advanced stage. During an interval of stationary water level a nip or line of low cliffs is cut, and in front of this there is a narrow shelf, partly cut and partly built, which remains as a *lake terrace* when the water level falls (figs. 471, 472). Where deltas occur the terrace becomes wider, and in other parts its surface may be diversified by spits and bars. Emergent deltas are deeply trenched by the streams that built them (p. 204). Below the lake-shore terrace the initial form of the under-water slope may be scarcely modified by deposition. Successively lower terraces generally mark successive shorelines during progressive lowering of the lake level; but where rapid rise of the water level takes place in a closed basin owing to decreasing aridity shore terraces may be submerged, and they may be still recognisable

Fig. 471.—Terrace marking a former shore-line 115 feet above the present lake-level, north side of Lake Taupo, New Zealand.

Fig. 472.—Lake terrace 130 feet above the present level of Lake Wakatipu, New Zealand.

V. C. Browne, photo.

Fig. 473.—Ancient lake-shore terraces cut during the final shrinkage of Lake "Bonneville" to become Great Salt Lake, Utah.

Douglas Johnson, photo.

as such when they re-emerge as the lake shrinks again, though they will be then less sharply defined than those formed during intermittent sinking of the lake, for they will be smoothed over by the layer of fine lake-bottom sediment deposited upon them. Lake-shore terraces formed during submergence as well as during emergence of the shores occur around the margin of the large ancient lake of which Great Salt Lake, Utah, is but a shrunken remnant 1000 feet below the level of the highest shoreline (fig. 473).

Unlike river terraces, ancient lake shores are strictly horizontal except in so far as they have been tilted or warped by earth movements.

APPENDIX

Reading References

Several textbooks of Geomorphology have recently appeared in the English language. The following may be consulted with advantage:

Wooldridge and Morgan, *The Physical Basis of Geography: An Outline of Geomorphology* (London: Longmans, 1937).

P. G. Worcester, *A Textbook of Geomorphology* (New York: Van Nostrand; London: Chapman and Hall, 1939).

A. K. Lobeck, *Geomorphology, an Introduction to the Study of Landscapes* (New York and London: McGraw-Hill, 1939).

The last-mentioned book provides excellent lists of further reading references and also a rich store of photographic illustrations and drawings of landforms, which are so arranged that they may be studied either parallel with the text or independently of it.

Various aspects of vulcanology are developed by G. W. Tyrrell in *Volcanoes* (Home University Library, 1931); and Douglas Johnson's *Shore Processes and Shoreline Development* (New York: John Wiley and Sons, 1919) provides an advanced treatment and is still the standard work on coasts.

For more information regarding sources and a fuller treatment of some doctrines and theories than it has been possible to find space for in this volume the reader may consult the author's *Landscape as Developed by the Processes of Normal Erosion* (Cambridge: University Press, 1941) and *Climatic Accidents in Landscape Development* (Christchurch: Whitcombe and Tombs Ltd., 1942).

INDEX

631

PRINTED BY WHITCOMBE & TOMBS LIMITED G2271